TURKEY

Archaeologist
İlhan Akşit

akşit

AKŞIT KÜLTÜR VE TURİZM YAYINCILIK

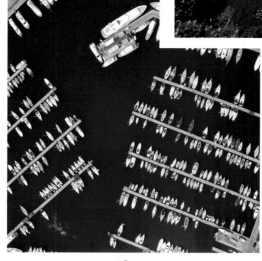

Contents

Published and distributed by:

AKŞİT KÜLTÜR ve TURİZM YAYINCILIK

Cağaloğlu Yokuşu Cemal Nadir Sk. Nur İşhanı
No: 2/4   34112 Cağaloğlu / Istanbul - TURKEY
Tel : +(90.212) 511 53 85 - 511 67 82
Fax: +(90.212) 527 68 13

Text by : İlhan Akşit
Graphics by : Hasan Basri Özsu
Photograhps : Korhan Sezer, İzzet Keribar, Hasan Basri Özsu, Kadir Kır, Şemsi Güner, Tahsin Aydoğmuş, Güngör Özsoy
Colour separation by : Akşit Yayıncılık
Printed in Turkey by : Seçil Ofset

Gold Bowl Alacahöyük, (2200 BC.).

Anatolian Civilization

Anatolia, the land of sun and history, is one of the rare places in the world which have been inhabited ever since the first man was seen on the earth. The Paleolithic Age, which we call the Stone Age, reigned between the years 600.000-10.000 BC. in Anatolia and was followed by the Mesolithic and Neolithic Ages. The men began to leave their caves between the years 8000-5500 BC. during the Neolithic Age, and to establish villages on the meadows. We can conduct studies on this culture in ancient localities of habitation such as Diyarbakır, Çayönü, Konya Çatalhöyük and Burdur Hacılar. The men lived the Chalcolithic age, which we call the metal-stone, after Neolithic Age. The early Bronze Age followed the metal-stone age and it was lived through very gloriously in Anatolia. An indigenous tribe called Hatti lived in central Anatolia during this age. We see the golden works of art of this magnificient civilization belonging to the years 2300-2000 BC., in the royal tombs in Alacahöyük. A civilization similar to this one was lived in Troy II during the same age in Anatolia.

The Hittites who came to Anatolia in the ears of 2000 BC. lived in principalities for a while, and then in the years of 1800 BC., they, established a state and made Hattusas the capital. We can study the art of the Hittite people who created a great civilization in Anatolia between the years 1800-1200 BC. in the localities such as Hattusas (Boğazköy), Yazılıkaya and Alacahöyük. The Hittites were destroyed by the unceasing attacks of the sea tribes

Gold Pitcher. Early Bronze Age. Alacahöyük, (2200 BC.).

Gold twin idol, early Bronze Age. Alacahöyük, (2200 BC.).

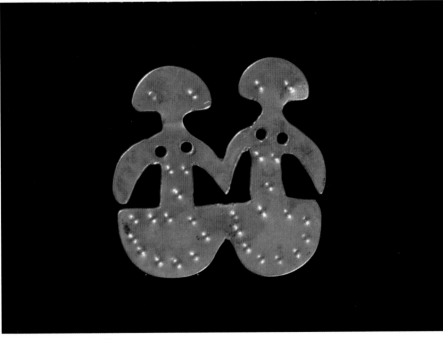

Aizanoi Zeus temple. (117-138) Euromos Zeus Temple. 2nd century.

during the years 1200 BC., But their usage and customs survived until 650 BC. in the south Anatolian cities such as Malatya, Maraş, Kargamış, Zincirli, which are called the late Hittite city-states. When the Hittite State ceased to exist, the Urartu people founded a state in eastern Anatolia, made Van the capital city and stepped on the scene of history (860-580 BC.). The works of art made of ivory and bronze which showed their master workmanship were discovered as a result of the excavations carried on in the Fortress of Van, in Urartu cities such as Toprakkale,

Altıntepe and Çavuştepe. When
the Urartus were utterly destroyed
by the Ischits in the year 580 BC.,
the Phrygians founded a state in
central Anatolia, with Gordion as
the capital, but they also disap-
peared from the scene of history at
the beginning of the 8th century
BC. by reason of the raids of the
Kimmers. The Phrygian works of
art found in the tomb of their legendary King Midas, are exhibited
at the Museum of Anatolian
Civilizations in Ankara. The
Lydians succeeded the
Phrygians by founding a
state in western Anatolia and
made Sardes the capital. When the

Sultanahmet Mosque. (1609-1617).

Sivas Gök Medrese (1271).

Lydians were defeated by the Persians in the year 546 BC., the whole Anatolia was conquered by the Persians.

Anatolia was taken over by Alexander the Great when he defeated the Persians in 333 BC., and by his inheritors after his death. So, Anatolia was the site of the Hellenistic period between the years 330 and 30 BC. We observe that the Kingdom of Pergamum developed and became more powerful during this period. Many works of art created during the Hellenistic Period were inspired by the style of art, called the Pergamum style. Since Attolos III. the king of Pergamum, had no inheritors, he ceded his territory to Rome in 133 BC., and Anatolia was wholly integrated to Roman territory in this way. Anatolia was furnished with magnificient structures during the Roman period, too. The structures of the Hellenistic Period and those of the Roman Period are seen to exist in an intermingled manner with each other in antique cities.

When Rome was divided into two as the Eastern Rome and Western Rome in the year 395 AD., anatolia was left in the possession of the Eastern Roman Empire. The most important works of art belonging to this empire, briefly called Byzantium, are the magnificient works in Istanbul such as Hagia Sophia, Chora and Hagia Eirene. The exquisitely beautiful Byzantine mosaics are seen here. In many localities of ruins, the works of art belonging to the Byzantine period are seen to have succeeded the works of art belonging to the Roman period.

The Seljukiyans who defeated the Byzantine people in 1071 during the pitched battle in Malazgirt, took possession of Anatolia

Rock-crystal flask, 16th century. (Topkapı Palace).

gradually. They founded the Seljukiyan State of Anatolia and made Konya the capital. Medresses with magnificient stone doors, caravanserai inns and mosques have also survived until today from the time of the Seljukiyans. The most famous ones among these are Buruciye in Sivas, The Medresse With Double Minarets in Sivas. Yakutiye in Erzurum, The Medresse With Double Minarets in Erzurum, the Medresse With Fine Minarets in Konya, the Medresse of Karatay Sahip Ata. The mosques such as the Grand Mosque of Divriği, the Grand Mosque of Malatya, the Mosque of Alaaddin in Konya, the Grand Mosque of Beyşehir are some of the mosques belonging to the Seljukiyan period. In addition to these, many caravanserais built in order to provide halting places for the carvans

Gold pen box. 16ᵗʰ century.
Steel helmet gold, rubies, turquoises, 16ᵗʰ century.

and monumental tombs which have survived standing magnificiently until today, are the most beautiful examples of the Seljukiyan art. Owing to the fact that the Seljukiyans were left powerless by the Mongolian invasion and ceased to exist officially later, the principalities subjected to the Seljukiyans declared themselves independent in certain places. One of them was the Ottoman principality which declared independance in Söğüt in the year 1299. The Ottoman

principality became more powerful day by day and enlarged its territory continually thus transforming itself from principality to an empire. The Ottomans ruled over Anatolia for 600 years between the dates 1299 and 1923 and they provided training facilities for architects, like Sinan the Architect, leaving behind magnificient works of art such as the Mosques of Selimiye, Süleymaniye, Sultanahmet and many other architectural works such as palaces, kiosks and fortresses. They created wonders in handicrafts of carpet making, tile-making and miniature, besides the architectural works. The Ottoman State collapsed after the World War I and the young

İznik tile, 17th century.
Polychrome ceramic tankard.
16th century, İznik.
Mosque Lamp, 1512.

Rebuplic of Turkey was founded in its place in 1923, with Ankara the capital city. In addition to many antique cities that can be visited in Turkey there are other interesting places which have a varied history, namely Cappadocia, the Mount Nemrut, Lycian Region. The Black sea is a land of greenness in itself. It is an inconceivably beautiful travel to experience through history in the crystal blue waters during the Blue Voyage from Bodrum to Antalya.

Istanbul

Istanbul, which had been the capital of Rome, Byzantium and the Ottoman Empire, is one of the most interesting centers of the world owing to its natural beauties, in addition to the historical structures which are the heritages of these cultures.

Istanbul is situated like an open air museum on both shores of the strait which is 33 kms in length and seperates the continents of Asia and Europe. We know that habitations had existed in the whereabouts of Istanbul during the Neolithic age. The first habitation

General view of Kanlıca.

View of the Bosphorus Bridge, which links Asia and Europe.

succeeding these ones, came into existance in Kadıköy which was named Khalkedon in the VII century BC. The city that was founded later on the opposite shore of Khalkedon, namely Byzantium, progressed rapidly because of its importance and became an important center. This progressive city became subject to Roman sovereignty, was adorned with temples and public squares during the period of Constantinus, and was surrounded with city walls. The city was made the capital of Rome in the year 330 and named Constantinapolis and, after Rome was divided into two parts as the Eastern Rome and

Western Rome, it was made the capital of the Eastern Roman Empire. Finally, when the Ottomans captured Byzantium in the year 1453, Istanbul was converted into the capital of the Ottoman Empire. Many historical works of art showing traces of these empires, have been able to survive up to date. The obelisks belonging to the Roman period, which were used as ornaments of the public square Sultan Ahmed, are still maintained in their places today. One of these is the obelisk which Theodosius I had ordered to be brought from Egypt in the year 390; it is 18.54 m in height and

General view of Hagia Sophia.
View of St. Eirene.

An aerial view of Topkapı Palace.
An aerial view of St.Sophia and Sultanahmet Mosque.

seems magnificient today with the hieroglyph scripture on it. Another column which is seen here is the braided column with a height of 20.68 m, which Constantinus VII had ordered to be erected in the year 944. The third column, formed by three winding snakes, was ordered to be brought from the Temple of Apollon in Delphi in the year 360 by Constantinus I.

The most important historical remain belonging to Byzantium is Hagia Sophia. Justinianus had this most magnificient temple of the world constructed between the years 532-537 in the place of a

View of the Fatih Sultan Mehmed Bridge.
Ortaköy Mosque (1853).

temple which had existed there formerly, and it contains very valuable mosaics and is still visited as a museum today. St.Eirene located at its side which Justinianus had ordered to be constructed in the year 537, is also being used as a museum today.

The monastery of Chora, which attracts attention owing to the mosaic art works inside, and the mosque of Fethiye are also historical works of art belonging to Byzantium and being visited as museums at present.

When Istanbul was conquered by Fatih Sultan Mehmet in 1453, the buildings of Byzantium were

repaired and new ones were built, and the architecturel activities were continued. For example, the magnificent Topkapı Palace the domicile of the Sultan and center of government administration, was constructed. The palace which was built between the years 1472-1478, later acquired the identity of a great city of 700.000 m² owing to the extensions which the other sultans ordered to be made and to its population exceeding 10.000. It is a magnificent museum today which contains the seraglio and where the treasures belonging to the Ottoman Empire are exhibited. The Dolmabahçe Palace was constructed during the years

General view of Anadolu Hisarı.

1843-1853 and the Ottoman sultans started to live in it. Sultan Abdülaziz had the Palace of Beylerbeyi Palace constructed on the opposite shore of the Bosphorus between the years 1861-1865.

In addition to these palaces, many historical mosques, which form the silhouette of Istanbul, are also places worthy of visiting. Istanbul is adorned with the works of the great architect Sinan, who was a master of perfection during the Ottoman period in the 16th century. Some of Sinan's master works which show his genius are; the Şehzade Mosque which he built for Prince Mustafa, son of Süleyman

Exterior and interior views of Süleymaniye Mosque (1550-1557).

20

Exterior and interior views of Sultanahmet Mosque.

the Law Maker in the years 1543-1548; the Mihrimah Mosque which he built in 1548; the Süleymaniye Mosque which he built in the years 1550-1557; and the Rüstem Paşa Mosque, completely adorned with encaustic tiles of Iznik, which he built in the years 1550-1557.

The Sultan Ahmet Mosque, which Sultan Ahmed I had ordered Sedefkar Mehmet Ağa to construct between the years 1609-1617, is one of the most important works of art worthy of seeing in Istanbul because of the encaustic tiles therein.

Bursa

The city of Bursa, founded at the foot of Uludağ which is one of the most important ski centers of Turkey, is called Green Bursa owing to the abundant verdure there. The city was founded by Prusias the I. (230-192 BC.) King of the Bythnians who were the first comers in that region, and was named Prusa as attribution to the King's name. Today this name has been converted to Bursa. The Seljuks began to rule over Anatolia in the year 1071, after the successive Persian, Hellenistic, Roman and Byzantine periods. Later on the Ottoman Principality, founded in Söğüt in the year 1299 and subjected to the Seljuks, proclaimed independence and increased in size in a short time. In the year 1330 Ottomans conquered İznik and made it the capital city. In the year 1335 the capital of the Ottoman State was Bursa succeeding İznik; and later, Edirne was conquered and made capital.

Bursa is full of historical works of art. The Ottoman Sultan, Yıldırım Beyazıt, had the Mosque of Yıldırım constructed in the year 1399. Another one of the interesting works of art in the city is the Ulu Cami located at the center of the city. It was constructed between the years 1396 and 1400, and was placed on twelve elephant feet and has 20 domes. There is a fountain and a remarkable niche inside the mosque and there are also examples of the art of ornamental calligraphy of that time. This mosque was the greatest mosque of the Ottomans in those years. Another one of the most favorite works of art in Bursa is the Green Complex situated in the district called Yeşil. The mosque in the complex was built by the order of

Uludağ, Turkey's skiing centre. Bursa.

Çelebi Sultan Mehmet in the year 1419, and the ornamental designs of the mosque could be completed in the year 1424. The architect of the Complex, composed of the Mosque, Medresse and Mauseloum, was Hacı Ivaz Paşa, the engraver was Ali Bin İlyas Ali and the master workman who made the encaustic tiles was Mehmet El Mecnun. The Medresse adjacent to the Mosque, is used as a museum today. Another work of art in Bursa is the Green Mauseloum which is regarded as the symbol of Bursa today. The mauseloum is octagonal shaped and its outer surface is also covered with encaustic tiles as the and inside. Çelebi Mehmet's sarcopha-

Exterior and interior views of Yeşil Türbe.

gus, is placed at the center of the mauseloum and it is made of encaustic tiles. Another important complex in the city is the Complex of Muradiye. Sultan Murad the II. had this complex constructed between the years 1424-1426, it is composed of the mosque, medresse, bath, kitchen for the poor and mauseloums. Besides the mauseloum of Murad the II. there are twelve mauseloums in the courtyard of the mosque such as those belonging to Gülşah Hatun, Mukime Hatun, Sultan's son (Şehzade) Mahmut, Sultan's son Mustafa and to Sultan Cem

Interior view of the Cem Sultan tomb in Bursa.

Interior view of Selimiye Mosque, Edirne (1569-1575).

whose name was given to the mauseloum and who was buried together with Mustafa, and all are ornamented with beautiful encaustic tiles. In addition to the Ottoman House nearby the mauseloums of Osmangazi and Orhangazi in Tophane, the Fortress of Bursa, the Mosque and Medresse of Murad the I. in Çekirge, there are many historical and modern hot springs in the vicinity. Villa Atatürk near Çelik Palas, the Museum of Archaeology in the park, are also places to be visited here. Uludağ, to which we referred shortly above, is also another place of excursion.

Edirne

The Mosque of Selimiye in Edirne, is the symbol of Edirne, Sinan the architect built this Mosque which he defined as his master work succeeding the mosques of Şehzade and Süleymaniye in Istanbul, for Selim the II. between the years 1569-1575. The mosque is encircled by its four minarets in a well shaped manner and has a magnificent appearance when it is observed from far off. The dome which has a diameter of 31.30 is supported by 8 pillars and flying butresses placed at the back. The mosque is ornamented with many windows and therefore the inside is

Interior and exterior view of the Selimiye Mosque.

25

very luminous. The encaustic tiles decorating the niche, are beautiful examples of the Ottoman art of tile-making. The pulpit of the muezzin is at the center of the mosque and supported by 12 marble columns, and there is a marble pond under it. The inside of the dome which is 43.28 m high, is ornamented with engravings. The four minarets which are 70.89 m high, surround the mosque gracefully. Owing to the fact that Edirne was an ancient Ottoman capital city, there are great number of historical works of art in it. The locality where the traditional wrestling activities of Kırkpınar are organised, is the place where the ancient Palace of Edirne was

View of interior and dome of the Selimiye Mosque.

situated. The covered bazaar of Alipaşa built by Sinan the Architect in 1569, the ancient Mosque dated 1414 which Çelebi Sultan Mehmet had ordered to be constructed and the market of antiques adjacent to it and dated 1417, the Market which Murat the III. had ordered to be constructed. The Building Complex of Beyazid which Beyazid the II. had ordered to be constructed in 1488, the Mosque with three minaret-galleries dated 1443, the Caravanserai of Rüstempaşa are some of these historical works of art.

Troy

Troy, situated at a distance of 30 km from the Dardanelles. Troy, which had been founded in the year 3000 BC., and was demolished and reconstructed nine times until the year 500 AD., was inhabited incessantly for 3500 years.

Troy I. which had been founded in the year 3000 BC., was demolished in the year 2500 BC., and Troy II. that was founded in its place, was brought to its end by a fire in the 2300's BC. Troy III, IV. and V. were founded successively. After these strata which were not indicative of a great deal of activity, Troy VI. was founded between the years 1800-1275 BC. This Troy which is worthy of attention today with its city walls in good condition, was succeeded by Troy VII which is the stratum where the famous war was made. This stratum is divided into strata VIIa and VIIb respectively, and the Trojan war, which was the first war in the world between the east and the west, took place in Troy VIIa in the years of 1200 BC. During this war many people came to the aid of Troy from various places of Anatolia, but because of the trick of the "Wooden Horse", the city fell and Troy was burnt and destroyed. The Trojans who could save themselves from this massacre, built their city over again and kept on living there.

Troy VIII. which followed Troy VII, acquired the properties of the Hellenistic period, and Troy IX became the Troy of the Roman period. Schliemann conducted excavations in Troy in 1870; following him, Dörpfeld and later in the year 1935, Blegen from America, continued the excavations there.

Wooden Horse, a symbol of Troya.

Pergamon

Pergamon was a small settlement during the Archaic Period. Lysimachos, who had become the sovereign of Anatolia after 301 BC., delivered the war expenditures, at the amount of 9000 talents, to Philetairos who was the commander of Pergamon, and the kingdom founded by Philetar by using this sum of money following Lysimachos's death, flourished and became the most eminent center of culture of the Hellenistic period during 150 years.

Eumenes the I., Attales the I. and Eumenes the II. were enthroned successively after Philetairos. Eumenes the II. took acropolis of Athens as an example and had the acropolis of Pergamon adorned with works of art which reflected fine taste, and Pergamon became one of the most graceful cities of the world. Attales the III. who succeeded Attales the II., handed over his land to in 133 BC.

In Acropolis, the remains that we see on the left hand side while entering the ruins, are the monumental tombs built for the kings of Pergamon during the Hellenistic period. Shops are situated at their side. When we enter the Acropolis, the remains seen at our left side, are the foundations of Propylon which Eumenes the II. had ordered to be constructed. Today, this Propylon has been reconstructed at the Museum of Berlin. From here, we pass to a square surrounded with three stoas of the Doric order. This is the abode of Sacred Athena, built during the time of Eumenes the II. The Temple of Athena built in the 3rd century BC., is just above the theater. The famous Library of Pergamon which con-

View of the restored Traian Temple. Pergamon (117-138).

Figure of Nike. (Pergamon Museum).

tained 200.000 books, was situated north of the square. As it is already known, Antonius had made a present of this library to Cleopatra. The remains near the library, are the remains of houses belonging to the Hellenistic period. When we turn back and go up the stairs, the remains of the palaces of Eumenes the II. and Attales the II. are seen. Towards the inside of the Acropolis, there are houses, military barracks and, at the farthest end, there are military warehouses called "Arsenals". The building that has been restored at present, is the Temple of Trajan. Emperer Hadrian (117-138) had

this temple constructed in the Corinthian order and it was placed upon a terrace with dimensions of 68 x 58 m. Attempts have been continuing since the year 1976 to erect this temple which has 6 x 9 columns and a peripteros plan.

The Theater of Pergamon, one of the steepest theaters in the world, has the capacity to include 10.000 people and had been constructed in the 3rd century BC. The theater underwent changes during the Roman period. There is a stoa 246.5 m long and approximately 16 m wide in front of the theater. The road in front of the theater leads to the Temple of Dionysos. The temple had been constructed in the 2nd century BC. and was reconstructed in marble during Caracalla period (211-217 AD.) and its dimensions are 11.80 x 20.22 m. The temple, which arouses interest because of the staircase in front with a height of 4.5 m and 25 steps, has an exquisite appearance.

The famous Altar of Zeus in Pergamon is on the south of the theater. Eumenes the II. (197-159 BC.) had it constructed as a memorial of the victory attained against the Galatians. This Altar has the shape of a horseshoe and its dimensions are 36.44 x 34.20 m. It is composed of four parts and the high reliefs on it describe the war between the giants and the gods. The Altar which was taken away from Pergamon in the year 1871 and carried to Germany by the German engineer Carl Humann, is exhibited at the Museum of Berlin, in a manner conforming to its original. On the south of the Altar, the Agora belonging to the 2nd century BC., is situated. At the extreme north end of the Agora, there is the Temple of Agora. Downwards in the Acropolis, the central city is placed; and inside Pergamon, there is the Temple of Serapis,

Columns of the asklepieion.

View of the Asklepieion.
Pergamon Theater.

built for the Egyptian Gods and called the Red Courtyard by the people. This is a basilica shaped building constructed during the period of Hadrian, and its magnificent form attracts attention today. The museum is in Pergamon and Asklepieion is out of the city. It is comprehended that Asklepieion, built in the name of the God of Health, has existed since the 4th century BC., and it contains premises such as the theater, rooms where the patients were cured by the sound of water and music, the Temple of Asklepie and the library. A road turns off into the direction of the city of Rome. An Amphi-theater for 50.000 people is situated here.

Sardis

In Anatolia, during the fall of a state, a new state was already at the stage of being founded, thus making this region a land of civilizations. Following the fall of the Hittites in 1200 BC., the Phrygians appeared in central Anatolia; and when they were withdrawing, the Lydians made Sardis their capital in the year 7 century BC. thus stepping on the scene of history. As we know, the first king of the Lydians was Gyges (680-652). Gyges was succeeded by Ardys, Sadyattes, Alyattes respectively as the Lydian kings. When Kroisos, who had been enthroned in the year 560 BC., lost the war that he made against the Persians, the Lydians were forced to quit from the scene of history in the year 546 BC. Sardis, the capital of the Lydians who had minted the first gold coin in history, is located today within the village of Sard comprised within the boundaries of the township of Salihli the city of Manisa. The building seen on the road in Sardis, which is situated at the 72nd km of the İzmir-Ankara overlandroute, is the Gymnasium restored and set

Artemis Temple, Sardis.

up. This building was constructed in the 3rd century AD. during the period of Geta and Caracalla, and a Synagogue was annexed to it later. The Gymnasium and Bath Complex which is an ostensive edifice with its ornamented two-storey front, interests the visitors. In addition, the House with Bronze (a Roman buillding belonging to 550 BC.), the Byzantium Church, the Roman Stadium, the Hellenistic Theater with a capacity of 20.000 people, the structures belonging to the Lydian period in the vicinity of

village, have been discovered as the result of excavations. The pyramidal monumental tomb at the foot of the Acropolis, is the grave of Abradates who was a nobleman of Susa. Kyres, the Persian King, had this monumental tomb built for this man who had died at war and for his wife who had committed suicide on his grave. Another one of the most magnificent works in Sardis is the Temple of Artemis. It has been understood by means of the excavations that the foundations of the temple dates back to the Lydian period and Kybele was worshipped here, and that Kybele and Artemis had been joined in 300 BC. and thus a temple was constructed. Over this temple which had the dimensions 23 x 67.52 m a second temple was constructed between the years 175-150 BC. It was attempted to complete the lacking parts of this temple, in the year 150 BC., In this way the temple was completed in three stages and acquired the form of a great temple with 8 x 20 columns and dimensions of 45 x 97.94 m.

The temple which had been

Gymnasion at Sardis.

appropriated to Antonius and his wife Faustina, was used until the year 400 AD., and then it was abandoned and a church was built adjacent to it.

In Bintepeler, northwest of Salihli, the greatest tumuluses of Anatolia are seen. It is comprehended that the 90 tumuluses here belong to the Lydian kings and the rich, nd that the greatest tumulus with a diameter of 335 m and height of 69 m belongs to the Lydian King Alyettes.

Kuşadası

Although the history of Kuşadası is quite old, hardly any traces of early settlement here remain today other that a section of a cyclopean wall. The town is conveniently located for those wishing to make visits to such famous sites as Ephesos, Miletos, and Priene and so it can be for given if it lacks much in the way of history itself. Trips can also be made from Kuşadası to the ruins of the ancient oracular cities of Claros with its temple to Apollo

View of Kuşadası.
View of Kuşadası at night.

Güvercin Island, Kuşadası.
Öküz Mehmet Pasha Caravanserai.

and Teos with its temple to Dionysos.

Kuşadası means "Bird Island" and the town takes its name from the little island (whose name in Turkish means "Pigeon" or "Dove Island") that is in the harbor and is now connected by a causeway to the shore. The little fort on the island was built in 1834 as a military outpost during the Morean rebellion. About the only other old buildings worth examining are the Kale içi mosque, built in 1618 and the Ottoman

Views from modern Kuşadası.

caravanserai built by Öküz Mehmet Pasha in 1618. The latter has been restored and is now used (appropriately enough) as a hotel.

Accommodations are what Kuşadası really stars in and there are numerous hotels, motels, and holiday villages located in and around the town that cater to every taste and pocket. Thanks to the marina and good harbor, Kuşadası is a favorite calling place for yachts and tour vessels with the result that there are many good shopping of fortunities to be found.

Ephesos

The findings obtained in this region where the native people, namely the Lelegs and the Carians have lived since the beginning, indicate that the city is dated back to 2000 years BC. As far as the years of 1000 are concerned, it is assumed that the Ions came to this region, lead by Androckles.

Ephesos was captured by the Kimmers in 7th century BC., by the Lydians in 560, and later in 546 BC. by the Persians; and was rescued from the Persian domination when Alexander the Great defeated the Persians. Lysimachos, a commander of Alexander's, had the settlement removed from the hereabouts of the Temple of Artemis to the zone between the Mount of Panayır and the Mount of Bülbül, and had a wall built around the city.

The city was taken by the Kingdom of Pergamon after 190 BC., by Rome in 133 BC., and later by Byzantium, Ephesos maintained its importance during the period of Christianity, and the apostle St. Paul arrived there during the years of 50 AD. It is also a known fact that St. John was buried on the hill of Ayasuluk at the beginning of the 2nd century. Ephesos lived through its third glorious period during the reign of Justinianus in the middle of the 6th century AD. and, at this time, the Church of St. John was built on the hill of Ayasuluk. The Temple of Artemis is also one of the places to visit in Ephesos besides the Church of St. John. The Temple of Artemis, which had been built at first during the archaic period, was one of the seven wonders of the world later during the Hellenistic period and, in the year 356 BC. when Alexander the Great was born, it

Statue of fine Artemis, 2nd century.

was destroyed by a maniac and was reconstructed by the people of Ephesos. It has 127 columns and its dimensions are 55 x 115 m. Some of the bases of the columns of temple are ornamented with raised relief design. The other places to visit in Ephesos are the Cave of the Seven Sleepers, the house of the Virgin Mary, the Mosque of İsa Bey built in 1375 and the Museum of Ephesos where the ancient remains found in the ruins of Ephesos are displayed. The ruins of Ephesos, situated near Selçuk, are centers of interest owing to the ancient remains that are still

Hadrian Temple (117-138).
Gate of the St.John.

The Celsus Library.
Memmius Monument.

existent. When you enter through the Magnesia Gate from above you see the State Agora. The Temple of Isis is situated at the center of the Agora, and Stoa is placed on the North side of it. The Odeion with a capacity of 1400 persons is placed behind it and the Prytaneion where the sacred fire used to burn, is on its flank. The Baths of Varius are placed on the east side of Odeion. On the west of the Agora, the Monument of Memmius built in the late Hellenistic period, the fountain of C. Sextilius Pollio built in the year 93 AD., and the Temple of Domitian (81-93 AD.)

are placed. On the south of the Agora, the fountain of Laecanius Bassus is situated. The Curetes street starts downwards from the Temple of Memmius. The Gate of Heracles is placed on this avenue. After passing through this part, the fountain of Trajan built in the years 102-114 is seen on the right hand side and after this, the Temple of Hadrian appears in front of us, in all its splendid beauty (117-138 AD.). The Scholastica Baths, built in the 4th century AD., are situated behind the Temple of Hadrian. The houses of the rich people of Ephesos which were in front of it, have been restored and opened for visits at present.

General view of Ephesos Theater. Fountain of Traian (102-114).

At the corner formed by the Curetes street and the Marble Road, the House of Love is placed and the Library of Celsus, restored and reestablished in recent years, stands right in front of this. The library which had been built in the name of Gaius Celsus complated in the year 135 AD., is entered by way of a stairway, 21 m in width and having 9 steps. The south-eastern gate of the Trade Agora opens to the Library of Celsus. Agrippa's slaves, Mazaeus and Mithridates, liberated by him had this gate built in the year 4 BC.; it

comprises three sections and has been restored today. The columns of the Stoa encircling the Trade Agora with the dimensions 110x110 m, are standing erect today. The Temple of Serapis built in the period of Antonine (138-192 AD.) is placed behind the Trade Agora.

One of the magnificent buildings of Ephesos is the theater, which had a capacity of 24.000 people and is in a rather well preserved condition. The construction had started during the Hellenistic period but it could only be complet-

ed during the time of Trajan (98-117 AD.) Festivals are celebrated in this theater today. The Port Avenue extends in front of the theater. The avenue is 11 m wide and 600 m long, and it has been called Arcadiane because it was renewed during the time of Arcadius. On the whole north side of the avenue, there are the Port-Gymnasium, baths and the Theater Gymnasium. The avenue that passes along the front of the theater, extends towards the Stadium built during the Neron period (54-68 AD.) and towards the Vedius Gymnasium. The Church of the Virgin Mary built at the beginning of the 4th century AD. is situated behind the Port Gymnasium.

Herakles gate. 4th century.

Ephesus Museum in statues and Mother Mary's house.   42

Priene

Priene which is in Güllübahçe at a distance of 15 km from Söke,was carried to its present locality in the year 350 BC. from the original place where it had been founded earliar. At the point of entrance of the ruins, a road on the right leads us to the Theater of Priene. The theater had been built during the Hellenistic period, and underwent modifications during the Roman period. The theater consists of 50 rows of seats and

Priene Athena Temple. 4ᵗʰ century BC.
Priene Theater. 4ᵗʰ century B.C.

is capable of holding 5.000 people and, in the section of the orchestra of the theater, there are marble armchairs reserved for eminent people. On the right side of the theater, the Themenos of Egyptian Gods is situated. The upper Gymnasium is in front of the theater and the Byzantine church is at its side. You pass to the famous Temple of Athena from here. The Temple of Athena belongs to the 4th century BC. and it is the work of the architect Pytheos. The temple, with 6 x 11 columns, has dimensions of 19.55 x 37.20 m. A few columns of the temple, which is a classical example of Ionian architecture, have been erected. Alexander the Great had the eastern half of the temple completed. The altar in the front was decorated with high reliefs in the past, and it belongs to the 2nd century BC. The Stoa that displays a graceful example of stoneworkmanship, is on the south of the Temple of Athena. When you go downwards from the temple, you see the Agora of Priene which belongs to the 3rd century BC. The sacred Stoa belonging to the 2nd century BC. is situated north of the Agora. Bauleuterion (the assembly building) which looks like a small theater, with dimensions of 20 x 21 m and capacity for 640 people, is adjacent to the Stoa and, adjacent to it, there is Prytaneion (2nd century BC.) where the sacred fire used to burn. Temenos of Zeus Olympios and the food market are situated east and west of the Agora respectively. There are houses on two sides of the avenue which connects the Agora to the western gate. Temenos of Kybele and the house of Alexander the Great, are situated at the western gate side of the avenue. In the extreme south of Priene, the lower Gymnasium and the Stadium are situated.

Bouleuterion, Priene. 150 BC.
Miletos Theater.

Miletos

Miletos which is in the vicinity of Söke, was on the seashore in the ancient times. The Miletos people who had founded about 90 colonies in the Mediterranean and Black Sea regions, after 650 BC, had resisted the Persian invasions in Anatolia, but they were defeated finally and the city was destroyed by the Persians.

When you arrive at the zone of the ruins, the magnificent theater

Miletos Theater. 4th century BC.
Propylon of gymnasion.
Miletos 2nd century.

Columns of Apollo Temple, Didyma.

of the city appears in sight at first. The theater had been constructed during the Hellenistic period and, it acquired its present characteristics by means of the annexes made during the Roman period. The walls of the front façade of the theater, are 140 m long and 30 m high, and are an interesting example of stone workmanship. This theater was large enough to hold 15.000 people, and a fortress was built upon it during the Byzantine period.

On the opposite side of the theater there is a Seljukiyan Caravanserai and the baths that Faustina the II., wife of Marcus Aurelius (161-180 AD.) had caused to be constructed, are situated adjacent to the theater. The Temple of Serapis, belonging to the 3rd century AD., is behind the baths. The rectangular buildings seen on one side, are warehouse buildings. The adjacent Southern Agora building which has dimensions of 164 x 196 m and is surrounded by stoas, belongs to the 2nd century AD. and its southern gate is at the museum of Berlin today. When you go out through the northern gate of the Agora, you see the Bishop's Church, Martyrion belonging to the 5th century AD. beside it, and the ceremonial road which is 100 m long and 28 m wide, extending in front of the Agora. On the east side of it, there is the fountain in the Public Square (Nymphaion) belonging to the 2nd century AD., and Bouleuterion (the Senate Building) is situated opposite to it. It is known that this building had been constructed during the years 175-164 BC., and the Temple of Asklepios and the Sacred Place are situated at its side. At the side of these, the Northern Agora extends along the sacred road and at the right hand side of the sacred road, there is the Gymnasium belonging to the 2nd century BC. the entrance of which has been brought to an erect position at present.

The baths that Vergilius Capito had ordered to be constructed during the time of Claudius, are situated north of the Gymnasium; and some of these baths were used during the Seljukiyan Period. At the northern end of the Ceremonial Road, the Port Gate which was a passage with 16 columns is situated; and on the east of this road there is Delphinion which is a work of the Archaic period. When you go towards the north from here, the port stoa, the Port Monument built in the year 31 BC., the Small Port Monument and the Synagogue are located at the left hand side. The statues of the lions which watch over the port can be seen here; on the opposite side, the Roman Baths are seen.

Apollo Temple, Didyma

Didyma, sacred place near Miletos, had ritualistic links with the latter. The temple of Apollo, of great fame in the archaic age, was sacked in 494 BC. The year 311 BC. saw its revival and the temple was rebuilt. Under the Seleucids, the construction of the temple received large contributions and its dimensions were enlarged. The said construction continued until Roman times.

View of Apollon Temple. Didyma. Head of Medusa.

Interior view of Apollo Temple.
Columns of Apollo Temple.

Circa 250 AD. it lost most of its importance, and in 385 it was closed down by order of Theodosius, and the expansion of Christianity the erection of a church irr the adyton of the temple. The temple itself, which was already in ruins, collapsed during the earthquake which occurred in 1493.

The construction of the temple had been realized in three stages. The first saw the erection of one section during the archaic period, the second stage related to the construction which had previous-ly been begun in the 4th century BC. The third stage saw the erection of the sections the construction of which had begun in the Hellenistic periods, and which had been completed in Roman times and which we see today.

This temple measuring 51 x 109 m is built on a dipteros. It is surrounded by columns, namely. 10 x 21 columns outside and 8 x 19 columns inside the temple. The oracle room is very impressive. One gains access to it by a flight of stairs from the adyton. In the middle stand two columns. To the west of the adyton is naiskos, the main spot on which rituals took place.

Aphrodisias

Aphrodisias is situated in the Village of Geyre within the district of Karacasu in Aydın, and it is at a distance of 37 km to Aydın-Denizli motorway. When you reach Aphrodisias, you pass the parking place and come to the museum. The remains of Sebasteion, belonging to the 1st century AD. This building had three storeys formerly, and now the first storey is visible. The eastern gate of the Agora is located between the Sebasteion and the theater. This gate belongs to the 2nd century BC. and was

Views of Restored Tetrapylon, Aphrodisias.

converted to a fountain during the 5th century AD. The theater, was constructed during the late Hellenistic period, and repaired during the time of Marcus Aurelius. The theater which has the capacity of including ten thousand people and contains twenty seven rows of seats, has been brought to light completely today. There is a public square in front of the theater. The remains belonging to the theater bath are seen at the side of this square. The gymnasion and Byzantine house are located south of the baths. And beyond them, there is a building that could have been a Byzantine church or Martyrion.

View of tetrapylon.
Odeion, Aphrodisias. 2nd century.

Aphrodite Temple, Aphrodisias.
1ˢᵗ century.

You reach the Bath of Hadrian by
going around the Acropolis on
which the theater stands. The
Portico of Tiberius, with dimensions of 212 x 69 m, extends in
front of these magnificient
remains of the bath. The portico
constructed during the time of
Tiberius (14-37 AD.) extends
south side of the agora, it
includes one of the greatest pools
of the antique world at the center
an its three sides are surrounded
with columns of the Ionian order.
The northern area of the agora,
situated between the bath and
the odeion, covers an 205 x 120
m area, and is surrounded by column of the Doric order at three

sides. A footpath leads us to the magnificient odeion of Aphrodisias. The odeion, made of white marble, belongs to the 2nd century AD. and it had been covered with a roof formerly. The bishopric palace stands in the west of the odeion and constitutes a building complex with it. Blue and gray coloured columns are seen in this building which belongs to the 5th century AD. Now let's go towards the Temple of Aphrodite, starting from the odeion. The temple which has an impressive appearance with its standing columns, had been built in the 1st century BC.; and Aphrodite, the goddess of beauty, had represented fruitfulness here together with

Aphrodisias Theater. 1st century BC.
Stadion of Aphrodisias. 1st century.

Stadion of Aphrodisias. 1ˢᵗ century.
View of the Sebasteion. 1ˢᵗ century.

Kybele, the mother goddes of Anatolia. The temple was converted into a church during the Byzantine period. A monumental gate with eight columns called "Tetrapylon" standing at the east of the temple, was restored an it was given a magnificient appearance. The stadion is located at the extreme north of Aphrodisias. A building decorated with mosaics and called the school of philosophy, is situated between the temple and stadion. The stadion which is in such a good condition that it can be used today, belongs to he 1ˢᵗ century AD., its dimensions are 262 x 59 m and it can include 30.000 people.

Pamukkale

Located 20 kilometers from the town of Denizli, Pamukkale is one of the most interesting places in the world, justly famous not only for the entrancing beauty of its unique geological formations but also for its historical remains. The calcium oxide-rich waters flowing down the southern slope of Çaldağ located north of the ruins have, over the millennia, built up deposits of white travertine on the plateau thus fully justifying both the site's ancient name of Hierapolis-Holy City-and its modern one of Pamukkale-Cotton Castle. -Let us now take a tour of this supernal spot.

Ancient Hierapolis appears to have been founded by King Eumenes II of Pergamon and its name is derived from Hiera, the wife of King Telephos, the legendary founder of Pergamon. The city became subject to Rome in 133 BC. In 17 BC. during the reign of Tiberius it suffered a heavy earthquake that substantially destroyed the city, requiring it to be rebuilt.
Preliminary excavations at Hierapolis were undertaken by a German team towards the end of the last century. Since 1957, excavation and restoration work has been going on under the direction of an Italian group of archaeologists.

The ancient city was strung out on either side of a long colonnaded street called the Plateia. Measuring 13 meters in width, this street ran north and south from the southern gateway to the Arch of Domitian in the north. It is paved with huge blocks of limestone. The first

Poetical views of Pamukkale.

Beautiful views of Pamukkale.

structure one encounters on reaching the plateau is the city baths, which are in a very good state of preservation. The baths are Roman and from the 2nd century AD. In the eastern part of the baths is a palaestra measuring 36.13 by 52.25 meters. Immediately to the north and south of the palaestra are two big rooms that were reserved for the emperor and ceremonial use. A large hall stretches the length of the western side of the palaestra and this was the gymnasium used by athletes. This salon led into the frigidarium from which one proceeded to the barrel-vaulted rooms of the calidarium. A small room

adjacent to the large hall now serves as a museum in which works discovered in the Hierapolis excavations are on display. Since Hierapolis was principally a luxury resort town it was richly adorned with magnificent sculptures showing the influence of the Aphrodisias (q.v.) school and is well worth a visit.

The well preserved theater of Hierapolis commands magnificent view of the plain below. The original theater was located above the northern gate, but when the city was rebuilt during the reign of the Flavian emperors (60 AD.) the theater was relocated here, and the seats from the old structure were used in the work. During the reign of Septimius Severus (193-211 AD.) the theater's skene was modified and richly decorated with reliefs. In 532 it was discovered that the sekene had been weakened by age and the almost daily seismic activity that takes place here and had to be reinforced. Since the theater has been restored, it is now possible to see the friezes of mythological scenes depicting Apollo and Artemis in their original positions. Thirty rows of the seats of this theater resting against the slope have survived. Originally there were 20 rows in the lower part and 25 in the upper separated by a diazoma. The cavea was divided by eight aisles.. Passing through the city walls above the theater we proceed to the Martyrion of St Philip. This is an octagonal building erected on a square measuring 20 by 20 meters. It was built in the early 5th century. Even in its present state of ruin it is an impressive structure. Retracing our footsteps to the theater we may now examine the ruins below the theater.

Near the road is the Temple of Apollo, the principal deity of the city. While the foundations of this temple go back to late Hellenistic times, the present remains of the upper structure are from the 3rd century A.D. Next to it is a cave (called the Plutonion) from which poisonous gases emerge. (According to Strabo, an ox thrust into this cave would keel over and die. He himself experimented with doves.) The temple measures 20 by 15 meters and sat on a platform that was 2.5 meters high. Before the temple is a monumental fountain. Built during the late 3rd century A.D., the walls of this rectangular fountain are very well preserved. There was also a pool located

Beautiful view of Pamukkale.

before the fountain and the structure was richly adorned with statues and columns. The water for this fountain was brought here by aqueducts, remains of which may be seen in the vicinity of Güzelpınar and between Pamukkale and Karahayıt. East of the present museum is a Christian basilica consisting of a nave and two aisles. It dates from the 6th century AD. Walking along the route of the Plateia (which now passes through the modern swimming pool and motel) reminds us that this main street dividing the ancient city was once decorated with colonnades, porticos, and important buildings located on either side. The street runs directly toward

the city walls passing through a gateway built in Byzantine times atop an earlier fountain. On the way is a basilical structure with two aisles and a nave whose eastern end terminates in an apse. The city walls were built in 396 AD. and were reinforced by twenty-eight towers. Passing through Byzantine gate we come to a rather well preserved section of the Plateia. This part was built during the reign of Domitian (81-96 AD.) and terminates with the Arch of Domitian. This monumental gateway was actually erected by Julius Frontinus, who was proconsul of

Swimming in these spring waters among vestiges of the past is a real delight.

Theater of Hierapolis. 1ˢᵗ century.
View of Domitian and Byzantine Gate.

the Roman province of Asia (middle western Anatolia) in 82 and 83 AD., and dedicated to the emperor. The gate has two round towers and three portals. Excavations are now in progress to reveal the remains of shops and houses that once lined both sides of this street.

Northeast of the street between the Byzantine and Domitian gates was the agora of ancient Hierapolis. The traces of the city's original theater may be seen above. As we follow the road in the direction of the necropolis we

pass by the imposing walls of a building originally erected as baths around the end of the 2ⁿᵈ century AD. It was converted to a church in the 5ᵗʰ century. The huge necropolis of Hierapolis spreads out on either side of the road for a distance of two kilometers. It contains tumuli, sarcophagi, and house-shaped tombs that range in date from the late Hellenistic period to early Christian times. It is one of the most extensive and best preserved ancient cemeteries in Anatolia and a stroll through it leaves a deep and mystical impression upon the visitor, particularly on a moonlit night. The road proceeds on to the hot springs of Karahayıt located 4 kilometers away.

Bodrum

Bodrum, the native land of the famous historian Heredot, is an important tourism center in our country, which attracts attention by reason of its natural beauties, besides its history.

We know that the native people, namely the Lelegs and the Carians had lived on the hills in the Peninsula of Bodrum. In the year 1000 BC., those who came here along with the Doric migrations settled in the locality where the fortress stands today and mixed with the native people here. So, the city of Halikarnassos was founded.

The city which was captured by the Lydians in the first half of the 6th century BC., and by the Persians in the year 546 BC., was joined with the Satrapy of Saird and later.

In the year 377 BC. Maussollos got hold of the Western Anatolia, had many cities constructed in the region of Caria, and had the capital of Caria removed from Milas to Halikarnassos. With the aim of enlarging the city, he had 6 of the 9 Leleg cities removed to this region, and he had the city surrounded with walls and had many palaces, theaters and temples built in the city.

The most important one of these, is the monumental tomb constructed for Maussollos and his wife Artemisia II. The construction had started in the year 355 BC. and at the time of its completion in 340 BC., it was one of the 7 wonders of the world. According to the information supplied by the historian Pilinius, the tomb consisted of 4 parts; there was a high base at the lowest level, a gallery of 36 columns upon it,

Yacht in the Blue journey.

View of Bodrum Castle (1402).
View of Bodrum.

and a roof of 24 steps upon which the statues of Maussollos and his wife were placed. The architect of the monumental tomb was Pytheos, and the relief engravings were made by sculptors such as Skopas, Leochares, Bryaxis and Timothes. The stones of the monumental tomb which was ruined by an earthquake in the 14th century, were used by the Knights of Rhodes in the construction of the fortress that exists today. The tendrils found in the tomb and the statues at the top, are kept at the British Museum today.

When Artemisia II died in the year 351 BC., she was succeeded by Idrius who was in turn succeeded by Ada, who was dethroned by her brother Pixodaros. Meanwhile Alexander the Great entered Anatolia and made Ada ascend the throne, The Queen's tomb, discovered in recent years, is displayed at the museum today. The city which was captured by Lysimachos following the death of Alexander the Great, was later subjected to Rhodes and Pergamum, and still later Rome got hold of Anatolia totally. Owing to the fact that Bodrum was founded upon the ancient city of Halikarnassos, not

General view of Bodrum.
Statue of Princess Ada in
Bodrum Museum.

much is left to our day from the ancient city. The theater, the stoa of Mars and Apollon situated within the gardens in the city, the theater on the hill belonging to the Hellenistic period have been restored today. Former sources of information state that, the temple of Mars and the stoa of Apollon were under the road in front of the theater, and the temples of Hermes and Afrodities were on the public square of today. The fortress is the city symbol. The Knights of Rhodes had it

Views of Bodrum.

constructed in the year 1402, and it was reinforced with the Italian, English, German and French towers. It was taken by the Turks in 1523, and it is used as an underwater museum today. The underwater section and the section of Princess Ada, are the sections which attract the greatest attention here.

There are not many Turkish works in Bodrum. The famous crafts called The Crafts of Bodrum today, were constructed here during the Ottoman period too.

Marmaris

Surrounded by pine-clad hills, Marmaris is located on the site of ancient Phykos of which nothing at all remains since the modern town sits atop the ruins. There are however numerous examples of Ottoman architecture from the reign of Süleyman the Magnificent since Marmaris was taken by him as part of his campaign against the island of Rhodes nearby. Among the

Aerial views of the Marmaris.

buildings that may be seen are
the castle built in 1521; a caravanserai built in 1545; Taşhan,
also built in the 16th century;
and the Mosque of İbrahim Agha,
dated 1789. Marmaris is deser-
vedly better-known for its natural
beauty: the lace-like coastline is
embellished with coves and inlets
where one may go swimming,
diving, or fishing. The sheltered
bay is excellent for windsurfing.
Accom-modations, restaurants,
and cafes are plentiful and tours
are available to coves like
İçmeler, Kumlubük, Turunç, and
Kadırga. Nearby is a sea cavern

A view of İçmeler.

General views of Marmaris.

called Fosforlu (Phosphorescent). The forests of fragrant storax trees around Marmaris offer tempting picnic spots.

Marmaris is a calling place on the Blue Voyage and boats may be hired here to go to Bodrum and Fethiye. Boat tours are also available to the nearby ruins of ancient Caunos. Good highway connections make it easy to visit more distant places like Knidos, Pamukkale, Aphrodisias, and even Ephesos.
The Marmaris marina is amply provided with everything a yachtsman might need.

Caunos

There are three ways of reaching Caunos which attract great attention today owing to its Venetion type of channel, Lycian type of tombs and ist suined remains. The visitors who come by means of their yachts, land on the island named Delikli Ada and reach the site of the ruins by starting off in small boats from here; those who come from Marmaris by sea route, drop anchor in the vicinity

Passing through Venetian-Lake canals and reach the ruins of ancient caunos.

Thefamous beach of Dalyan where are sea tortoises lay their eggs.

of Delikli Ada and also reach the site of the ruins in small boats; and those who come by land route, reach the ruins by starting boats from the Village of Dalyan which is at a distance of 27 km from Köyceğiz. The existance of the ruins of Caunos was first discovered in the year 1842, and excavations have been carried on there by the Turkish archeologists under the supervision of Prof. Baki Öğün since 1967.

Caunos, the son of Miletos, had been indicated as the founder of the city and therefore, it had been named Caunos. The city was first captured by the Persians and then by Alexander and in the year 189 BC., it was made subject to the Kingdom of Rhodes. We know that it continued until

the year 167 BC. Caunos was the subjected to the kingdom of Pergamon and was brought directly under the sovereignty of Rome after 133 BC. You reach the site of the ruins by means of channel adorned with Lycian type tombs belonging to the 4th century BC. The first place that we see is the acropolis of Caunos. The northern part of the city wall, which surrounds the acropolis, belongs to the period of Mausolos. The northwestern part has Hellenistic qualities. And starting from the harbour are seen the city walls of Cyclopean type belonging to the Archiac Period. The theater belonging to the

Views of Lycian tombs, Caunos. 4th century BC.

Caunos Theater. Roman period.
View of Lycian tombs.

Roman Period is located at the skirt of the acropolis and its southern part is carved in the rock; the other parts are shaped into seats supported by gable roof vaults. There are 33 rows of seats, the scene has collapsed and the part of the orchestra has been filled in.

A temple, revealed by the recent excavations, is located at far west of the theater, and a church and the magnificent walls of the Roman Bath are visible beyond it. Another temple belonging to the Roman Period is located behind the bath. As we go downwards,

see the remains of a wall built in the shape of three-fourths of a circle with a row of columns on it and, behind it, a temple of the Doric order.

The locality called Sülüklü Göl (Lake of Leeches) in Caunos today, was a harbour closed by means of chains during the Antique Period. The excavations performed at the north of this harbour have revealed a stoa which used to form a part of the port agora.

The fountain near the stoa has a plan of inantis style and has been restored recently, and the inscription which is seen on its side facing the harbour, contains the written decrees concerning the customs house.

Telmessos

The ruins of Telmessos now lie beneath the pleasant modern town of Fethiye. Fethiye is the center of tourism in Lycia. It contains many touristic facilities and is especially convenient for yacht tourism. From Fethiye one may visit the many ruins and important ancient sites in the surrounding area in comfortable, easy, one-day outings. There are many such places close to Fethiye, including Cadyanda, Pınara, Tlos, Xanthos, Letoon and Patara. Since the new town of Fethiye has grown over the ancient settlement, and no excavations have been carried out we do not know when the ancient city was first founded; however, the double "S" in the last syllable of the name suggests that it was a local name. In the 4th century BC. he also, Pericles of Limyra, who was trying to establish the Lycian confederation, advanced on Telmessos and included it among the settlements in the confederation. Alexander brought local rule to an end in Telmessos but the great leader had previous links with the town. The fruits and wise men of Telmessos were renowened throughout the ancient world. Philip, the father of Alexander called upon a sage from Telmessos to interpret his dream. The sage, Aristander, prophesied that Alexander would be born and he also prophesied the entire future of the prince. Alexander grew up to respect this sage and always had him by his side. Aristander was even to accompany him during Alexander's eastern campaign. It was thanks to the position of this sage that Telmessos surrendered to Alexander immediately, without any opposition, and no damage was done to the city.

Views of Calm Sea (ölüdeniz).

Alexander's commander took command of the fortress of Telmessos with some cunning. Nearchos, the commander of the fleet, entered the harbor of Telmessos and asked the citizens to allow his musicians to enter the city. When the citizens agreed, the musicians entered and during the night they took over the fortress with the spears and shields they bore with them. After this cunning trick, Telmessos was left under the command of the king of Telmessos once again by Alexander, who also left his commander as the governor-general of Lycia, thus trying to placate the king of Telmessos.

After the death of Alexander, Telmessos remained in Ptolemaian hands for some time and after 189 BC., it was joined to the kingdom of Pergamon for a period. Upon the death of the king of Pergamon, Attalos II, Telmessos was annexed directly to Rome together with all the lands of Pergamon.
In the year 168 BC., Telmessos entered the Lycian confederacy, and struck a coin to commemorate the event. During the Byzantine period, the city continued to exist as an important center in the area, but after the 7th century AD. its importance waned with the threat of Arab attacks.

At one point, during the 7th century, Anastasius II gave his own name to the city, calling it Anastasiopolis, but this name was soon abandoned. For some time during the Ottoman period it was called Megri, but this name was also abandoned for the modern name of Fethiye, which it has borne since the 19th century. C. Texier, who saw the city in the

View of Fethiye Bay

1850's, reported that the Apollo temple and the theater were then standing. Soon after his visit, the violent earthquake of 1856 destroyed these, and a second earthquake that took place a century later also destroyed Fethiye. The town of today was completely rebuilt after 1957, and the theater lies (appropriately enough) below the present open-air cinema. The original town stood on the site of the fortress. The lower part of the walls date from the Roman period, while the upper parts date from the medieval period.

The medieval battlements were reinforced by the Knights of

View of Fethiye.
Amynthas Tomb. 4th century BC.

Rhodes, who tried to gain control of the region from here. From Knights' Island, in the bay of Fethiye, where they built a fortress, they controlled the town of Fethiye. Today this island is a resort, adorned with villas. On the eastern cliff of the acropolis is the tomb of Amyntas, the magnificent rock tomb which has become the symbol of Fethiye and can be seen from every point in the city. The facade of the tomb is in antis in plan like a temple in the Ionic order. It belongs to

View of Fethiye at night.
Fethiye Bay.

Amyntas who was the son of
Hermapias, and was made in the
4th century BC. C. Texier, who
visited this tomb in the 1850's
carved his name in the upper left
corner of the tomb door. Beside the
Amyntas tomb is another similar
tomb, one of the columns of which
has broken off. Alongside this,
other rock tombs can also be seen.
In the town itself, there are many
sarcophagi of the Lycian type.
One lies almost beneath the rock
tombs, on the street below, and
another is situated between the
municipal buildings and the wharf.

Xanthos

The Persians took over Anatolia when they defeated the Lydians. When the Persians attempted to capture Xanthos chose to commit collective suicide with the aim of saving themselves form being taken as prisoner by the Persians. The people of Xanthos also resisted Brutus who attempted to recruit soldiers in Anatolia in 42 BC. after having killed Caesar, ant they again committed collective suicide when the city was falling.

When we start out to visit this city, surrounded with walls, we see a Hellenistic gate at the left hand side of us and another gate built for the Emperor Vespasianus. The ruins that stand on our right hand side are the remains of the Monument of the Nereids, which belongs to the years of 400 BC. and is kept at the British Museum today.

The center of Xanthos consists of the Roman theater. The Roman tower-tomb is located first adjacent to the theater. The Lycian monumental tomb, 8.59 m in height and belonging to the 4th century BC., is at the middle. The other monument adjacent to this one, is the Harpy monument which is 8.87 m in height and belongs to the year 480 BC. Owing to the fact that the reliefs of the upper part of this monument had been taken to the British museum, the ones that we see here today, are the copies made of plaster. The wide area adjacent to this monument, is the Roman agora of Xanthos. There is a monument in the eastern part of the agora; it is 11 m in height and there are inscriptions written in Greek and

Lycian monument at Xanthos.
4th century BC.

Xanthos Theater.
Xanthos Lycian and Harpy Monuments.

Lycian script on it. There is Lycian acropolis behind the theater. And immediately behind the theater, there is a Lycian monumental tomb. The remains of a Byzantine church are at the side of this monument.

The remains of a palace of the Lycian period lie at the center of the acropolis and, a little further, there is a Lycian pool carved in the rocks. The place of recreation of the Lycian King, is located at the extreme end of the acropolis at a point overlooking the lowland. The Roman acropolis is on the hill which is at the east of the

Xanthos Theater, Roman period.
Xanthos, Lycian monument 4ᵗʰ century BC.

theater. There is a Byzantine basilica in the acropolis. Many rock-tombs and their monuments are placed side by side in the southeast of the acropolis. The Lycian monumental tomb belonging to the 4ᵗʰ century BC. and located at a point near the city walls, is 6.39 m. The remains of the Monument of Payava are seen at a point a little further towards the right hand side of this; and the monument itself had been carried to the British Museum. Down below, at a point where the city walls from a corner, only the base of the tomb with lions, belonging to the date 540 BC., is seen.

Letoon

When you turn off from the Kaş-Fethiye motorway and advance towards the Village of Bozoluk, you reach Letoon. Letoon is a city that had been founded in the name of Leto, mother of Apollon and Artemis.

The first one, of the three temp-less here, belongs to Leto and it is dated to the years of 400 BC. It is of Ionian order, has six columns in the front and at the back and eleven columns at the sides. The smallest temple which is located

Letoon, Apollo Temple.
Hellenistic period.

Letoon Theater. Roma period.

Letoon Artemis Temple. 4th century BC. View from Portico.

adjacent to the above mentioned one, that is to say at the center, is dated to the 4th century BC. and belongs to Artemis. The third temple of Doric order which is situated at the extreme end, belongs to Apollon and to the Hellenistic period. The exedra in the form of semicircle which was used to place statues on, belongs to the Hellenistic period. There are the remains of a fountain belonging to the Hadrian period.

The theater belongs to the Hellenistic period and it has two entrances in the west and in the east which have vaults.

Patara

When you turn and enter the road that leads to Gelemiş, on your way from Fethiye to Kalkan, you reach the ruins of Patara at the 15th km. Patara continued to develop during the Roman Period, within the Lycian union, and carried on its fuction as a naval base where the Judicial procedures of the Roman governorships were carried out and the relations of Rome with the eastern provinces were maintained. Patara continued to be important during the Byzantine period and it is the locality where St. Nicholas was born. The harbour of Patara is filled with sand today.

You see the Arch of Triumph on your way to Patara; it was the gate of entrance to Patara. This arch was built in the years of 100 AD. during the time of Mettius Modestus, the Governor of Rome in Lycia. You see the tombs of Lycian type at the edge of the road. The temple of Apollon should have been probably situated on the hill above the arch. There are ruins of baths at the south of the hill. There are ruins of a basilica at the edge of the road, ruins of a bath on the west handside of this and further beyond, a temple of Corinthian order with its cella gate still standing. The theater which was built at the skirt of the slope of a hill in 147 AD., is covered with sand. The temple of Athena is located on the hill where the theater is set. There is a cistern with a depth of 8 m adjacent to this temple. There was a cereal barn in ancient times in the harbour which is filled with sand today. There is a monumental tomb adjacent to the barn building and the structures of the agora of Patara are situated at the back of the barn.

Patara Theater 147.
Monumental Gateway. 100.

Antiphellos

Kaş was originally called Habesos or Habesa in the ancient tongue of Lycia and later was given the name Antiphellos. It is one of the oldest settlements in the region of Lycia. Most of the ancient settlement is now covered by the modern town of Kaş. The rock-cut tombs to the north-east of the town date to the 4th century BC.

General views of Kaş.
Beach of Kaputaş near the Kaş.

On a rise between the open sea and the hill, which was probably the acropolis of the ancient city, lies a rock tomb formed like a Doric structure with Doric triglyphs on the facade. Inside the tomb is to be found a frieze of dancing female figures.

The acropolis was surrounded by a fortified wall, of which traces are to be seen on the facade facing the island of Meis (Kastellorizon).

No traces of fortifications are to be seen on the northern or western slopes. To the west of the modern town stands the ancient theater overlooking the sea.

Views of the Kaş at night.

This structure possesses a remarkable view. It was constructed of local limestone and today the tribunes and outer walls are still visible although no trace of the skene is left.

On the western edge of the acropolis are traces of a temple. Tombs of the Roman period are scattered about the town and along the coast.

Kekova

After leaving Kaş one sails past Uluburun and sets a course for Kekova, a spot that is like heaven on earth. One first encounters the Sıçak peninsula at the end of which are two islands: Toprakada and Karaada. Kekova island stretches out from here and it is because of this island that the whole area is called Kekova. Passing among the islands and arriving at Kekova, the safest anchorage is Üçağız, which is a good, all-round

Views of Kaleköy (Simena).

Views of Kaleköy (Simena).

harbor. Other places may be used for short periods during visits. At Kekova history and nature have merged and become inseparable. Such ancient cities are Aperlai, Kekova, Simena, and Theimussa are to be found in the vicinity.

Aperlai

Aperlai is located on the Sıçak peninsula, near the Sıçak jetty. A Lycian city, Aperlai's history is known from coins bearing its name that have been discovered and goes back to the 4th or 5th centuries BC. Aperlai was the head of the Lycian Confederacy, of which Simena and Apollonia were also members.

The city walls begin at the seashore and are fortified with towers at intervals. These walls, with their rectangular and polygonal construction, are from Roman times. Other remains at Aperlai are all from the Byzantine and later periods. The western reaches of the wall are of rectangular construction. There are three gates in this wall, two of which have a plain and the third a blind archway. The southern reaches of the walls are of polygonal construction and in a bad state of repair. This side is reinforced with two towers and it is here that the main gate was located.

Views of the Lycian Sarcophagus in the sea.

Views of Kekova.

Outside the walls are typical Lycian sarcophagi from Roman times.

Simena

From inscriptions that have been found, we know that the history of the ancient city of Simena goes back to the 4th century BC. If we go ashore via the jetty next to the sarcophagus on the seashore and climb the hill behind the houses, we reach the castle of Simena. This castle was used during the Middle Ages. In the medieval walls of the inner keep are a few blocks of all that remains of ancient temple. Inside the castle is

a small natural theater carved into the rock. This is the smallest of theaters among the cities of Lycia. West of the theater there are rock tombs here and there. Above the rock tombs is a Roman wall built of dressed stone and located on the wall are late-period embrasures thus giving one a glimpse of three eras simultaneously. On the shore are the ruins of public baths whose inscription is still legible and reads "A gif to the emperor Titus made by the people and council of Aperlai as well as by the other cities of the confederation."

Looking from the castle towards Üçağız it becomes clear how beautiful and safe a natural harbor this really is. Simena (or Kale Köy, its present-day name) is only a temporary shelter however. The actual shelter for yachts is Theimussa (Üçağız), a landlocked bay surrounded by green hills. There is a road overland that leads here. The ruins of the ancient city of Theimussa are located here. Very little is known about the history of the city however. One inscription indicates that its history goes back to the 4th century BC. One sees mostly the ruins of a necropolis here and no city walls or other major structures have been encountered. The oldest sarcophagus is from the 4th century BC. and is shaped like a house. Over it is the nude portrait of a young man. The inscription tells us that it belongs to "Kluwanimiye". The work is Roman and a later addition to the sarcophagus.

One may reach Kekova overland from Demre Çayağzı as well as in boats that you can rent at Kaş.

After leaving Kekova we pass Kişneli Island and Asırlı Island and come to Gökkaya harbor.

View of the Üçağız (Theimussa).

Views of Kekova.

Gökkaya is a beautiful bay and a fine harbor. On the way is a big sea cave that was used at one time by pirates. From here one comes to Çayağzı, also called Kokar bay, alongside of which are the ruins of Andriace. There are restaurants and souvenir shops here. From here, one may take a car to Myra, the city of St. Nicholas, which is quite close. This is also a place from which one may visit other Lycian cities as Isinda at Belenli, Apollonia at Kılınçlı, Istlada at Kapaklı, Kyaenai at Yavu, and.Trysa and Sura at Gölbaşı. The area is also filled with thousands of Lycian sarcophagi lying everywhere.

Myra

Myra is situated on the newly completed coastal road from Kaş to Finike, 24 km from Finike, in the region of Kale. After going through the small town of Bucak, we continue on to the banks of the river Demre, 15 km from the settlement. Leaving our car by the road, we cross the stream and through the fields can be seen the distinctive Lycian rock tombs, with facades almost like that of a multi-storied apartment building, pierced with innumerable windows.

Although the date of Myra's first foundation is not known, from some Lycian inscriptions found in the area it would appear that the habitation existed in the 5th century. Strabo counts it among the six notable cities of Lycia.

In the year 18 AD., the emperor Germanicus and his wife Agrippina visited Myra, and in honor of this visit, the statues of both the emperor and empress were erected in the harbor of the city, Andriace.

In the early years of Christianity in 60 AD., St. Paul met with his followers here on their way to Rome. During the 2nd century AD. Myra became a center of the diocese, and it was during that period that its theater was built. The theater and its portico were constructed by Licinus Lanfus of Oinoanda, to whom 10,000 dinars were given for its completion. The renowned Opramoas of Rhodiapolis, whose hand of patronage is to be seen in all the cities of Lycia, did not ignore this city, donating great sums to its development. Another notable patron was Jason of Kyaenai, through whose efforts the city was adorned with many great buildings. During the Byzantine period,

Myra, Lycian rock-cut tombs.
4th century BC.

Myra maintained its role as a religious center. During the 4th century AD., St. Nicholas of Patara, later to be known as Santa Claus, was bishop of Myra. His tomb and a church dedicated to him are to be found here.

The ruins of Myra are situated 5 km inland, between the modern town and the sea. The acropolis of the city is situated on top of the cliffs containing the Lycian rock tombs. The city walls, dating from the Hellenistic and Roman periods, are still to be seen protecting the acropolis.

The rock tombs cover the southern cliffs below the acropolis like a sheet of lace. Apart from the tombs beside the theater, others are to be seen on the river banks and in the surrounding cliffs. Many of the tombs cut into the rock near the theater are damaged and much worn, but some still have fine facades, with inscriptions and reliefs clearly delineated. Two damaged tombs can be reached by a steep pathway.

Another tomb with reliefs on the northern face of the rock has been cut in the form of a large sarcophagus. The owner of the tomb is seen buried here together with his family. The reliefs show him first in his prime and later as a corpse laid out on his heir with his family around him. The tomb is dated to the 4th century BC.

To see the tombs more closely and in order to examine them in detail, we can climb up to them via a flight of steps belonging to the theater, the river flowing by below. The most interesting tomb in the necropolis has a facade shaped like that of a temple. The facade contains two flanking columns of the Ionian order with floriate capitals containing lion

View of entrance of Myra Theater

Myra Theater.
Roman period, icona of St. Nicholas.

heads. The architrave frieze contains a relief of a lion attacking a bull, executed in a most convincing manner.

The theater is situated close to the rock tombs. It is in a relatively good condition. The cavea has been carved into a slope out of the rock. The galleries were supported at the sides with vaulting that was used both for access to the upper galleries and also contained shops. Below the diazoma were 29 rows of seats, and below them, six rows more.

The skene is still standing up to the second course in places and from the remaining fragments, it would appear that the facade facing the audience was extremely ornate. In the town namen Kale is situated the St. Nicholas Church, who was from Patara, and took office in Myra as the Bishop in the 4th century AC. and buried in this Church when he died, which was given his name. Town of Myra and the Church was demolished during the arab raids in the 7th and 9th centuries, and was totally destroyed in the naval raid made again by the arabs in 1034. Constantin

Monomakhos IX and Zoe the empress had made the Church reconstructed and also surrounded by walls. In 1087, merchants coming from Bari had stolen the bones from the church which were supposed to be belonging to St. Nicholas. This Church is the one built in the 9th century and restored several times. It is understood that the tombs belonging to the 2nd century AC. were used again in the lower storey of the Church. You can see the frescoes situated on the abscissa and the naves of the Church. Furthermore, the sitting places and columns reflect their restored appearances. You can reach the upper storey of the Church by using the stairs

View of the churc of St.Nicholas.
Statue of St.Nicholas.

located at the side way. The Church was subjected to another restoration in the recent past, and a statue of St. Nicholas was erected near it.

After the Church, you can see the mausoleum on the Myra-Kaş road, dating back to the 2nd century AC. which probably belongs to a rich Lycian. Port of Andriace, taking place in Çayağzı at a few kms. distance to Kale, is known as the port of Myra town, where the Hadrian Granarium (granary) with dimensions of 36 x 45 m still stands erect.

Olympos

Olympos is situated between the holiday resort of Kemer and the village of Adrasan. We follow a sign leading from Ulupınar to the ruins of Olympos, where we find not only the ruins of Olympos but volcanic terrain which has formed from constantly fuming geisers of natural hot gas. The ruins of the city areset along the banks of a small stream, and

Aerial view of the porto-Ceneviz near Olympos.

Aerial view of Olympos.

although small, it is a very interesting site, unforgettable in its striking position by the sea, and curious for its everburning light.

The left bank of the stream is completely covered with undergrowth, and with great difficulty, one can make out the remains of a wall, and over it a door on certain ruins. This is all that remains of a temple on that side of the stream. What stands now is probably the wall seperating the pronaos and the cella of the temple. From the inscription of this temple we understand that it was built during the reign of the Roman emperor Marcus Aurelius. It had a plan of the in antis type, and was of the ionic order. Beyond the temple, other buildings still standing date from the Byzantine period, and on the side facing the sea can be found the remains of a bath. To the south of the stream, opposite the foot of a bridge crossing it can be seen the ruins of a large Byzantine basilica, while the remains of the bath stretch down to the shore behind it.

Between the basilica and the theatre of Olympos lies a building in ruins, with columns in the centre. It is not known what this may have been, although it is possible that it represents the remains of a gymnasium.

Beyond this, below the necropolis is the theatre of Olympos. Large pieces of rubble spread over the surrounding area and piled up in the ochestra show this to have been a theatre of the classical Roman type. Beyond the theatre can be seen a ramp constructed of polygonal stone coursing which leads into the city's necropolis. Buildings from the medieval period can be seen on the hills overlooking the sea.

Ruins of Olympos.
View of the beach at Olympos.

Phaselis

Phaselis is. in Tekirova, at a distance of 35 km from Antalya. Phaselis was founded in the year 690 BC. as a colony of Rhodes. Then it maintained its existance under the dominitaion of the Persians, of Alexander in 333 BC., the Kingdom of Rhodes, Rome and Byzantium successively, and finally it became extinct in the

Aerial view of Phaselis.
South port of Phaselis.

11th century AD. when the Seljukiyans began to consider Antalya and Alanya more important.

The aqueducts which attract attention at first sight, belong to the Roman period. There are three harbours in Phaselis; one of which is the Military Harbour in front of the aqueducts, the second one is the wide Northern Harbour adjacent to the military harbour and the third is the Southern Harbour in the south.

There is a wide avenue at the

View of aqueducts of Phaselis.
Phaselis Theater. Roman period.

Aerial view of the Kemer.
Aerial view from Beldibi.

center of Phaselis which starts from the Military Harbour, and ends here with the Gate of Hadrian. At the starting point of the avenue, the Trade Agora is located at the right an there the remains of shops here. The Domitian Agora and the new agora are situated on the avenue at the side of this agora. And on the left hand side of the avenue, the theater of Phaselis, belonging to the Roman period. The necropolis of the city is on the hills at the left and side of the incoming road, and at the seaside.

Antalya

Attaleia, the ancient name of Antalya, is derived from that of the Pergamon King Attalos II Philadelphus, who founded the city on the Pamphylian seacoast around 150 BC. Settlement of Antalya and its environs stretches back to the dawn of humanity however as attested to by Paleolithic finds discovered in the neaby Karain and Beldibi caves and Early Bronze Age finds discovered at Semahöyük. Today it is part on Turkey's "Gold Coast", an exquisite land of sun, sea, and history.

In 133 BC. Antalya, together Pergamon's other possessions in Asia Minor, were taken over by Rome. Antalya (or "Attalia" as the Bible calls it) is where Paul set sail from together with Barnabas on his first missionary journey: "They passed through Pisidia and reached Pamphylia. Then after proclaiming the word at Perge they went down to Attalia and from there sailed for Antioch..." Acts xiv 24-26). In 130 AD., Hadrian visited the city during his peregrinations of his empire and to this we owe the monumental arch (7) built in his honor. During Byzantine times Antalya was an archdiocese. Following the Seljuk capture of the city, Antalya continued to be an important commercial and military port.

Because the modern city sits atop the remains of its predecessors, very little remains of old Antalya. Of the fortifications that once surrounded the city, only Hıdırlık tower is still standing. Hadrian's Gate, as we have said, was originally constructed as a victory arch. Kesik ("cut-off") minaret and Yivli ("fluted" or "grooved") minaret are works

View of Antalya at night.

Hadrian's Gate, Antalya.

General views of Antalya.

from the reign of Alaeddin Keykubad I (1219-1236). The former is located on the site of a temple from the 2nd century AD. while the latter has become a symbol of modern Antalya. Another of the architectural works of importance in Antalya is the Karatay medresse, built during the reign of the same sultan. The ancient castle overlooking the ancient harbor with its old houses nestled inside is worth exploring and the Antalya Museum is a must for anyone interested in this region's art and history.

The area around Antalya is full of places from which one-day trips may be made to ancient Lycian,

Different views of Antalya.

View of Düden Waterfall and Köprülü Kanyon.

Pisidian, and Pamphylian sites: Termessos, located amidst the lofty peaks above Antalya; Perge located 17 kilometers, Aspendos located 40 kilometers, and Side located 80 kilometers along the road to Alanya; and cities like Selge and Syllion located somewhat inland are but a few examples. In the direction of Kemer is Phaselis, a marvelous archaeological site where one may enjoy the ruins in the atmosphere of a seaside pine forest. In addition there are a number of scenic spots of natural beauty such as the waterfalls at Düden, Kurşunlu and Manavgat, which are a delight to visit on a hot, Mediterranean summer day.

Perge

Perge is situated in the district of Aksu at the 17th km of the Antalya-Alanya motorway. It has been understood by reading a clay tablet discovered in Boğazköy that Perge had existed during the Hittite period under the name "Parha".

The city was first captured by Alexander and the it was dominated by the Seleukos, the Kingdom of Pergamon and Rome respectively. Most of the remains seen today belong to the Roman period. The excavations which were started here in 1946 under the presidency of Prof. Dr. Arif Müfid Mansel, are being continued today.

The first structure we come across in the site of the ruined remains is the theatre of Hellenistic-Roman type which is capable to accomodate 15.000 people. The theater was constructed in the 2nd century AD. and gladiator fights had taken place here during the late Roman Period. The U-shaped stadion in front of the theater dates back to the 2nd century AD. The rows of 12.000 seats in the stadion were supported by vaults and its monumental gate is total ruined today.

The city walls of Perge, which belong to the Hellenistic Period, had been fortified by towers in certain places and the southern part, which is the entrance today, was enlarged in the 6th century and a patio was formed. A gate built during the time of Septimus Severus gives access to a second patio. The monumental fountain dedicated to the memory of Artemis Pergaia and Septimus Severus, is seen in the west hand and an ornamented Propylon belonging to this bath. We leave

Kurşunlu Waterfall, Antalya

these behind and come to a horseshoe-shaped patio which is accessed by means of a gate belonging to the Hellenistic period which has two towers. Plancia Magna, who had done many useful things for Perge, had this place constructed. The statues belonging to the two storied gate with three entrances which is located in the northern port of the patio, were found out during the excavations and are exibited at the Museum of Antalya today. An Agora built in the 4th century AD. is situated at the east of the Hellenistic gate, the portico with

Agora columns at Perge.
General view of Perge.

The city gate of Perge. Hellenistic period.
Colonnaded street at Perge.

columns is adjacent to it, and a
church and a bath are located at
the south of the gate. An avenue
with marble pillars, which is 300
meters long, extends from the
gate of entry towards the acropolis. This avenue ends with a
fountain. The Palaestra located
on the avenue that extends in the
west hand-side of this avenue is
in well preserved form and it had
been dedicated to emperor Claudius. There is a Basilica of the bishopric and, at the west of this basilica, they are situated the ruined
remains of a bath adjacent to the
city wall. The acropolis of Perge is
located above the fountain.

Aspendos

Turning off the Antalya-Alanya road at kilometer 30 in the direction of the village of Belkis we come to the best-preserved ancient theater in Turkey. According to Strabo, the city of Aspendos was founded by colonists who came from Argos under the leadership of Mopsos. Coins minted in the 4th and 5th centuries BC. give the city's name as Estwediya. (Aspendos had the distinction of being the only city besides Side that coined money in its own name at that early

Interior views of Aspendos Theater.

Aspendos Theater. (161-180 AD.)
Ancient bridge near the Aspendos.

period.) For a while, the city was a member of the Athenian maritime alliance (the Delian League). A naval battle was fought off Aspendos in 469 BC. during which the Persian fleet was defeated by the forces of the Athenian general Cimon. Despite this however we see Aspendos being used as a Persian base in 411 BC. With Alexander's defeat of the Persians in 334 BC., Aspendos was freed of Persian rule. It was ruled by various Hellenistic period kings following the death of Alexander and like most other cities in Asia Minor it came under Roman rule in 133

BC. The city particularly flourished in the 2nd and 3rd centuries AD. In the 5th century the city's name was changed to Primupolis. Aspendos was badly affected by the Arab incursions in the 8th century. The Seljuks, who arrived in the area in the 12th century, appear to have made use of some of the ancient structures, the theater being among them.

One may approach the ruins by car as far as the theater and we shall begin our tour there. The Aspendos theater is built of regularly dressed blocks of conglomerate while the door and window frames are of a cream-colored limestone. One enters the skene

through five doors, the one in the middle on the east being larger thaa the other four on located two on either side. The stage building is a two-tiered facade with four rows of windows, each row of which is of a different form and size. The niches contained decorative statuary. Even today the facade has an attractive appeal. From inscriptions at the theater we know that the structure was built during the reign of Marcus Aurelius (161-180) by two brothers, Curtius Crispinus and

Aquaducts of Aspendos.
Basilica of Aspendos.

Two different view of aqueducts, Aspendos.

Curtius Auspicatus, to be dedicated to the gods and the emperors. The architect's name was Zeno.

The auditorium is divided in two by a diazoma and there is a gallery of columns surmounting the top row of seats. While the theater appears to be built on barrel-vaulted substructures, parts of it do rest against the hillside. With a seating capacity of 20,000 the Aspendos theater is still usable today.

North of the theater at the same level is the stadium. The

Aspendos stadium resembles the one at Perge: the spectator's seats are also set on vaults.

To the south of the theater are the remains of a gymnasium and baths now in ruins.

If we ascend to the acropolis on the hill above the theater from the path connecting the theater and stadium we pass through the eastern of the city's three gates into the ruins of the city proper. Proceeding west from this gate, we come upon a basilica, part of which was used for government and civic affairs and as a courthouse. Much of this section is still standing. The triple-nave basilica extending 105 meters to the west was a commercial building while the agora lay to its west. The agora was surrounded by public buildings. West of the agora is a covered marketplace measuring 70 meters in length. The front was open consisting of a row of shops with a stoa in front. North of the agora are the remains of a nymphaion (fountain) of which only the facade measuring 32.50 meters in length and 15 meters in height remains. This elaborately decorated facade has two rows of niches.

Northwest of the fountain are the remains of the bouleuterion, which was used as the city-state's parliament hall. In the center of the ruin are the traces of the foundations of a monumental arch. At the southern end of the basilica are the remains of exedrae, which served both as pedestals for statues and stone benches for the public.

Another of the remains worth mentioning at Aspendos are the city's magnificent aqueducts, parts of which are in the nearby village and on the site of the ruins.

Statue of Heracles, Side Museum. 2nd century.

Side

A road which departs from the Antalya-Alanya motorway at the 5th km before reaching Manavgat, leads us to Side.

Side, which means "pomegranate" in the native language, had been taken over by Lydia, the Persians and Alexander in the 6th century BC., in 546 BC. and 334 BC. respectively. It was taken over by the Ptolemaios after Alexander died, and was subjected to the domination of the Seleukos in 218 BC. Its most glorious period was lived during the 2nd century BC. and was joined to the Roman territory in 78 BC. It survived in welfare until the 3rd century AD. and later was subjected to the attacks of the tribes who came from the mountaneous regions, it kept on getting poorer and was made the bishopric center during the 5th and 6th centuries AD. The city was abandoned after the arab raids in the 10th century.

When you enter through the main gate of the ground walls belonging to the 2nd century BC., you see the monumental fountain of three storeys belonging to the 2nd century A.D. The Roman bath, used as a museum today, is on the right hand side of the road here. The Trade agora of Side is located in front of the theater and museum. There is a round temple, built in the name of Tyche, at the center of the agora. The building that stands erect on the seaside, east of this agora, is the emperors' hall of the state agora of Side. This building which was used as library, too, stands together with its columns and some of its reliefs today. Byzantine structures such as the remains of churches and basilicas are situated on the shore between

Apollo Temple, Side. 2nd century.

this building and the fountain which stands at the entrance. When you turn back in order to see the theater, you come across the restored Fountain of Vespasianus at the side of the monumental gate. You can reach the theater by passing through here. The theater of Side, belonging to the 2nd century AD., was constructed upon galleries with two storeys and arched vaults. The stage-section of the theater which could seat 15.000 people, was decorated with statues and reliefs containing mythological descriptions.

Aerial view of Side.
View of colonnaded street, Side.

Side Theater. 2nd century.
Imperial Hall at state Agora, Side.

The Temple of Dionysos which belongs to the early Roman period, is situated at the side of the theater and on the road. The avenue with columns that extends towards the village passing by the theater, is the continuation of the avenue with columns through which we passed on our way here. This avenue lies under the buildings today. There were a bath and Byzantine house at the right hand side of this avenue in ancient times. The temple located at the end of the avenue with columns, is ascended by means of

stairs. It belongs to the 3rd century AD. It is the Corinthian order, has a semicircular plan and belongs to the god named Men. The temple of Apollon and the Temple of Athena in Corinthian orders, which have been restored today, belong to the 2nd century AD. A Byzantine basilica had been constructed on these in the 5th century AD. And later, a church was built within the basilica. The Temple of Apollon which is in restored form today has 6 x 11 columns and dimensions of 16.37 x 29.50 m; and the Temple of Athena adjacent to it,

View of fountain, Side.
Aerial view of Side.

Apollon Temple, Side.
Manavgat waterfall.

has dimensions of 17.65 x 35 m. There is a harbour at the north of the temples; it is full of sand today. There are Roman harbour baths behind the harbour. If we walk along the seaside starting from the temples, we can see the ruins of baths among the houses of today and also the Byzantine house. We can also reach the square where the theater is located, starting from here.The necropolis of Side is out of the land walls. The western necropolis is located where there are the hotels and the eastern necropolis is behind the sand beach.

Alanya

Alanya is a touristic centre on Turkey's Mediterranean coast, 135 kilometers east of Antalya. Excavations have shown that the Alanya area was inhabited as early as prehistoric times. Alanya first appears in the 2nd century BC. as a pirate lair and it was known then as Korakesion. The Romans later captured the town in their campaign to suppress piracy in the eastern Mediterranean. It came under Byzantine rule after 395. In 1220 the Seljuk Sultan Alaeddin Keykubad I took the city and had the great castle and dockyards built. Known then as Alaiye, a name derived from that of the sultan, the city was used

Aerial view of Red Tower (1227), Alanya.

120

General view of Alanya.
View of Alanya.

by the Seljuks as their naval base in the Mediterranean and it remained an important military post in Ottoman times. A century later the Arab traveler İbn-i Batuta visited Alanya and described it thus:

The city of Alaiye is a large town on the seacoast. It is inhabited by Turkomans and is visited by the merchants of Cairo, Alexandria, and Syria. The district is well-wooded and wood is exported from there to Alexandria and Damietta, whence it is carried to the other cities of Egypt. There is a magnificent and formidable citadel, built by Sultan Alaeddin at the upper end of the town. The "magnificent and formidable

citadel" was built by Alaeddin Keykubad I in 1226 on the site of an earlier fortress. (Strabo refers to one being here in Roman times.) It consists of three sections: an inner keep, the central castle, and an external redoubt.

The inner keep contains cisterns, the ruins of a Seljuk palace, a fresco-decorated courtyard, military fortifications, and a Byzantine chapel in the middle. At the northwestern corner is a place where prisoners condemned to death were hurled over the precipice by means of catapults. The central castle contains a

General view of Alanya.
Damlataş cove, Alanya.

Adamatacağı, Alanya.
Church in the Alanya castle.

masjid built in 1230 by Akşebe Sultan as well as her tomb. Süleymaniye Mosque was originally constructed in 1231 but was rebuilt during the reign of Süleyman the Magnificent when an Ottoman arasta (row of shops) was added. There is also a 17th century Ottoman khan. Located on the outer walls of the castle is Kızıl Kule (Red Tower), so called because of the red bricks used in its construction. This octagonal structure was built in 1227 and stands in all its magnificence even today. (It is particularly impressive when illuminated at night.) Adjacent to the tower are

the dockyards where five vessels could be worked on at a time. Next to the dockyards is a tower called Tophane Kule (Arsenal Tower) where cannons were cast during Ottoman times. Nearby close to the seashore is a cave called Damlataş. The humid air inside this cave is supposed to be good for those sufffering from asthmatic problems. Alanya's archaeological museum contains numerous interesting works and is well worth a visit. Owing to its vital importance as a naval base, Alanya was connected by roads that went east and west and into the hinterland. (The Seljuk capital was up country in Konya.)

Beach of Ulaş near Alanya.
Alara Castle near Alanya.

Termessos

Termessos, the earliest ancient city of the Pisidia Quarter is situated at 30 km north-west of Antalya on Güllük Mountain with an altitude of 1050 m which was known as Solymos in the antiquity.

Coming into existence in the historical scene of this city dates back to 334 BC. with the arrival of Alexander the Great to the region, which commenced the first period welfare, second of which was experienced during the Roman Period. As you arrive the city by passing through the National Park situated on the Antalya-Korkuteli Motorway, the first ruin you can see is a tomb of which the podium is still erect. Then attracaks your attention a Propylon built in the Ionic order in the Hadrian Period, located in front at the right side. You can reach the gymnasium of the city as you follow the street with columns. You can see the official buildings of the city as you arrive the platform. First remain you see there is the agora. West part of this agora, surrounded by porticos, was made built by Attalos II, King of Pergamon.

The most well-preserved unit of the city is the theater with a capacity of 4200 persons, overlooking the Antalya Bay. At southwest of this theatre was built in the Hellenistic Period, takes place the Bouleuterion belonging to the 1st century AD. example of cut-stone workmanship. And just behind it takes place the Zeus Solymeus Temple nearby of which is situated the small Artemis Temple belonging to the Roman Period. The bigger Artemis Temple, dating back to the Antonin Period (138 AD.) is situated behind the small one. At the north of this Temple, consisting of just its foundation today, is situated a small holy area in Corinth order.

The building standing at the left-hand side of the Attalos II stoa is a temple designed in Corinth order, and the one near to it is a small Corinth temple dating back to late Roman Period. The building situated at extreme southwest end of the architect of the city. Necropolis of the city take place at south, west and north where very interesting rock graves and templeformed graves are situated.

Hadrian's propylon, Termessos.
Termessos Theater. Hellenistic period.

Ankara

The history of Ankara, the capital of Turkey, dates back to very ancient times. Ankara and its whereabouts include findings belonging to the Paleolithic and Chalceolithic ages and it can be seen that habitation had existed during the early Bronze Age. The statuette called Hasanoğlan belonging to the early Bronze Age. The Bitik vase that belongs to the Hittite period. Indicetes that the Hittite period had been reigned in the region. We learn by studying the ancient works of art discovered in the vicinity of Ankara that there was an intensive habitation here during the succeeding Phrygian period. The fact that Gordion, the capital city of the Phrygians was near Ankara, indicates the origin of the discovered Phrygian works of art. The works of art found in Midas' tomb in Gordion, are being exhibited in the Museum of Anatolian Civilizations in Ankara. During the period of the Galatians the name of Ankara as Ankyra an later it was changed to Engürü; and still later the name Angora was changed to the present form Ankara. The Seljukiyans got hold of Ankara, following the Roman and Byzantine Periods, in 1071 and we see that the fortress which is a symbol of Ankara, had been used during all the different periods. Ankara was made capital in 1923 and it is an interesting place today owing to the ancient works belonging to the past and to many museums. The city of the antique period lies beneath the modern city of today. It is known that there is a theater today under the former assembly building in Ulus.

The Temple of Augustus, built during the years 25-30 BC., is

View of Atakule at night.

View of Ankara at night.
View of Anıtkabir at night.

situated adjacent to the Mosque of Hacıbayram. The Temple was converted into a church in the 4th century. Another ancient work that has survived until today, is the Column of Julien, erected in order to commemorate Julien's visit to Ankara in the year. The Roman Bath is located between Ulus and Dışkapı. The remains of the bath, constructed during the Caracalla Period in the name of Asklepion the god of health, are visible today. Atatürk's Mausoleum is located on Rasattepe overlooking Ankara. The construction of the Mausoleum continued between the years 1944-1953. It also

comprises a museum which includes Atatürk's belongings. The most important museum in Ankara is the Museum of Anatolian Civilizations. The works of art exibited here are, golden cups'dated to 2300 BC., also garland and sun disks all of which were found in the royal tombs in Alacahöyük. The works belonging to the Hittite period, the metal works discovered in the tumulus of Midas and the work of the Urartus who had founded a state and made Van the capital of it, are exhibited in the Museum of Anatolian Civilizations, too. The most beautiful examples of wood carving and embroidered rugs are exibited in the Museum

Bronze ceremonial symbols, Alacahöyük (2200 BC.) Museum of Anatolian Civilisations in Ankara.
Augustus temple. Roman period. Ankara.

of Ethnograpy. The fossils belonging to the early ages are kept in the Museum of Natural History. The most important mosque of Hacı Bayram Veli, belonging to the date 1427 and adjacent to the temple of Augustus. The other historical mosques of Ankara are, the Mosque of Aslanhane dated 1289 and famous for its niche, the Mosque of Ahi Elvan, the Mosque of Alaaddin (1178) in the fortress, the New Mosque dated 1865, the Mosque With Chains dated 1865 and the Mosque of Karacabey dated 1444.

Cappadocia

Cappadocia is a picture drawn on the earth by nature, it is a poem. Cappadocia, which is situated within the triangle of Nevşehir, Aksaray and Kayseri is bounded by Erciyes with a height of 3916 m in the east and by Hasandağ, a volcanic mountain of 3268 m high in the south. The tough rocks, formed by the lava spurted by these two mountains during geological times, had kept on taking constantly changing shapes with kind effects during the course of time, and the wonders of the world of today were created.

During the early times of the spread of Christianity, the people who needed to hide themselves from the Arab raids, carved out these tough rocks thus constructing churches and built underground cities to defend themselves against the raids.

The settlements in Cappadocia had come into existance, mostly in the valleys of Göreme, Ihlara and Soğanlı. The people who had settled here, worshipped in the churches that they carved out of the rocks, and they dealt with agriculture to meet their own needs. The water sources in the valleys made this region productive.

The most intensive settlement was in the vicinity of the township of Göreme. It is possible to see many churches together today in the locality made into an open air museum. Let us begin discussing the churches in Cappadocia, by describing the churches in this open air museum. In Göreme, at a distance of 7 km from Ürgüp, the first ancient structure that appears in front of us is the Maidens

Everywhere in Cappadocia, you may meet sometimes single and sometimes multipletopped fairy chimneys.

Poetical view of Cappadocia.
Fairy chimnys in Cappadocia.

Monastery. The monastery, belonging to the first half of the 11th century, and is an interesting building of six storeys. The Chapel of St. Basil is situated on the opposite side of the promenade road in the museum. The Church with Apple, one of the most important churches in Göreme, appears in sight thereafter. The church, planned in the shape of a closed Greek cross, ends with three abscissas. The church belongs to the 12th century and the frescos in it display the scenes based on the contents of the Bible and also inspired by the Pentateuch. The Church of St. Barbara is situated

beyond the Church with Apple. In this church which belongs to the first half of the 11th century and the descriptions of Pantocrator Christ, Georgios, Theodoros and Saint Barbara are worthy of attention. The Church with Snake, situated here, also belongs to the 11th century and the scene of Deisis is displayed on its long wall. Descriptions of Saint Onesimos Georgios, Theodoros, Constantine and Helena are seen here. On the rocky mass that heightens from the south of the open air museum towards the west of it, there are monasteries grouped together and 8 churches, 7 dining halls, grave chambers

View from the underground-cities.

and wine factories. The church which is situated here, has two storeys and the frescos inside have been recently restored and fortified. The events included in the contents of the Bible and the Pentateuch, are described in vivid colours in the frescos. The church with Sandals (Çarıklı Kilise) is situated at the extreme north of the valley. The Church with Sandals belongs to the 12th century, has a dining hall under it, and there descriptions of the scenes from Christ's life and from the Pentateuch inside the church. The church with Buckle, located on the road to Göreme, consists of four sites namely: The Old

A view of Cappadocia.
A bell tower in Zelve.

Church, The New Great Church, The adjoining chapel and the church underneath. The Old Church, forms the entrance of the New Church today, and it is decorated with the descriptions which are dated to the 10th century and concern Christ's life.
The New Church which has a rectangular plan, is decorated with the descriptive scenes from Christ's childhood adolescence and showing the sorrows of his life. This church is dated to the end of the 10th century. The

Churches in open air museum, Göreme.
The fresco of the Karanlık Church, Göreme.

annexed chapel and the church underneath, belong to the following period. At a distance of 300 m from the zone of the museum, there is the Church of Virgin Mary; and the Church of El Nazar, belonging to the 10th century and the Hidden Church are situated at the left hand side on the way to the township of Göreme.

The missile-shaped fairy Chimneys within the Zemi Deresi near these churches, create very interesting scenery. There are many churches in the township of

Göreme, such as Yusuf Koç, Durmuş Kadir. While travelling in Göreme, the fortresses of Uçhisar and Ortahisar suddenly appear in front of you as a magnificent sight. Here, the Valley of Güvercinlik is so beautiful that one doesn't get tired of watching it. Aktepe and the Valleys of Uçhisar, Kılıçlar, Uzundere are places which display very interesting sights. The Pink Valley, placed between Avanos and Ürgüp arouses interest by reason of its natural scenery.

The Church of Çavuşin, situated on the road of Avanos at a distance of 2 km to Göreme, is decorated with frescos belonging to the 11th century. One can walk from Çavuşin to the Valleys of Güllüdere and Kızılçukur. The 12 churches in this region can also be visited during this walk that will be a pleasant thing for you to remember. We come across interesting scenery in Bağıl Deresi which extends towards Killik or Kaya Harmanı in the north of Avanos-Göreme road and towards Uçhisar in the south of it.

The locality called Cinnes on the road to Zelve past Çavuşin and the locality named Paşabağı or Keşişler Vadisi (Valley of Monks) are also worth seeing. Zelve is a region which extends-towards the interiors of a hill called Aktepe where there are about 15 churches. There are many underground cities in Cappadocia too. Within these soft rocks carved out as a means of defense against the enemy, interesting underground cities were formed, and all kinds of needs could be met in them. The most important ones among them are the cities of Kaymaklı, Derinkuyu and Özkonak and

The fresco of the Karanlık Church, Göreme.

there are underground cities in many other places too. In addition to the Valley of Göreme, there are churches of importance in the Valley of Soğanlı too. Churches such as Karabaş, Yılanlı, Kubbeli and Gök Kilise are situated in this valley which are at a distance of 30 km to Ürgüp.

In the Valley of Ihlara which is arrived at by diverging from the Aksaray-Nevşehir road, there are 36 churches each one of which is more interesting than the other. When one descends the steps and reaches the valley at the end of the road, the Churches of Ağaçaltı, Sümbüllü, Kokar and Yılanlı can be seen in the Open

Views of Ihlara valley.

Air Museum of Ihlara. The other churches of importance such as those of Eğritaş, Pürenliseki, Karagedik, Kırkdamaltı, Bahattin Samanlığı and Ala Kilise are also situated in this valley.

The Church of Gümüşler belonging to the 11th century and are located at a distance of 7 km to Niğde, is a church of interesting appearance. The Churches called Yüksek Kilise and Kızıl Kilise which are located in Güzelyurt, are made of stone.

Konya

When we speak of Konya, the first thing that we are reminded of is the Mausoleum of Mevlana. But it also acknowledged that the Neolithic habitation of Çatalhöyük, dating back to 6000 BC., existed in its whereabouts. The region where the Hittite period had been lived through, was captured respectively by the Persians at first and than by Alexander, the Romans, and by the Byzantines in 395. It was later exchanged between the Omayyads and Abbasids and in 1097, following the foundation of the Anatolian Seljuk Sultanate in 1097, Konya was made the capital. During the Seljukiyan period, Konya was adorned with many medresses, mosques and kiosks. It was subjected to the Mongolian invasion after the year 1243, and the Ottomans captured Konya in 1467 and included it in their domain.

Another historical work belonging to the Seljuks in Konya is the Mosque of Alaeddin which was completed by the order of Sultan Alaeddin Keykubad the I in 1221. The pulpit of the mosque is one of the most beautiful samples of Seljukiyan wood workmanship. Other magnificient Seljukiyan works of art in Konya are the building complex of Sahip Ata dated 1258-1283, the Mosque of Konevi dated 1274, the Medresse of Karatay dated 1252, which is worthy of attention owing to the ornaments of encaustic tiles and the marble stone door and the Medresse With Fine Minarets (İnce Minareli Medrese) dated 1264.

There are many Seljukiyan mausoleums in Konya, the most important of which is the Mausoleum of Mevlana that has

The Tomb of Mevlana, Konya.

View of Mevlana Tomb at night.
İnce Minareli Medresse, Konya 1264.

become to be accepted as the symbol of the city. Mevlana's father, Bahaeddin Veled, was buried here as he had bequeathed to be and was buried at his side when Mevlana died; a dome was constructed on the spot in the year 1273. Karamanoğlu Ali Bey had the green dome of the mausoleum constructed in 1397. The religious verse Ayet-el Kürsi is inscribed on the exterior point where the green conical cap made of 16 foils is joined with the cylinder.

In the Mausoleum of Mevlana, which was opened as a museum

in the year 1926, are exhibited the clothes of Mevlana, musical instruments, books written by hand and fabrics. The Archeological Museum, the Museum of Ethnography, Atatürk's Hause and the Museum of Koyunoğlu are other Museums in Konya which are worthy of visiting.

The inns constructed by the Seljukiyans on the trade roads also make up a historical group. The most important of these are the in named Altun Aba Hanı, Horozlu Han dated 1248, Zazadin Han and Kadın Han.

The sarcophagi of Mevlana.
The whirling dervishes performing the sema

Boğazköy

Hattuşaş (Boğazköy) which was the capital city of the Hittites, is located in Boğazköy within the administrative boundaries of the township of Sungurlu in the city of Çorum. The excavation that had been initiated in Boğazköy by Hugo Winckler in the year 1906, is being continued by the German Archaeologists today.

The city is surrounded by walls with a height of up to 6 m and an impressive appearance. A hidden tunnel (potern) 71 m long, extends south of the city walls.

There is a gate, called the ground gate upon this potern and there are sphinx shaped reliefs on its two sides.

The Lion Gate and the King's Gate are situated west and east of the Ground Gate respectively. The original of this gate is at the Museum of Anatolian Civilizations in Ankara. There are many remains of temples between these two gates. The largest temple in

Lion's Gate: 14th century BC. Boğazköy.
A relief of twelve figures on the walls of the open-air temple at Yazılıkaya.

View of the ancient city of Boğazköy.
Open air temple, Yazılıkaya.

Boğazköy is the big temple located in the zone near the village. The construction of this temple had started in the 14th century BC. and could be completed merely in a century. It covers an area of 160 x 135 m.

This temple was built for the Sky God of the Hittites and for the Sun God of Arinna. The temple consists of many rooms and there are magazine rooms around it.

The earthenware jugs found here, indicate that provisions were stored here.

It is also understood by means of the tablets that another building here, was the artist's house and 208 people lived in it.

The Acropolis of Boğazköy is called he Great Fortress. This inner fortress surrounded by walls, contains a room, the building of archives, and in the extreme north, Palace buildings and fortresses such as the Southern Fortress, Nişantepe, Sarıkale, Yenice Kale are located south of this Acropolis.

Alacahöyük

Another important city of the Hittites is Alacahöyük in the village of Höyük within the township of Alaca. In this mound, which has a diameter of 350 m, 4 culture strata and 14 structural strata have been confirmed. These comprise, the strata II and III of the Chalcolithic Age and the Early Bronze Age, between the 14th and 9th structural

Entrance of the open air temple.
View of Potern, Boğazköy.

The Sphinx gate, Alacahöyük.
Relief of the King Tuthalia IV., 1250 BC.
Yazılıkaya.

strata. In the 13 rich King's tombs discovered in this stratum, there are great numbers of instruments called sistrums which were used during religious ceremonies, statues of animals such as bulls and deers, and golden ornamental objects. These precious works of art belonging to the years 2300-2100 BC., are exhibited at the Museum of Anatolian Civilizations in Ankara. The subsequent strata include the Hittite stratum reflecting the history between 2000-1200 BC. and indicate the cultures that extend from Phrygian to Ottoman periods. The gate with the Sphinx belonging to the Hittite imperial period (1466-1190 BC.), is the first ancient work of art seen in Alacahöyük. The two magnificent sphinxes that watch over the city gate, are the typical examples of gate architecture of the Hittites. There are various reliefs at their sides. There is a great building behind the gate and it might have been a palace or a temple. A water channel and its remains are seen at the center of the ruins.

Trabzon

Trabzon is another city of ours in the region of the Black Sea, which is famous for its natural characteristics and verdure. As far as we know, Trabzon was founded by the people of Miletos in the year 756 BC., and was named Trapezus, but the historical facts go back further into the past. We know that Trabzon had been under Roman domination between the years 20 BC. and 395 AD. When the Latin people captured Byzantium in 1204, Alexios of the Commenoses left this region and founded the independent Greek State of Trabzon, making Trabzon the capital.

Owing to this rich history of Trabzon, the city walls, many churches and monasteries have survived until the present. The most important one among the mentioned churches is, without doubt, the Hagia Sophia of Trabzon. Emperor Manuel the I. had it constructed in the year 1245. The church which has survived until today with the frescos inside also in good condition, has three entrances. The bell tower adjacent to the church was constructed upon the order of Alexios the IV. in the year 1427.

Another center of tourism in Trabzon is the Monastery of Sumela. The monastery is at a distance of 54 km from Trabzon, and is positioned like an eagle's nest within the forest at a height of 1628 m. The general belief is that, two monks had used a rock cavity as a church during the time of emperor Theodos the II. (408-450). Later on, Justinianos (527-565) had this church repaired and enlarged. The monastery flourished in the real sense,

View of the Black sea region.
Sumela Monastery.

during the time of Alexios Comnenos the III. in the year 1360. Annexes with a height, length and width of 17 m., 40 m. and 14 m. respectively and containing 72 rooms were built. The Ottomans, after they captured Trabzon in 1461, supplied aid to the monastery. A narrow staircase ascends to the monastery, and the church, the chapel, students rooms, guest rooms and the kitchen sections are built in the rock. The descriptions of saints which were renewed in the year 1732 by the monk named Matheos and the frescos pictured

View of the Uzungöl (1110 m.), Çaykara.
St. Sophia of Trabzon (1245).

Daily activity in a small mountain village above the Black sea, Trabzon.

by Savaş, the painter from Ünye, are inside the church. In addition to the Monastery of Sumela, the monasteries of Kuştul and Vazelon are the monasteries that have survived until today.

When the Turks captured the city, the churches in the city were transformed into mosques. The mosques of Yeni Cuma, Fatih, and Kudrettin are mosques of this kind. The city walls of Trabzon, which Hadrianus had ordered to be built, were repaired and used by the Ottomans. The Villa Atatürk dated to 1890, is also among the visited places.

The Palace of Ishak Paşa

The Palace of Ishak Paşa which stands like an eagle's nest at a distance of 5 km from eastern Beyazıt, is an interesting building worthy of seeing. The construction of the palace had been initiated at the date 1685 by the order of Çolak Abdi Paşa, the Governor of Çıldır, continued 99 years and could finally be completed in the year 1784 during the time of Ishak Paşa II. The styles of Baraque and Rococo were used in an intermingled manner

on the main gate on which the Seljukiyan effect and also, in places, the regional effect are observed. The palace has two storeys and is located in an area of 7600 m². It is known that it used to contain 366 rooms in the past. In this palace, which has a very impressive aspect even today, the Persian ambassador had stayed as a guest. And it is rumoured that when the ambassador came to Topkapı Palace and said that the other one was more impressive than Topkapı Palace, Ishak Paşa became a

General view of Ishak Paşa Palace.
Entrance gate of Ishak Paşa Palace.

A view of hall of Ishak Paşa Palace.

Personal non grata you enter by the main gate and reach the first courtyard. The servise premises on the left hand side have fallen down. The second courtyard is also entered by means of a main gate. The left part of the courtyard has fallen down and the section reserved for the males, namely "selamlık", is located on the right and includes a large hall. The mosque made of stones with horizontal lines and its minaret, and the mausoleums of Ishak Paşa and Çolak Abdi Paşa are situated adjacent to the selamlık section. When you enter through the magnificient main

gate of the "harem", namely the women' section, you reach a marble courtyard in the center which has columns. This section is decorated with inscriptions an black and white marble. The magnificient premises of the harem are located at the side of this courtyard. The second storey of the harem has fallen down completely. There is a bath in the harem. The ventilation in the kitchen is worth of attention. There is a central heating system in the palace in addition to the fireplaces. The ruined remains of the ancient Eastern. Beyazıt are located lower below the palace. The Mosque built during the time of Selim I is seen opposite to these.

Van

The history of the city of Van established on the coast of Lake Van in Eastern Anatolia, is dated back to very ancient times. It is known that the Hursi people had lived in the region during the years of 2000 BC. During the Urartu period Van had become a very important city. We observe that after the 9th century BC., the feodal Principalities of Urartu and Nairi had united and founded a state. King Sardur the I. who founded the Urartu State (840-830) made Van the capital

View of Akdamar Church.
General view of Van Castle.

View of Akdamar Church in Van Lake.
Hoşap Castle near Van. 1643.

city and had a fortress constructed. This fortress was 1800 meters
long and 1200 meters wide, and
he had the epitaph of foundation
engraved on the tower of Sardur
of the fortress. Sardur was succeeded by his son Ispiuni and following him, Menua was enthroned, Menua took advantage of the
weakness of the Asurian people at
that time and had his territory
extended towards upper Azerbai-
jan on the north and towards to
the region of Tigris River on the
south. The epitaphs of Ispiuni and
Menua are situated in Meher
Kapı in Akköprü. The epitaph
on the fortress indicates that

Enteresting Seljuk tombstones in Ahlat.
Halime Hatun Kümbet, Gevaş 1358.

Argisti I. was enthroned (780-760 BC.) successively and he made wars with Assyria. Then he was succeeded by Sardur II (760-730 BC.) who made great attempts in respect to the public improvements and cultural activities of the Urartu State. Sardur II. also had Çavuştepe constructed on the road to Başkale. In 730 BC. Rusa I. became the Urartu king and he had the Temple of Haldi and the Earthen Fortress constructed. He was later succeeded by Argisti II (713-685 BC.) who also had to combat the Kimmers like his father had done. Rusa II. was enthroned after him

Emir Bayındır Kümbet, 1481. Ahlat.

(685-645 BC.) and continued the activities related to the publicimprovments on large scale; he had the capital of the state removed to Toprakkale, had the Fortress of Kef constructed in Adil cevaz and had also built a palace with 140 rooms. As successors of this king, Sardur II., Erimena and Rusa III. were enthroned (590-580 BC.), and during the reign of this last king, the Urartu State was overthrown by the Iskits. This is the short summary of the Urartu state which has become to be identified with the city of Van. It is of course possible at present to see many Urartu cities in Van

and ancient works of Urartu in the museum. The Ulu Cami (the Great Mosque), dated to 1389 in ancient Van at the foot of the Fortress of Van, and the Mosque of Hüsrev Paşa dated to 1565, are historical mosques that can be visited today.

The Church of Akdamar at Lake Van, is one of the main touristic sites of ours which are visited. The cupola of Halime Hatun in Gevaş, which can be seen on the way to the Church of Akdamar, is dated to 1358. The Church of Akdamar was constructed by the architect Manuel during the years 915-921, upon the order of King Gagik I, one of the kings of the Vaspurkan dynasty. The outer surface of the church is ornamented with raised relief design.

Mount Nemrut

Mount Nemrut is at an altitude of 2150 m from the sea level, and the tumulus which includes the tomb of the King of Commagene, Antiochos Epiphanes the I. is there.

Mithradates the I., father of Antiochos to whom the tumulus belongs, took advantage of defencelessness of the Seleukos who ruled in Syria after Alexander's death, and founded the independent kingdom of Commagene in the year 80 BC. Mithradates the I. was succeeded

Apollon and fyche heads, Nemrut.

154

Vest terrace of Mount Nemrut.
Statue heads at Nemrut.

by his son Antiochos the I. (62-32 BC.) who brought great fame to his country. The King who pointed out in his inscriptions that his maternal lineage had been traced back to Alexander the Great, and his paternal lineage to the Persians, joined the two cultures for this reason. Mithradates the II. was enthroned after him, and he was succeeded by Antiochos the III, during whose reign the country became powerful. After his death, Vespasianus united Commagene to the province of Syria (72 AD.). The tumulus is at a distance of 65 km to the township of Kahta in Adıyaman; the tomb is placed in

Statue trunks on the eastern terrace of Mount Nemrut.

Head of Apollon, Nemrut.

the middle of the tumulus and is covered by a small hill which has a height and diameter of 50 m and 150 m respectively and made of small pieces of stones. Terraces are built on the four sides of the cumulus. There is an altar in the eastern terrace and there are also statues arranged in a line, with their backs turned to the tumulus. The heads of the statues have rolled down to the terrace in front, but the bodies still stand erect. These gigantic statues with dimensions of 9-10 m, are the statues of Apollon, Tyche, Zeus, of Antiochos himself and of

Heracles. Statues of eagles and lions are placed on the two sides of these and, on the low walls adjacent to the two sides of the terrace, there are inscriptions which explain how the ceremonies were performed. The statues on the western terrace are arranged in the same sequence. On the side of this terrace, there are many reliefs. The relief discovered in Arsameia, capital of Commagene and located in the village of Kocahisar near the Stream of Kahta describes Mithradates and Heracles shaking hands and is a very interesting piece. The epitaph in the grave chamber of Mithradates the I. which contains an inscription of 256 lines, is also interesting.

Zeus and Apollon heads. Nemrut.
The second tumulus on Nemrut.

The Bridge of Cendere over the Stream of Kahta was built during the Roman Period. There is a second tumulus on the mound named Karakuş, at a distance of about 10 km to this bridge. It is believed that this tumulus had belonged to the ladies of the court. Mount Nemrut, which can be considered as the eigth wonder of the world, is an interesting place to visit because of its impressive appearance and the unique beauty of the sunrise there.

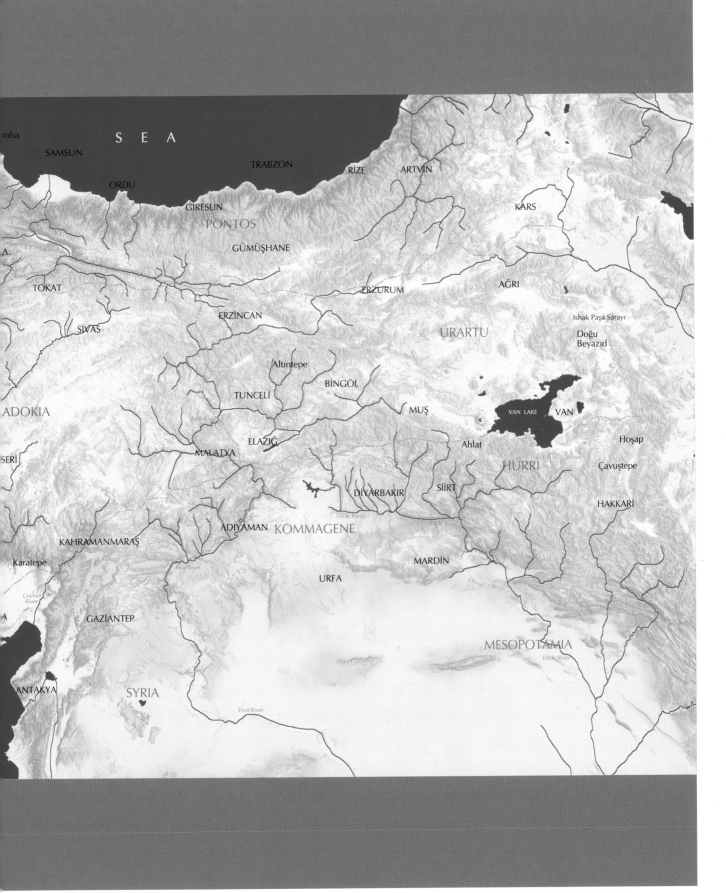

SEA

mba
SAMSUN
TRABZON
RİZE
ARTVİN
ORDU
GİRESUN
KARS
PONTOS
GÜMÜŞHANE
ERZURUM
AĞRI
TOKAT
ERZİNCAN
URARTU
İshak Paşa Sarayı
SİVAS
Doğu
Beyazıd
Altıntepe
BİNGÖL
TUNCELİ
MUŞ
VAN LAKE
VAN
ADOKIA
Fırat River
ELAZIĞ
Ahlat
Hoşap
SERİ
MALATYA
HURRİ
Çavuştepe
DİYARBAKIR
SİİRT
Dicle River
HAKKARİ
Ceyhan
River
ADIYAMAN
KOMMAGENE
Dicle River
KAHRAMANMARAŞ
MARDİN
Karatepe
URFA
Ceyhan
River
GAZİANTEP
MESOPOTAMIA
Dicle River
A
ANTAKYA
SYRIA
Fırat River
Fırat River

PUBLICATIONS LIST

İLHAN AKŞİT

İlhan Akşit was born in Denizli in 1940. He graduated as an archeologist in 1965. When he was assigned to a post related to the excavation of Aphrodisias. He was director of the Çanakkale-Troy Museum between 1968-1976, during which time the replica of the Trojan horse we now see on the site was constructed. He directed the excavation of the Chiyse Apollo temple over a period of five years. From 1976-1978, the author acted as director of the Underwater Archeology Museum, Bodrum and was appointed Director of National Palaces in 1978. During his directorship, the author was responsible for the restoration and reopening of these palaces to the public after an extended period of closure. In 1982 the retired from his post to take up a career as an author of popular books on Turkish archeology and tourism. He has nearly 3 titles to his credit to date, including. The Story of Troy', The Civilisations of Anatolia', The Blue journey', Istanbul' and The Hittites'.

THE GOLDEN BOOK
CUBA

Text by Renato Recio, Eduardo Jiménez *and* Milena Recio

BONECHI
EDITORIAL
José Martí

© Copyright by CASA EDITRICE BONECHI
Via Cairoli 18b - 50131 Florencia, Italia
Tel. 055/576841 - Fax 055/5000766
E-mail: bonechi@bonechi.it - Internet: www.bonechi.it
ISBN 88-476-0186-X

© EDITORIAL JOSÉ MARTÍ
Publicaciones en Lenguas Extranjeras
Apartado Postal 4208
La Habana 10400, Cuba
Tel. (537)333541 / 329838 - Fax (537)333441 / 338187
E-mail: cclfilh@artsoft.cult.cu
ISBN 959-09-163-8

Project: CASA EDITRICE BONECHI
Editorial Director: Monica Bonechi
Graphic Design and Picture Research: Serena de Leonardis
Editing: Magaly Silva *and* Giovannella Masini
Video Page Making: Fiorella Cipolletta *and* Laura Settesoldi
Cover: Laura Settesoldi
Texts: Renato Recio, Eduardo Jiménez *and* Milena Recio
Translation: Richard Dunbar

The photographs contained in this volume, taken by
Marco Bonechi *and* Paolo Giambone
are property of the Casa Bonechi Editrice Archives.

Printed in Italy by
CENTRO STAMPA EDITORIALE BONECHI

INTRODUCTION

Contrary to what some might think, Cuba has been a land of many discoveries over the centuries. In fact, before Christopher Columbus reached its shores on October 28, 1492, the island had already been visited by "foreigners": natives most probably coming from the Caribbean mainland, who, in the course of their explorations, had often sailed towards this new land seeking fair shores on which to settle. It is possible to imagine that these "indios"—as Columbus called them in the belief he had reached India—lived peacefully, surrounded by a nature that provided all their needs for a sustainable life. The European discovery of the New World, dividing the earth into hemispheres, ended the peaceful existence of the original inhabitants, marking the start of five centuries of history that up until present times has also been, in different ways and in different moments, a history of encounters with Cuba.

It was especially Cuba's status as an island and its privileged location in the Caribbean Sea that made the land attractive. The warm temperatures and tropical rains have shaped a landscape that is remarkable for its variety and uniqueness. This virgin and fertile nature seduced not only Columbus, who stated, "This is the most beautiful land that human eyes have ever seen." German naturalist and geographer Alexander von Humboldt (1769-1859), who was considered the second discoverer of Cuba, provided the first scientific description of its fascinating mountains, endless beaches and the variety of its flora and fauna. Linked to the island's nature, which had so impressed Columbus and Humboldt, was another discovery that would prove to be even more important.

Between 1920 and 1950, ethnologist and author Don Fernando Ortiz made an in-depth examination of the most intimate secrets of that impalpable and complex atmosphere that had developed over the centuries, which came to be known as cubanía. The scientist, born in his beloved Havana, the Cuban capital, thus earned for himself the title of the third discoverer of the island.

If Columbus had revealed to the world the existence of Cuba, and Humboldt had described the land, Ortiz was able to sketch its profile, defining the Cubans as the most generous fruit of this land, and their boasting of it as their greatest quality. Through a complex process, which Ortiz called "transculturation," the inhabitants of Cuba evolved in a world apart and sprung from diverse ethnic roots, with the white Spaniards and other Europeans who emigrated to

The Malecón, Havana's popular seafront avenue.

Cuba mixing with the black Africans, brought to the island as slaves starting in 1526.

The mulatto, which refers not only to the color of skin, expresses one of the most important symbols of Cubanía, a fusion of diverse cultures that has created its own identity. Under the Cuban sun, which beat down with equal intensity on the Spanish merchant, the Creole proprietor and the African slave, the diverse religious beliefs, customs and many psycho-social differences of all the inhabitants melted together in a particular syncretism, even despite the barriers erected by the white dominion and Catholicism.

Other nationalities, though not predominating in Cuba, have by their mere presence contributed their own characteristics and participated in the creation of this fusion that makes up the Cuban identity. Among them have been the Chinese, brought to the island and subjected to slavery, the French and Haitians, who came when they fled the bloody Haitian Revolt of 1791 and promoted, among other things, the cultivation of coffee in the east of the country, and the North Americans, present in the country since the 18th century. There has even been an Arab contribution, which had exerted influence on the Spanish culture over the centuries.

Cuba has always had an ambiguous relationship with the seas that surround it. From them came the conquerors, pirates and corsairs, the cyclones and hurricanes, and the slaves; they also brought scientific discoveries and such technologies as the printing press, the steam engine and the railroad. Because of the constant action of the waves, vast sandy white beaches developed, gently sloping into the clear waters of the bays that abound on the island's long coastline.

From across the sea also arrived, at the end of the 19th century, the United States navy, with the mission of intervening in the Spanish-Cuban conflict, but in reality interfering with the real independence of Cuba. And disembarking on the south coast in 1956 were the 82 young Cubans led by Fidel Castro, who once again took up the struggle for the sovereignty of their country, a half republic since 1902 and governed by the interests of the United States of America. Surround entirely by water, buffeted on all sides by winds, the object of countless foreign passions, oppressions, conceits and plots, the island and its inhabitants finally became their own masters with the historic event that radically revolution-

ized the political, social and cultural life of Cuba. The 1959 triumph granted the people a heretofore unknown dignity, which itself generated new energies and other unknown quantities contributing to the Cuban personality and identity.

The city of Havana, whose history since its beginnings has gone hand in hand with the history of Cuba, still continues to be one of the places that best exemplifies the memories of the past and the excitement of modern times, Cuban style.

Among the elegant buildings from past centuries, saved thanks to a keen interest for the preservation of their heritage, and old American cars, whose impressive numbers testify to their unusual mechanical longevity, the Habaneros, like most Cubans, demonstrate what they have lived through and what they have adapted to: that which they themselves call the "culture of resistance."

Living in a paradoxical dialectic of survival and development, of immobility and international leadership, the Cubans have developed into one of the most interesting peoples in the world, especially if one considers that the country is neither particularly large nor populous.

But the mystery of Cubanía reveals itself with difficulty. The question, "What is a Cuban like?" can be answered in a thousand different ways, many of them contradictory. Lively and extroverted, profound and tenacious, able to joke even in the most difficult situations and ready for sacrifice and extreme abnegation. While not neglecting their prevalently sensual side, they are romantics and pragmatics, patriots and cosmopolitan, austere and spendthrift ...

As soon as we meet a Cuban, many adjectives come to mind in describing him. However, there are still no precise words for a people who, despite their short time as a nation, have been at the forefront of so much history, have faced such powerful enemies and have dreamed in such an enormously impassioned way.

Modern Havana, seen from the sea.

The Cathedral, one of the symbols of Havana.

HAVANA
Old Havana

Near the spot once known as Puerto de Carenas, a group of men, following the currents of the Gulf of Mexico, decided to found the fifth settlement on the island of Cuba on the basis of the colonization plan drawn up by the conquistador Diego Velázquez. It was the third attempt of these men, led by Pánfilo de Narváez, to find a suitable place for the settlement. They first looked near the mouth of a river on the south coast. Then they moved towards the north coast, near the mouth of a river today called the Almendares. They then went to a hospitable bay, well protected by the fury of the ocean, which would become the point of convergence for all the ships that traveled between Spain and her American colonies. The village built on the bay became with time a populated city, rich in history and culture.

The original area of present day Havana, known as Old Havana, and in particular its famed historic center, declared a Heritage Site for Humanity by UNESCO in 1982, is made up of numerous buildings, plazas,

churches, parks and streets. This old city center recounts the story of a culture that was formed by a unique mix of Spanish, African and American (in the true sense of the word), and its special charm makes it the most popular spot for the hundreds of thousands of tourists who visit the Cuban capital every year.

The buildings along the narrow but well laid-out streets, though not reaching the architectural levels of those built in Europe between the 15th and 19th centuries, create a unique grace that represents, as described by one of the main scholars of Cuban architecture, the most accomplished and personal exemplification of colonial architecture. The functional architectural design of these buildings provides remarkable testimony to the country's society, life and customs, and demonstrate the variety of materials that the island's inhabitants have produced from their land and their industry over the ages.

This architecture helps to create the special atmosphere that one breathes in throughout much of the

7

historic center, which covers some 150 hectares. In the 1950s, the construction of the bay tunnel, which led to the development of the city around Old Havana, increased the land value in this area to such a degree that the people who most ardently promoted the preservation of the country's cultural heritage came under serious threat. The fear turned into reality when plans were announced for the construction of a heliport on the grounds of the oldest university in Cuba.

With the Cuban Revolution of 1959, this trend, which would have virtually destroyed Old Havana, was fortunately halted, and the buildings in this section of the city were converted for governmental and commercial use.

Today, taking advantage of the swift growth in tourism, new ideas are being studied for the financing of the costly works of restoration and preservation of the historic center: government funds have been earmarked to carry out these works, and the Oficina del Historiador de La Habana (The Havana National Historical Society) has been instituted for the collection and disbursement of the funds.

La Plaza de Armas

Although the five original plazas created at the dawn of the urbanization of Havana are still preserved, the Plaza de Armas continues to provide natural access to the historic center. At the beginning of the 16th century, the Plaza and the surrounding area made up the first nucleus of San Cristóbal de La Habana, the point where the wide bay of Havana and the natural canal that connects it with the open sea meet and where the first colonizers settled. The Plaza de Armas is therefore the oldest of Havana's squares, and it was the center of the lives of the founders of the early village. At the far eastern side of the square is El Templete (the Temple), a small Neo-Classical building erected in 1828 to mark the spot where in 1519 the first mass was held and where the first *Cabildo* (government) operated, in the shade of the giant *ceiba* tree.

In the middle of Plaza de Armas, the statue of Carlos Manuel de Céspedes, called the "Father of the Nation" for being the courageous initiator of the armed fight for national independence.

Used book vendors are an integral part of Plaza de Armas.

El Templete stands out among the colonial buildings that surround Plaza de Armas, constructed to perpetuate the memory of the first mass and the first Cabildo in the city.
In the photo, the building during restoration.

Important buildings dating from the colonial era around Plaza de Armas. Among them is the Palacio del Segundo Cabo. In front of its large and shaded archways can be found stands of used book vendors and artisans.

From Plaza de Armas, looking north, stands the Palacio del Segundo Cabo, built in 1772 as the Real Casa de Correos (Royal Post Office).

The small courtyard of the Palacio del Segundo Cabo features lowered arches supported by columns and pedestals, constituting a Classical stylistic composition of Adalusian inspiration.

Inside of the elegant Neo-Classical memorial are still the frescoes by the French painter Jean-Baptiste Vermay, who reproduced the inauguration of the Templete and the first mass. The Habaneros have always ensured that next to the Templete a ceiba has grown, and every year on the day commemorating the founding of the city they circle the tree in silence three times so that three wishes they make to Saint Christopher, protector of Havana, come true.

The Plaza de Armas was originally named Plaza de la Iglesia (Plaza of the Church), since it was the custom during the times of Spanish colonization to place the parish church in the area where the main citizens of the new village lived. In that period, however, the dwellings, like the church, were humble *bohíos*, rustic buildings like those of the natives. The site began to lose its original name when the *Castillo de la Real Fureza* (Castle of the Royal Army) was built, another of the main elements still visible along the square. The garrison stationed in the castle often used the adjoining square to carry out their drills and maneuvers, so that around 1580 the people began calling the square Plaza de Armas.

Much time passed before the original plaza took on its final appearance, and it was only in the last third of the 18th century, after Havana was taken over by the English and the city and the island were affected by new economic impulses that changed the policies of the royal administration, that the site was adorned with fountains, trees and decorations. This was also the period in which the surrounding streets were graced with monumental buildings symbolizing Spanish colonial prowess: the Palacio de los Capitanes Generales (Palace of General Captains, or the Palace of Government) and the Palacio del Segundo Cabo (Palace of the Second Chief or the General Vice-Captain), both today perfectly preserved. From this period, the chroniclers and travelers began to leave frequent testimony of the importance of Plaza de Armas during the colonial era.

The entrance to the main stairway, located at the rear of the courtyard of the Palacio del Segundo Cabo, was designed to produce a strong sense of depth.

The mixed-line arch of the entry to the main stairway of the Palacio del Segundo Cabo.

Partial view of the facade of the Palacio de los Capitanes Generales. The palace was begun in 1796 and completed in 1834. Note the roof terrace with iron railings interrupted by crenellations.

Elegant carriages continually circled the plaza, carrying the aristocratic women of Havana, while the men strolled in the park or sat on benches, awaiting a discreet glance or a prudent greeting from a woman on the verge of falling in love. This era provided the prints that served as models for the restoration of the plaza in 1935, bringing it back to its appearance of 1841.

Whoever strolls in Plaza de Armas today sees not only the faithful reproduction of its original layout and of the buildings that remain around its edges. They can also enjoy the musical bands that perform concerts in the same spot that military marches once took place. In the surrounding area it is still possible to see an occasional horse carriage pass by, driven by a liveried coachman, while lovely women walk through the park in 19th century dress.

Palacio del Segundo Cabo

The Palacio del Segundo Cabo, as it has come to us from the 19th century, was built starting in 1772 in a measured Baroque style, a manifest prelude to the Neo-Classical. Located in the northern section of the plaza, near the Castillo de la Real Fuerza, the Palacio was originally the Real Casa de Correos (Royal Post Office). Subsequently, it was the seat of the Real Intendencia de Hacienda, until the colonial era ended and it became the residence of the Segundo Cabo in 1854. Now the building houses the Cuban Book Institute and every day, at the opening of its majestic door, decorated by huge and elegant pilasters, one can catch a glimpse of its square arcaded patio whose columns and pedestals reveal its Andalusian origins.

Palacio de los Capitanes Generales (Municipal Museum)

The Palacio de los Capitanes Generales was built several years after the Palacio del Segundo Cabo, using the same local limestone that was used for the former in order to maintain stylistic harmony. The Casa de Gobierno (Government Palace), which also reflects a sort of Classical Baroque in its facade and in much of its interior, occupies all of the western side of the Plaza de Armas and is today the home of the Municipal Museum and of the Oficina del Historiador de La Habana (Havana National Historical Society).
The Municipal Museum contains an extremely rich account of Cuban history in the splendid setting of the antique palace of the Spanish governors, who from the balcony watched the nighttime military parades that took place in the plaza, which reached its splendor with the construction of these two buildings.

The statue of Christopher Columbus, by Italian sculptor J. Cucchiari, was placed in the beautiful courtyard of the Palacio de los Capitanes Generales in 1862.

Baroque style arcades look out onto the central courtyard of the Palacio de los Capitanes Generales.

Dominated by sets of medallóns (Isabellean furniture with wicker added to suit the Cuban climate), this 19th-century style room of the Municipal Museum recreates the lifestyle of the Creole aristocracy.

Known as the Music Salon, this was the ante-chamber of the main hall of the Palacio de los Capitanes Generales. Visitors can admire the emblem of the monarchy (foreground) and of the city. On the central table are two 18th-century Meissen porcelain vases.

The Green Room was originally the ante-chamber of the public office of the Capitanes Generales. The furnishings and rug are original.

The Main Hall. The original 19th-century Venetian mirrors witnessed, among many important events, the end of Spanish dominion in 1899 and the entry into power of the president of the Republic in 1902.

Guéridon Table from the 19th century. The images are of Napoleon and his generals. The table was in the Kuquine property of the dictator Fulgencio Batista, from where it was brought to the Municipal Museum.

Throne Hall of the Palacio de los Capitanes Generales. The hall was built for the Spanish royalty out of respect and subordination, although no royalty ever came to Cuba. Small receptions were given by the General Captain in this hall.

Wicker furniture in the Municipal Museum reached Cuba at the end of the 19th century, and Art Nouveau at the beginning of the 20th century.

This salon is known as the Coffee Room, a beverage that became over time a fixture in the life of Cuban families. The display case to the right holds a collection of valuable fans produced with precious materials such as coral, mother of pearl, ivory, amethyst and emeralds.

The bath of the Palacio de los Capitanes Generales, containing two original large marble bathtubs. The screens are also of great value.

The first Flag Hall of the Municipal Museum, containing the three most important flags in the history of Cuba and flags of the nations that supported the island in its fight for independence. The Hall also holds the uniform of Máximo Gómez and one of the machetes used in battle by Antonio Maceo, two key figures in Cuban history.

One of the many treasures housed in the Municipal Museum: the flag raised by Carlos Manuel de Céspedes at Demajague to mark the beginning of the Ten Year War in 1868.

The second Flag Hall of the Municipal Museum. On the right are the combat flags carried by the Mambí army; on the left are the flags of the patriot associations that supported the struggle from abroad. In the display cases are objects that testify to the most important events of the War of Independence.

In the rear of the second Flag Hall, The Death of Maceo, an oil painting by Armando Menocal.

Oil portraits of the patriots of the War of Independence in the Municipal Museum. This collection by Federico Martínez contains 110 paintings from the beginning of the 20th century.

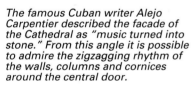

The brick pavement of the Plaza de la Cathedral hosts the stands of artisans selling their crafts.

This side view of the great Havana church does not make its suggestive Baroque facade any less majestic.

The famous Cuban writer Alejo Carpentier described the facade of the Cathedral as "music turned into stone." From this angle it is possible to admire the zigzagging rhythm of the walls, columns and cornices around the central door.

The Cathedral and Plaza

For a very long period, the development of colonial architecture in Cuba and Havana depended substantially on the kind of economy that Spain established on the island when it was realized that no gold or gems would be found there.

For much of the period, the economic life of Cuba was marked by self-sufficiency, with the exception of Havana, whose main source of wealth depended on the great traffic of ships, forming large fleets that linked the New World with the main Spanish ports. This role of the capital, and the fact that is was constantly under the threat of pirates and corsairs under the employ of other European powers, meant that most of the investments went towards strengthening the city's defenses during the 16th and 17th centuries, while works of a religious nature were less important than they were in other Latin American colonies.

With the native population almost totally extinct, it was not necessary to undertake a mass conversion of the population to Christianity, nor to develop a strategy aiming at their ideological submission with the use of magnificent symbols of religious power.

On the other hand, the economic resources in the early centuries were very limited, making it necessary to construct modest buildings. The first church in Havana was a hut. When it became a building, however humble, the French corsair Jacques de Sores set it on fire without hesitation, destroying it along with the rest of the city on July 10, 1555. It was only rebuilt in 1574, although the church had, as the testimony of the period reveals, "neither paintings, nor books, nor ornaments, nor bells." The church was rebuilt and enlarged around 1666, dedicated to Saint Christopher, Patron Saint of the city, and, with the founding of the parishes of the Holy Spirit, Christ, Safe Voyage and the Guardian Angel, it took the name of Parroquial Mayor (Main Parish).

However, this hierarchical role did not provide any formal advantage to the church, so much so that it was stated that it looked on the outside "so plain that it seems a private home rather than the house of God." On June 30, 1742, a bolt of lightning struck the powder magazine of the ship *Invencible*, anchored in the harbor, causing an explosion that razed numerous building in the city, including the Main Parish.

The demolition of the ruins was hurried to build the Palacio de los Capitanes Generales on the same site in the Plaza de Armas. On December 9,1777, the Main Parish was transferred to a church then under construction near the small plaza of the Ciénaga by Jesuit fathers, who then saw it confiscated a short time before the expulsion of the Society of Jesus from Spain and her dominion. The church was transformed into a Cathedral and after the work of rebuilding and restructuring, begun in 1788, the small plaza around the church received its definitive name and gained importance and prestige.

The church forms a rectangle of 34 by 35 meters, divided internally by large pilasters in three naves and eight side chapels. The floor is in white and black marble tiles. The oldest chapels include one dedicated to the Virgin of Loreto, consecrated in 1755 and thus much earlier than the transformation of the small church into the Cathedral, and the chapel called the Sagrario, with its own entrance corresponding to the parish linked to the Cathedral. The sculpture and goldwork of the main altar and its tabernacle in marble and precious metals were almost all produced in Rome in 1822 by the Italian artist Bianchini, who worked under the direction of the famous Spanish sculptor Antonio Solá.

Behind the main altar are three large frescoes by the Italian painter Giuseppe Perovani, as well as paintings by Jean-Baptiste Vermay. To understand better the value of the facade of the Cathedral, we can cite the eminent Cuban architecture historian Joaquín M. Weiss, who wrote: "Stylistically, this building goes much further than any of our other Baroque architecture." Weiss, in one of his best known works, calls attention to the cornice placed above the central door, which uses undulate forms and broken lines to express the freedom and the fantasy with which the facade of the great church was designed.

The Cathedral has thus come to the Cubans of today as a cultural and spiritual symbol of its past and as a synthetically expressive example of the country's colonial architecture. It is therefore not strange that the plaza, along with the buildings around it and the Cathedral that takes up its entire north side, is for many the most beautiful and representative image of Old Havana. In this plaza, between the streets of San Ignacio and Empedrado, is the Callejón del Chorro, a

One of the colonial buildings that surround Plaza de la Cathedral, the antique palace built by the marquis Aguas Claras. Today it houses the prestigious restaurant, bar and cafe El Patio.

The cupola of the Cathedral, viewed from the central nave near the main altar.

The main altar of the Havana Cathedral. The sculptures and goldwork that one can admire there were produced in Rome in 1820.

memory of other times when springs bubbled up there and the Zanja Real flowed, furnishing water to the people and the ships. One can still spot, in one of the walls along the Callejón, the original plaque that recalls: *This water was made to flow by Regiment Colonel Ivan de Texada. Anno 1592.*

The elegant buildings around the plaza are for the most part similar to many of the colonial buildings that can be found throughout the historic center and which have been copied in other Cuban towns. Generally, they are homes in the Moorish style with facades featuring monumental doorways, windows and balconies. They also feature spacious entryways and are usually characterized by an internal courtyard or patio surrounded by tile-covered porticoes.

These buildings were constructed like fortresses, endowed with a precise form. The interior was conceived for the comfort of the inhabitants, including the servants. On the corner of Empedrado and San Ignacio streets, near the Cathedral, is the building that belonged to the Marquis of Aguas Claras, today occupied by El Patio restaurant. From the restaurant's terrace, diners can appreciate a close-up view of the top of the church's famous facade.

The southern side of the plaza is occupied by the building that was the property of Don Luis Chacón, the governor of the island. It is said that some of the elaborate surfaces of this building, dating from the 18th century, are the most beautiful examples that can be found in Old Havana. Perfectly integrated within the setting of the plaza and with the scenario of this building is the Museum of Colonial Art, of the Havana National Historical Society, with an exhibition of furniture, lamps, porcelain and other objects and works of art that reflect the taste and customs of the period. Leaving the Cathedral and going left, one finds the home of the Count of Lombillo, whose family owned this palace in the 19th century, although in reality the building has occupied this site since the first quarter of the 17th century. Today the antique palace houses the Museum of Education, where visitors can admire, among the various displays, vivid testimonials of the literacy campaign carried out in Cuba in 1961. Next door, under the same portico, is the home of the Marquis of Arcos, another very representative colonial palace that is today the home of the Taller Experimental de Gráfica (Experimental Workshop of Graphic Arts).

The Plaza de la Cathedral is visited each day by thousands of tourists and Cubans, who enjoy the beauty of the area and its lively atmosphere. Traditional Cuban music, played by small bands, provide the background in the El Patio restaurant, with the echo of the singers and guitars drifting to the nearby Bodeguita el Medio. The Bodeguita specializes in Creole cooking and is famous throughout the world for its *Mojito de ron*, made of rum and mint, one of the favorite drinks of Hemingway. For many people, the restaurant begins or caps off a visit to the Plaza de la Cathedral.

Other religious buildings

Of the many religious structures built within the historic center of Old Havana, at least a dozen of them are worthy of mention. Following is a brief description of the most important churches.
In 1574 a small community of Franciscan monks settled in Havana, where ten years later they began work on the church and convent of Saint Francis of Assisi.

At the far end of the plaza on the opposite side of the Cathedral is the palace that today houses the Museum of Colonial Art, run by the Havana National Historical Society. A visit to the museum is obligatory for an understanding of the atmosphere and customs of the city in times past.

The attractive central courtyard of the Museum of Colonial Art is surrounded by galleries. Note the lowered arches on the ground floor and the lack of arches on the top floor.

The church and its monastery, located near the present day streets of de Oficios and Brasil (Teniente Rey), were reconstructed and enlarged numerous times in the course of almost two centuries, until in 1738 the complex reached its present shape.

A short distance from the harbor and surrounded by an irregularly shaped plaza, the Franciscan building was for a long time the most elegant church of colonial Havana, characterized by an unusual and tall bell tower, by far higher than the towers of any other church in the city. Starting in 1841, when the Spanish government took over the property of the religious orders, the church was put to many uses, for the most part quite different than its original purpose, until the present day. At present, the Minor Basilica, thanks to its extraordinary acoustics, is used as a hall for concerts and chamber music.

As if it were a sort of relic among the buildings of colonial Cuba, the surviving section of the church of San Francisco de Paula, once a part of a women's hospital, is worthy of a visit. Located on a small traffic circle near the bay, at the meeting point of the streets of Leonor Pérez (Paula), San Isidro and San Ignacio, the impressive bulk of the antique church stands in view of the numerous drivers who crowd this spot with their cars. The dome of the church of San Francisco de Paula is particularly interesting for its pre-Churrigueresque Baroque style. Inside of the church are the remains of the great Cuban violinist Claudio José Brindis de Salas, while the hospital that stood next to the church was the scene of several pages of the first Cuban novel, *Cecilia Valdés*, by Cirilo Villaverde.

Among other religious buildings of Old Havana is also the Seminary of San Carlos and San Ambrosio,whose construction dates back to the 18th century and

A room recreating 19th-century fashion, with sets of medallóns. To the left is a piece in the Louis XVI style. The small tree in mother of pearl on the table is an example of the works produced in jails and convents. The crystal chandelier is French.

Bedroom with furnishings from the second half of the 19th century. Note the bronze cradle and the opaline chandelier.

Nineteenth-century dining room. In the glass case to the right are examples of China that belonged the Creole bourgeois of the era.

therefore prior to that of the Cathedral. The experts maintain that the only merit of its exterior is the doorway; however, they agree with admiration on the quality of the interior, with its quadrangle delimited by galleries and its fine examples of doors and finely carved wooden grilles, with high quality reproductions still on display. In addition to its many architectural qualities, the Seminary was for many years, during the entire colonial era, an important center of lay education in which numerous important national patriots developed their culture and conscience.

Very characteristic of Creole crafts is the production of applied glass above doors and outside-facing windows. These decorative elements serve to let in softer light. This late 19th-century skylight with decals is in translucent and ground crystal.

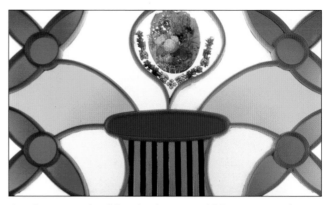

Another example of Creole glass art, which, as opposed to the usual lead crystal, uses glass and wood for the decoration. This is another 19th-century skylight with decals, in translucent and ground glass.

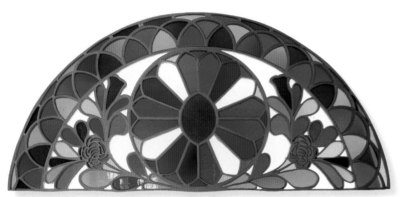

Cuban glass art began in the mid 18th century, continuing till the end of the 19th century. Similar works can be admired throughout the country in the homes of the middle classes and aristocracy. This piece was found in a home dating from the second half of the 19th century.

Flower holder with its pedestal.

This English porcelain flower holder is in the Museum of Colonial Art.

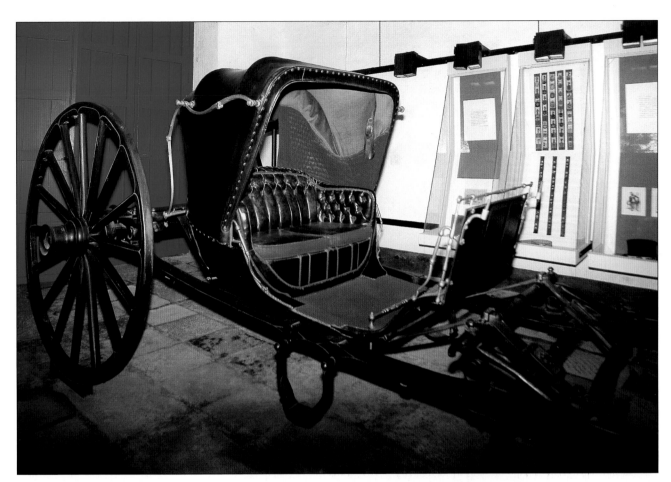

The most luxurious means of transportion in the 19th century was the gig. This carriage, on display in the Museum of Colonial Art, was manufactured in Cuba.

A back view of the gig exhibited in the Museum of Colonial Art. Its beauty and excellent craftsmanship can be admired.

The Plaza de San Francisco hosted, during the earliest settlement of Havana, the public market. The first mention of it dates back before 1559.

The church of San Francisco was first built starting in 1584. Rebuilt in 1738, the church and its convent are important sites in Cuban history.

The church of San Francisco de Paula, on Avenida del Puerto, is characteristic of the Cuban Baroque style of the first half of the 18th century.

The Seminary of San Carlos and San Ambrosio was rebuilt in the 1950s in a style defined by some experts as Cuban Neo-Baroque.

In 1836, the center of the Plaza de San Francisco was graced with this beautiful fountain, la Fuente de los Leones. The fountain is the work of Italian sculptor G. Gaggini, who also made the famous Fuente de la India, or the Noble Habana.

The facade of the Seminary of San Carlos and San Ambrosio clearly recalls the facade of the Cathedral, although without the same solemnity of the latter.

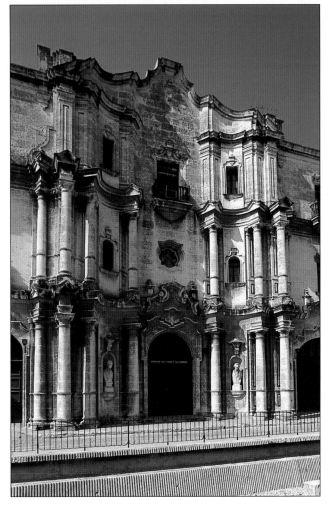

General view of the Castillo de la Real Fuerza, the first military fortress built in Cuba and one of the first in the Americas.

Partial view of the moats of the Castillo de la Real Fuerza. The design of the fortress, like that of the other colonial forts of Havana, was influenced by the style and the architectural concepts of the Renaissance.

The only tower of the Castillo de la Real Fuerza. Atop the cupola is La Giraldilla, *the symbol of the city of Havana.*

The Main Forts of Havana

The treasures that Havana accumulated in the course of its economic development thanks to its strategic port was reason enough to siege the city for pirates, corsairs and fleets of the European powers, who fought over the centuries with Spain and disputed her rule in many areas of the Americas. The danger that threatened Havana became evident a very short time after the founding of the city, when the first inhabitants had to suffer numerous attacks and sackings, including that of the terrible French corsair Jacques de Sores, who in 1555 destroyed all that stood in his way. The Crown then became convinced of the immediate need to provide Havana with military protection able to repel any attack and decided to begin fortifying the city.

Castillo de la Real Fuerza

The first of these military fortifications was begun in 1558 and finished in 1577. A side of Plaza de Armas was chosen for its location, probably because this was where the main settlement was situated and the highest city officials lived. The Castillo's wide moat, its appearance of a medieval castle complete with drawbridge and its thick walls set over a polygonal plan give it the impression of being a seemingly impregnable fortress.

In little time, however, the Castillo de la Real Fuerza showed its inability to sustain enemy attacks. The fact that it was built in a somewhat less than fortuitous location from a strategic standpoint, and the lack of combat stations which had become evident from the outset, immediately provoked heated polemics. The composition of the first garrison that occupied the Castillo was also laughable. In fact, the garrison consisted of that blend of cultures which, in the course of the following centuries, would constitute one of the salient features of the Cuban national identity: of the 50 men, 19 were born in Portugal, two gunners were Flemish and one was German, and, to further increase the ethnic diversity, the first drummer of the Castillo de la Real Fuerza was an old Negro slave. The unmistakable landmark that this fortification provided for the city was made even more conspicuous when between 1630 and 1634 a small tower was added to one of the highest points of the complex and was topped with one of the enduring symbols of Havana: the *Giraldilla*, a bronze statue molded and cast in 1630 by Havana artist Gerónimo Martín Pinzón and depicting a woman watching over the city and in the distance far beyond the harbor.

Despite the building's lack of functionality as a fort, it was never demolished, even though several attempts were made to raze it. The Castillo de la Real Fuerza ended up being used as barracks and offices during the colonial era and as the headquarters of several institutions during the 20th century. At present it houses the National Museum of Artistic Ceramics. The Castillo de la Real Fuerza, despite its lack of military activity, gained a place in the coat of arms that King Philip II presented to Havana when he granted the settlement the title of city in 1592.

First placed as pennant in 1630, the original Giraldilla *was toppled by hurricane winds in 1926. Today it is kept in the Municipal Museum, with a copy taking its place atop the tower of the Castillo de la Real Fuerza.*

The front of the Castillo de la Real Fuerza, with the drawbridge. At present, the fortress houses the National Museum of Artistic Ceramics.

The esplanade in front of the entrance of the Castillo de la Real Fuerza. The cannons of different caliber and range were manufactured between the 18th and 19th centuries.

A detail of the stairway that leads to the embattled terraces that held the artillery of the Castillo de la Real Fuerza.

Castillo de los Tres Reyes del Morro

Another fort of Havana that has a place in the city's insignia is the Castillo de los Tres Reyes del Morro (Castle of the Three Kings of Morro), the second fort built in Havana. It was completed in 1630, after 40 years of work. Its construction was commissioned by the Italian engineer Gian Battista Antonelli, and the location chosen for it was a rock promontory that closes the line of the bay on its northern side. From here, the view of the sea was better and its location was farther from the dwellings than that of the previous fort of Real Fuerza. These facts, in addition to its superior arms, led people to believe that once the new castle would be in operation, the city would have become an impenetrable bastion.

A century later, however, at the dawn of June 6, 1762, a multitude of vessels belonging to the large British fleet was spotted on the horizon from here. The fleet had regrouped near the Florida peninsula and was sailing southwards in the direction of Havana, whose territory it was evidently intent on

In front of the Morro, the small fort of La Punta dating from 1630. It was built on the norternmost point of the bay channel to create a line of crossfire on enemy ships. Pictured is a frontal section of one of its bulwarks.

View of the Castillo de la Real Fuerza from the fortress of the Cabaña.

Panoramic view of the Castillo de los Tres Reyes del Morro, built at the beginning of the 18th century.

capturing. After 44 long days of siege and despite the tireless defense of the populace, Havana fell into the hands of the English. The final blow dealt by the British was the placement of several mines among the stones of the Morro, where the valiant defenders of the city's last bulwark fought.

The English remained on the island for a year until an agreement was worked out with Spain to exchange their dominions, with the latter regaining possession of its "most faithful Havana" and the former receiving the North American territory of Florida. The conquest of Havana by the English not only deeply shook Spain's military predominance and political control of the island, but—a fact that was even more terrible for the city—it spelled the decline of commerce and traffic that ended once and for all economic monopoly of the Spanish. The Creoles began to look more attentively towards other horizons and to understand gradually that independence from Spain would be fundamental for the economic and political interests of Cuba.

The bitter lesson learned from the period in which Havana was no longer under the firm control of Spanish colonial power could not, however, allow itself to be repeated. For this reason, one of the first plans of the Crown for Cuba, once it had reestab-

Entry to the loophole gallery that provides access to the Castillo de los Tres Reyes del Morro and view of bastions and moats, now dry, that circle the fortress.

The Castillo del Morro and part of the lighthouse, seen from the fortress of the Cabaña.

The lighthouse of the Morro, the oldest in Cuba, was built in 1845. The lighthouse is 48.5 meters high, and provides a view of 43.5 nautical miles.

Detail of the sentry box placed on the extreme of the Austria Bulwark, one of the two main bulwarks of the Castillo del Morro. Below is the entrance to the loophole gallery.

Old barracks inside of the Castillo del Morro. In the background are the lighthouse and the coastline of Havana.

lished its control over Havana, was that of rebuilding the Castillo del Morro and adding another fortification to the city. In 1845, a new tower, reaching 48.5 meters above sea level, was built on a hill and inaugurated at the Morro. The light of this tower, like those before it—though not as tall or elegant, but of equal utility—served to pinpoint the harbor to ships approaching the bay at night, while to departing ships it signaled their last farewell and lit their path to the open sea.

The jar room, original clay vessels where rape-seed oil was stored to keep the lighthouse lit at night.

"The Evolution of Mapmaking" in the Hall of Great 15th and 16th Century Voyages of the Castillo de los Tres Reyes del Morro.

Reproduction of a caney, a native dwelling with walls of tree branches and a conical roof of palm branches. Inside of the crude dwelling exhibited in one of the rooms of the Castillo del Morro is a hammock and original work and hunting tools as well as some semies (idols) worshipped by the first inhabitants of the island.

Vestibule of the Hall of Great Voyages. The displays provide an interesting overview of the geographic knowledge at the time Christopher Columbus came to Cuba.

Esplanade of the Twelve Apostles, located on a low area of level ground overlooking the entry to the harbor.

Main entrance to the Castillo de San Carlos de La Cabaña, built by the Spaniards at the end of the 18th century following the end of the English takeover of Havana. Partial view of the now dry moats.

Castillo de San Carlos de La Cabaña

Several small castles, such as the Atarés and del Príncipe, are located within the city of Havana. But the third most important fortification of the city and the largest in the Americas was the Castillo de San Carlos de La Cabaña, built next to the Morro and completed in 1774. "A work that cost so much, one should be able to see it as far away as Madrid," said King Carlos III, according to the chronicles, when he was informed of the cost of Havana's new castle. Fourteen million pesatas, a true heresy, were paid from the city's coffers to construct the new defensive structure of the city, whose size and solid appearance should have at least awed potential enemies. And that was apparently the case, since once all the cannons of the Cabaña had been forged and emplaced, they remained silent. Or at least all of them except for one, used for the ceremony of the Cañonazo, a tradition that began in the 16th century in another part of the city and today takes place in the Cabaña.

It is said that the blast indicated the opening and closing of the walls of the city and of the port, which was made unapproachable by a chain of enormous links

The Plaza de Armas inside of the Castillo de San Carlos de La Cabaña.

View of the main road inside of the Cabaña and of the old barracks, now transformed into exhibition halls for ceramic goods, military history and antique arms.

Battery of 21 bronze cannons cast in Seville in the 18th century, used to protect the entry to the bay from the fortress of the Cabaña.

strung across the channel. The opening shot occurred at 4:30 a.m. and the closing shot at 8 p.m. So it was at least until the occupation of the United States, when the first shot was abolished and the second shot moved to 9 p.m. The well known signal thus changed its time and function, but it continued nevertheless to sound each evening, with the exception of the last years of the Second World War (1942-45), when it was decided that Cuba shouldn't waste

Church of the Castillo de La Cabaña.

Sentry box in the north bulwark of the fortress of San Carlos de La Cabaña.

Historical reenactment in period uniforms. Every evening at 9 o'clock, a cannon shot is fired from the Cabaña, at it was in the times when the gates to the walled city were shut.

gun powder for shooting blanks. The rule was undoubtedly over cautious, and the populace managed to overturn it through persistent pressure.

Today the large fort next to the Morro, completely restored and perfectly preserved, is the headquarters of the Parque Histórico Militar Morro-Cabaña, where visitors can look over the past and admire one of the most beautiful views of Havana from the high walls.

Photograph of Commandant Ernesto Che Guevara taken on January 3,1959, the day in which he took command of the fortress of the Cabaña several hours after victoriously entering Havana at the head of a column of his soldiers.

CHE GUEVARA AT THE CABAÑA

On January 2, 1959, late at night, Che Guevara reached Havana for the first time in an olive-green Chevrolet, together with several jeeps and trucks that carried the 400 guerrillas of his military column. The Cuban Revolution was on the verge of triumphing and the Argentinean Ernesto Guevara, first commander designate by Fidel Castro, who himself was in the Sierra Maestra, had orders to take the second most important fort of the capital, the Castillo de San Carlos de La Cabaña, while commander Camilo Cienfuegos, his friend and disciple, was given the task of occupying the Columbia barracks, the headquarters of the troops of a dictatorship whose leader had already fled.

The city, occupied by the troops of the Movement of the 26th of July after that January dawn, breaks into celebration. Everyone wants to meet the mythical Argentinean soldier with the thin beard who had joined Fidel Castro in Mexico to take part in the expedition of 82 men pledging to be "free or martyrs," that man of 31 years of age with a tough and at times ironic temperament, the guerrilla who dealt the decisive blow to the dictatorship in the city of Santa Clara.

But Che, his arm in a sling after the battle of Santa Clara, moves unhesitatingly towards the fortress of the Cabaña. The sentinels of the old regime, under the watchful eye of the militia men on the outside of the encampment, fear for their lives, and keep hold of their weapons. Without hesitation, Che walks into the fort, which for five months will serve as the fighter's headquarters. At dawn of January 3 he calls the 3,000 soldiers before him and says: "The guerrillas must learn discipline from you, and from them you must learn how to win a war."

From that day onwards, Che lived in the Cabaña in a building constructed at the end of the 19th century, where the governor of the fort had resided. With time, the old palace, where the asthmatic fighter received constant visits by journalists, celebrities, friends and war comrades, took on a sort of air of sacredness. At the end of the 1980s, it was made into a museum which houses a large exhibit of objects belonging to the "Heroic Guerrilla," as the Cubans usually call Che. The original weapons that Che used in the mountains of Cuba, in the forests of the Congo and in the Bolivian Andes, his eye glasses, and his camera that he kept during the first years of the revolution, are some of the objects that allow us to imagine the person, along with the photos and the papers that trace the steps of the life of this emblematic man: his childhood, his travels as a young man across Latin America and the most important revolutionary events that he took part in.

The plazas and the barracks of the Cabaña were not only the scene of his short military career before being named the president of the National Bank of Cuba and, subsequently, the Minister of Industry. During the five months in which he was the head of the garrison, the fortress was transformed into a key seat of revolutionary theory and practice.

Immediately after his arrival he in fact created the Military Cultural Academy, which followed up on a practice that he had begun in the Sierra Maestra, despite the urgency of the war: literacy and education of his troops, most of whom were farmers who had never attended school. He instituted several workshops, the so-called "Cabaña Libre," in the fields around the old fortress, where the soldiers produced artisan goods to make themselves self-sufficient. He also created the nursery school "Los Barbuditos" in which children listened to the enterprises of the war heroes and where they were taught to load and unload old rifles, which they did before modest fiestas for new soldiers. Today, from the window of his perfectly conserved office in the Cabaña, it is possible to see the same Havana that Che contemplated for the first time, perhaps with a certain amazement, on that dawn of January 3, 1959.

The office used by Che Guevara in the Castillo de La Cabaña during the first five months of the triumph of the Cuban Revolution.

Havana beyond the walls

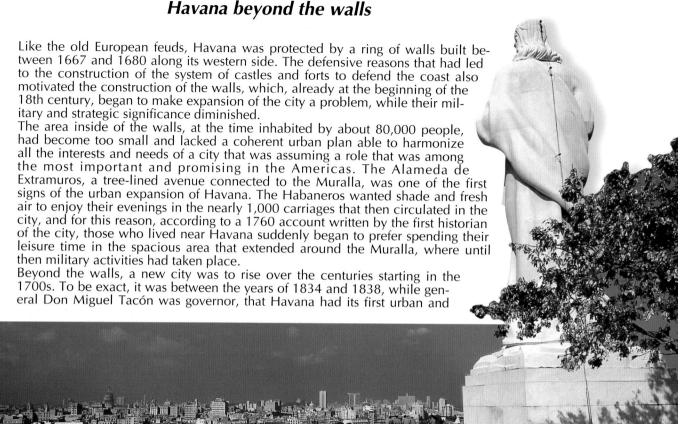

Like the old European feuds, Havana was protected by a ring of walls built between 1667 and 1680 along its western side. The defensive reasons that had led to the construction of the system of castles and forts to defend the coast also motivated the construction of the walls, which, already at the beginning of the 18th century, began to make expansion of the city a problem, while their military and strategic significance diminished.

The area inside of the walls, at the time inhabited by about 80,000 people, had become too small and lacked a coherent urban plan able to harmonize all the interests and needs of a city that was assuming a role that was among the most important and promising in the Americas. The Alameda de Extramuros, a tree-lined avenue connected to the Muralla, was one of the first signs of the urban expansion of Havana. The Habaneros wanted shade and fresh air to enjoy their evenings in the nearly 1,000 carriages that then circulated in the city, and for this reason, according to a 1760 account written by the first historian of the city, those who lived near Havana suddenly began to prefer spending their leisure time in the spacious area that extended around the Muralla, where until then military activities had taken place.

Beyond the walls, a new city was to rise over the centuries starting in the 1700s. To be exact, it was between the years of 1834 and 1838, while general Don Miguel Tacón was governor, that Havana had its first urban and

architectural plan, which mostly focused on the area around the walls. One of the works in the plan was the famous Tacón Theater, inaugurated in great pomp in 1838, as described by the countess of Merlin: "This theater is both rich and elegant; ... the governor's box is larger and more ornate than that of the king in other theaters. Only the leading theaters of the great European capitals can compete with the beauty and decorations, the splendor of the lighting, the elegance of the spectators all in yellow gloves and white trousers, of that of Havana."

This theater was one of the most obvious symbols of economic well-being that the country was enjoying. Thanks to the trade in slaves, to scientific progress, and to access to new markets, especially with the United States, Cuba began to become an important producer of sugar at the end of the 18th century. The profits of this industry began to fill the coffers of the municipal treasury and made many men rich. Most of these were Creoles, as the natives of Cuba were called, and they in turn began to demand independence for the island. Out of the need to maintain political hegemony, the government of the island, represented by Tacón, promoted new works to demonstrate by their magnificence the advantages of the defense of Spanish interests in Cuba.

If up until then most of the buildings of the old city were religious, military or residential, during the process of urban development in Havana there appeared a great profusion of new works for a wide variety of uses, such as markets, theaters, cafes, ice cream parlors, ballrooms, shops, hotels, villas, the railroad station, boardwalks, avenues ... a whole network of city services.

This Christ by sculptor Jilma Madera has blessed the city of Havana since 1958.

The Christ of Havana looking towards the city. Sculpted in white Carrara marble, it is 15 meters tall. Thanks to its position at the top of the hill of the Cabaña, the statue stands 79 meters above sea level.

Monument to Generalissimo Máximo Gómez. In this view it is possible to see the tunnel running beneath the bay, connecting its two sides.

View of the Havana waterfront from the Castillo de San Carlos de La Cabaña. The domes of the Capitol and of the Presidential Palace (Museum of the Revolution) stand out.

Main entrance to the old Presidential Palace, built in 1918 and today home of the Museum of the Revolution.

Still preserved in front of the Presidential Palace is this section of the walls of Havana: the sentry box of the Guardian Angel bulwark, or the Angel Bulwark.

Small factories were also built, the result of the modernization of the urban economy. Still existing among these are the tobacco works, a product that distinguished itself among all of those that were exported from Cuba and which today continues to be unequaled. The residential buildings began to express more obviously the economic differences of the new owners. Along with the luxurious homes that gave an air of opulence to Havana, one could encounter houses that were much more modest, conserving the typical austerity of the city of the 16th and 17th centuries. These homes continued to be found in quarters far from the new city beyond the walls, close to what is today called Old Havana. The program undertaken by Tacón was so extensive that many experts agree that there was not another of the same breadth until almost a century later, during the republican period under the government of dictator Gerardo Machado. With the arrival of the 20th century and the end of the Spanish colonial regime on the island, a new period began for the development of Havana. Despite the years of war against Spain (1868-78, 1895-98), the Cubans could not achieve real independence: as soon as the Spanish surrendered their domination, another foreign power flung itself on the country. In 1898, the United States intervened in the Spanish-Cuban conflict to win a future protectorate in Cuba, which enabled them to establish the basis for a new kind of domination, neo-colonial, that lasted for the entire first part of the 20th century.

The foreign influence over the economic, political and cultural life of Cuba also left its mark on the architecture of Havana. The Baroque style, for example, which was predominant during the Spanish colonial period, was considered a symbol of the defeated regime and rejected. The fashion shifted towards the most diverse stylistic currents: Neo-Renaissance, Neo-Baroque, French Art Deco or Art Nouveau from the Catalan masters. In the first years of the 20th century, Neo-Classicism also had a marked influence. The style was one that recalled the republican civil virtues from the Roman tradition, exalted by the French Revolution and assimilated by its heirs, the most developed European societies and especially the United States.

It was thus that monumental works were built in Havana, many of them for civic purposes, with appearances typical of those found in the great European capitals, if not, as in some cases, imitations of existing buildings.

The Hall of Mirrors, the former receiving room of the Presidential Palace.

The second and third floors of the Museum of the Revolution seen from their broad marble staircase.

A room in the Museum of the Cuban Revolution, in one of the halls that once belonged to the Presidential Palace.

Presidential Palace (Museum of the Revolution)

Inaugurated in 1920, this civic work is the most eclectic building among those used by government offices. It was the seat of the executive power starting in 1959 and for this reason the building is of great historic importance, which is further reinforced by the fact of its having been the scene of one of the most shocking successes of those years.

Photographs, objects and documents of the revolutionary history of the Cuban people exhibited in the rooms of the museum.

In 1956, a group of young University of Havana students attempted to attack the palace and execute Fulgencio Batista to end his dictatorship. Bullet marks are still visible today on the walls, in addition to a large collection of objects and documents pertaining to the event. Today the palace houses the Museum of the Revolution, one of the most important in the country, which covers the entire history of Cuba from its discovery up to the present.

The Capitol of Havana. Its elegant dome, at some 91 meters, can be seen from many areas of the city.

The Capitol Building of Havana

Completed in 1929, the Capitol was the result of the most extraordinary architectural imitation. However, it is possible to identify some innovations in the Cuban tradition, such as the inner courtyards, very similar to those that abound in the buildings of Old Havana, and the use of precious domestic hardwoods.

Beneath the large dome, which is the axis of the entire building, stands the third tallest statue in the world (17 meters): a Minerva Protectoress, symbol of the Republic, in cast bronze. At her feet, in a small display case, is a diamond—with obvious reference to the Arc de Triomphe in Paris—that marks the beginning of the Carretera Central, the first road to cross the island and built under the Machado government.

The two symmetrical lateral pavilions at the base of the dome were for the legislative bodies of the House and Senate, incarnating the liberal conception of the balance of power.

Their interiors have rich decorative elements in diverse styles of great opulence and an almost idolatry rhetoric, based on the image of the Republic which had just been constituted.

Since 1962, the Capitol has been the headquarters of the Academy of Sciences of Cuba and more recently of the Ministry of Science, Technology and the Environment, as well as other institutions that have relations with the world of information and scientific documentation. The main floor, with its 15 fine halls and carefully restored galleries, is the home of the Capitol Center of Havana, in charge of organizing meetings, fests and tours of the majestic building.

The old Centro Gallego, today the Grand Theater of Havana, one of the most beautiful architectural monuments of the city.

Statue of José Martí, dominating the Parque Central. It was the first statue erected in honor of the "Apostle" of Cuban independence.

Centro Gallego (Grand Theater of Havana)

In the spot originally occupied by the Tacón Theater in the 19th century, Havana exhibits another of its most beautiful monuments. The Centro Gallego, today the Grand Theater of Havana, was built facing the Parque Central in 1912 and has one of the richest exteriors of any building in the capital. With its spiral scrolls and turrets embellished with statues of angels and Muses, the Centro Gallego endowed the areas of old Havana beyond the walls with a strong cosmopolitan sense and became one of the unequivocal incarnations, as Alejo Carpentier wrote, of "this style without style that in the long run, by symbiosis, by amalgamation, becomes a Baroquism."

Carpentier was a well-known Cuban novelist, who also had architectural training. He often looked intently to discover the hidden treasures of Havana, and to direct distracted eyes at that which, although obvious, is sometimes missed: "little by little, from the multi-colored, from the extreme, from the elaborate that incarnates itself in realities very different one from the other, have arisen the constants of a general appearance that distinguishes Havana."

Parque Central

Starting from the 19th century, the Parque Central has become the Habaneros' most popular location. Situated where colonial Havana blends with the new city, this tree-filled plaza constituted the beginning of the famous Paseo de Extramuros. But with the frenetic urbanization that took place in this section of the city at the beginning of the century, the park gradually lost its central location, even thought it still is an important geographic, historic and cultural point of reference.

In the middle of the plaza, with its lovely gardens of flowers and majestic ceibe trees, there originally stood a statue of Queen Isabella II, which was toppled with the end of Spanish dominion. Subsequently, the first statue in Cuba dedicated to José Martí was placed there, which still occupies the spot.

Among the buildings on Avenida del Malecón is the so-called "Caryatids Building" with its design typical of the eclectic style combining Neo-Classical and Deco elements. The building houses the Center of Spanish Culture.

This small palace with its eclectic design was strongly influenced by the styles of the Italian Renaissance, quite atypical in the context of Old Havana. In was built in 1905. Today it is home to the National Music Museum.

The Hotel Nacional of Cuba, emblem of Havana, built in only 13 months in 1930, is one of the most beautiful and luxurious in the country.

El Vedado is now considered the most central area of the city of Havana.

Modern Havana

The long avenue known as Malecón de La Habana is a sort of balcony that looks out at the waters of the Gulf of Mexico. A seafront avenue extremely popular with Habaneros, the Malecón begins in front of the Castillo de la Real Fuerza and ends in modern Havana, near the Torreón de La Chorrera, a military construction of 1665.

In the section running along El Vedado are many buildings from the 1950s, with a marked American influence (from Art Deco to modern monumental), that co-exist with eclectic buildings of the Cuban middle classes from the beginning of the century. Starting from the 1930s, this area of the city began to become one of the city's most attractive neighborhoods due to its shining modern image, and it continues to be so today. The popularity that El Vedado enjoyed prompted the most powerful families to seek isolated and peaceful areas towards the west in which to build their houses. Thus, neighborhoods like Miramar arose, which today contains the most sumptuous examples of Cuban architecture from the first half of this century.

Host to some of the most important personages in the world, the Hotel Nacional conserves photographs of some of these guests in the so-called Hall of Fame.

52

Hotel Nacional

The biggest and most luxurious hotels in Havana were built in El Vedado following a tourism development plan promoted by the Mafia in the United States. The plan aimed at transforming the seafront of Havana into one enormous Las Vegas casino.

The Hotel Nacional, where a multitude of persons linked to international crime met and lived, was built in 1930 on a hill a short distance from the Malecón. Special care has been taken to conserve the original decorations in the majestic building. Its several levels, embellished with small and lovely artistic mosaics, its marble columns and scagliola that support the roof, and its public areas have all been preserved to look as they did when the building was completed, endowing the Hotel Nacional with a very special appearance.

Celebrities from the international worlds of politics, culture, science and athletics have passed through the large doors and the gardens of this building, which is a fascinating and sober example of the Spanish plateresque style.

The monument to José Martí, national hero of Cuba, dominates the Plaza de la Revolución. The viewing terrace at the summit of the obelisk, at some 139 meters, is the highest point in Havana and offers a fine panorama of the entire city.

At the base of the monument is the José Martí memorial, with a permanent exhibit on the life and accomplishments of the National Hero of the Cuban Republic.

Plaza de la Revolución

One of the most emblematic and majestic constructions of contemporary Havana is the monument to José Martí, a mass of gray marble reaching 139 meters in height. Built between 1958 and 1959, this enormous monument pays homage to the national hero of Cuba, rising above the historic Plaza de la Revolución. The Plaza has witnessed the largest political rallies of the Cuban people, many speeches by Fidel Castro and one of the masses of Pope John Paul II. The modern monumental architecture surrounding the Plaza de la Revolución houses the main political-administrative institutions of the country, as well as the José Martí National Library and the National Theater. In front of the monument, on the facade of the Ministry of the Interior, an immense metallic structure holds the image of the venerated commander Che Guevara.

The Memorial also contains information on the construction of the Plaza and on the most important events that it has witnessed.

55

The seat of the José Martí National Library, founded in 1901. The design of the building (modern monumental) makes it the most characteristic among the buildings on Plaza de la Revolución.

Behind the José Martí Memorial is the building housing the most important offices of government: the State Council, the Council of Ministers, and the Central Committee of the Cuban Communist Party.

The most famous image of Che in the world, a unique work reproduced on the facade of the building that at the beginning of the Revolution housed the Ministry of Industry, which was directed by Che, and which today houses the Ministry of the Interior.

The Avenida Paseo, one of the most beautiful and greenest avenues of Havana. It begins at the foot of Plaza de la Revolución and crosses the area of El Vedado, ending at the Malecón and the sea.

HEMINGWAY IN HAVANA

It was almost without realizing it that the giant, reddish, childish individualist with his short pants and sunglasses came to live in Cuba. Havana, where he arrived for the first time in 1928 for a 48-hour tropical vacation, would become the only really stable residence of the fickle literary genius, Ernest Hemingway. All of his homes, more or less temporary, tell the story of 22 years of his intimate presence in this city, which strangely was never the explicit setting or protagonist of his novels.

It was never love at first sight between Havana and Hemingway. His first visits to the Cuban capital did not seem to show anything more than his desire to partake in the simple pleasure of fishing for impressive specimens of swordfish and needle-fish in the mysterious currents of the Gulf of Mexico. But later his sentimental relations with this country and especially with this city became lasting and profound. In 1954, when he was awarded the Nobel Prize for literature, he announced in perfect Spanish his decision to donate the prize to Our Lady of the City of Cobre, the Patron Saint of Cuba.

At the beginning, there were only relatively short trips. During his fishing expeditions, Hemingway came to know the humble seamen who lived in Cojímar, a fishing village east of Havana.

Among the "good folk," who ended up calling him "Papa," were to be many of his future and faithful friends. Some of them, who became protagonists and characters in novels such as The Old Man and the Sea and Islands in the Gulf, removed the bronze propellers from their boats when they heard of the suicide of the illustrious writer and friend and commissioned a sculptor to make the expressive statue that was placed in the old square of Cojímar, in front of the dock where Hemingway used to moor his boat, the Pilar.

The modest Plaza Hemingway was the first in the world to be given his name.

The Pilar, built in 1934, was skippered by Gregorio Fuentes, a fisherman and friend of the writer. Fuentes received the boat in Hemingway's will, and in 1961 he donated it to the Hemingway Museum.

Before departing as war correspondent on the front of the Spanish Civil War, Hemingway already had three favorite places for his sojourns in Havana: the Floridita, a bar-restaurant today famous throughout the world for its shellfish specialties and its Daiquiris, a cocktail that the novelist promoted all over the world; the Creole restaurant la Bodeguita del Medio, where he used to drink a Mojito and chat with friends; and a room on the last floor of the Hotel

The Finca Vigía, a few kilometers from Havana, has remained the way its owners left it in 1960. It is now the Hemingway Museum.

The trophies of animals hunted by Hemingway in Africa, Europe and the United States are displayed throughout the house.

Ambos Mundos, near Plaza de Armas and the Cathedral of Havana, which upon his return from Spain became his favorite hiding-place for writing.

But when Hemingway decided to spend long periods in Cuba, the Ambos Mundos became too popular with his friends and admirers. In 1939, his third wife found an ideal place where the novelist could finish For Whom the Bell Tolls: a home 15 kilometers from the city that was called Vigía, in the village of San Francisco de Paula.

The house was built between 1886 and 1887 by a Catalan architect. The luminous building, which, in the words of its owner "seemed like an old boat," took on much of the fame and myth of Hemingway. He spent almost all of his evenings in the large living room sitting in his favorite armchair, reading a good book and with the mobile bar designed by him always within reach.

In Vigía he wrote more than half of his works and threw parties for Hollywood celebrities, boxers, bull-fighters, authors and artists. But Hemingway had a characteristic that was particularly liked by the Cubans: he didn't act like a Señor, a master.

His home was open to whoever wanted to come in or was in need, humble as the person may be.

With the triumph of the Cuban Revolution in 1959, despite the pressures of the United States on Cuba, Hemingway remained in Vigía (now a museum) until he left for Spain in 1960. There he came down with his fatal illness that did not allow him to return to his island, and in 1961 he committed suicide in the United States.

This great American who preferred to live in Cuba, apparently distant from all the turbulent events of the island and dedicated to the pleasures of writing novels and drinking whisky, forever won the hearts of Cubans with one of his last comments, given to a journalist: "We will win. We Cubans will win."

The dining room, a simple room furnished with Spanish style country furniture. Here too the most notable decorations are the animal trophies: a kudu, an oryx from Kenya and a pronghorn antelope from Idaho.

The bedroom of Hemingway and his wife Mary.

The writer's private room, where he usually worked and rested. On top of the bookcase is his Royal typewriter. Hemingway always wrote standing up.

Under the play of shadows cast by the flowers of the climbing plants covering the trellis is the cistern for the house's water supply.

Kept in the gardens of Finca Vigía is one of the museum's exhibits, the Pilar, the boat used by Hemingway for his frequent fishing expeditions in the waters of the Gulf.

A short distance from the Cathedral of Havana is one of the finest Cuban restaurants, La Bodeguita del Medio. It walls, which almost have no room left for visitors to leave signatures, poems and comments, its characteristic rustic furnishing, and its typical Creole fare have made La Bodeguita a universally known spot.

The restaurant/bar Floridita, one of the places in Havana preferred by Hemingway. It is said that the American writer used to say: "My Mojito at the Bodeguita, at the Floridita my Daiquiri."

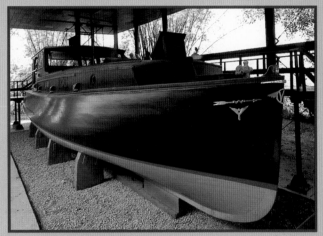

How to enjoy a day of sun and sea on the eastern beaches.

A number of beautiful beaches line the shores around Havana.

The Eastern Beaches

One can also discover Havana and the ways of its people by going to the beaches to the east of the city: a large number of magnificent beach resorts attract visitors almost all year round thanks to the warm and transparent waters and the fine sand beaches.

The beaches of Bacuaranao, El Mégano, Santa María del Mar, Boca Ciega and Guanabo attract thousands of tourists, who can enjoy the fine Cuban sea and the capital city at the same time.

Situated along the entire northern seafront as far as Matanzas are numerous campgrounds and two other excellent beaches, Jibacoa and Arroyo Bermejo, whose splendid sea bottoms are appreciated by enthusiastic scuba divers.

CUBA
from West to East

Valle de Viñales

Pinar del Río, where the best tobacco in the world is grown, includes some of the most fascinating and varied landscape in the entire country. Its geophysical contrasts enliven this province: from the southern plains, where the main tobacco producers and fields are located, to the north, where the Guaniguanico mountain range is formed by the Sierra del Rosario and the Sierra de los Órganos.

The Sierra de los Órganos is home to a singular display of Cuban geography, with the greatest peculiarity found in the Valle de Viñales. There, the *mogotes* rise to create unique cone-shaped limestone formations, among the oldest geological entities in the country and dating to the early and middle Jurassic era. Fossils, including those of dinosaurs, have been found within their bases. Not extremely high, but very voluminous and monolithic, these precipitous, nearly perpendicular crags with roughly shaped tops seem to form images of giant sleeping animals, or heaps of rocks mysteriously thrown from the heavens, or even enormous domes and decaying castles.

The vista point of Hotel Los Jazmines offers the most sweeping views of the Valle de Viñales, one of the most beautiful natural sites in the Pinar del Río and in all of Cuba.

The landscape of the Valle de Viñales is unique: rather than a simple valley surrounded by mountains, there are plateaus abruptly broken by mogotes.

The mogotes *of Valle de Viñales are the special feature of this valley. One cannot help but see strange forms in them, such as sleeping animals. This, for example, could be a giant elephant lying in a field.*

A landscape worthy of being immortalized by the paintbrushes of the greatest naturalist painters. Pictured is an element that characterizes cubanía, *the royal palm.*

Soroa: The Rainbow of Cuba

A short distance before Viñales for those traveling from Havana is another of the most beautiful natural areas of Pinar del Río, the site of a story that is worth recounting.

At the end of the 18th century, a French coffee grower, Jean Paul Soroa, arrived in Cuba, fleeing from the revolution in Haiti. Unlike many of his fellow countrymen, however, Soroa came to the western part of the island, settling in a little explored place in the Sierra del Rosario. He named this spot, overgrown with thick, luxuriant vegetation, after himself. Many years later, UNESCO declared the area a Biosphere Reserve because of its many natural wonders.

The Rainbow of Cuba, as Soroa also noted, is created by a waterfall formed by the río Manatiales, which plunges some 20 meters. From the so-called Soroa's leap, the cool waters flow into a small pool, where visitors refresh themselves after climbing the 279 steps that lead there.

Visitors to Soroa can also go up the mountain to the vista point of the Castillo de las Nubes, which offers a sweeping panorama of the Sierra del Rosario. On clear days, one can look south and discern, perhaps with same loving eyes as Soroa, the outline of Isla de la Juventud.

The Salto de Soroa. Around the falls it is common to come across trees as high as 35 meters and Cuban birds that are plentiful on the island: the tocororo—*the national bird—, the* tomeguines, nightengales, the *cartacubas and the* zunzún, *the tiniest humming bird in the world at only three-centimeters in length.*

The park at the house of Comacho. This bridge leads to a vista point that is the highest point of the orchid park.

The Orchid Garden of Soroa

In 1942, Tomás Felipe Camacho, a lawyer and native of the Canary Islands, purchased some land in an area of Soroa that he considered too beautiful to exclude from his property. And he thought of building a resort there, but some sad events ruined his plans: his daughter died while giving birth and his distraught wife passed away a short time afterwards. From that moment onwards, Don Tomás devoted himself exclusively to giving life, in honor of his lost loved ones, to an enchanting world of orchids.

When the park was completed in 1952, the cost of the enterprise had reached the figure of 1.5 million pesos (which was worth the same amount in US dollars at the time). Comacho hired a caretaker for the garden, the Japanese expert Kenji Takeuchi, a man who was short in stature, but great in wisdom. When Takeuchi arrived, he was met by Tomás with these sorrowful words: "Behind every orchid is concealed a great passion."

The man who created this monumental garden returned to the Canary Islands, where he died in 1961. At Soroa he left behind more than 700 varieties of orchids planted over an area of 35,000 square meters lying at an altitude of 206 meters above sea level. The area has a particular microclimate due to its abundant rains and an average annual temperature of 23.9° C.

Upon the death of Camacho, the park became a National Heritage site and fell under the management of scientific institutions. At the moment, the University of Pinar del Río is in charge of caring for the Orchid Park of Soroa, which now has some 950 varieties from all over the world, with about 25,000 plants. The period with the most intense flowering is between November and February. Besides the orchids, the park also hosts 70 species of trees, almost all of them exotic, and about 300 varieties of ferns.

The orchid park contains a large number of ornamental plants. Among them are Bromeliaceae *in different shapes and colors. In Cuba, these plants are known as* curujeyes.

Crotons (Codiaeum variegatum) *also decorate the park with their colorful leafs.*

Among the various species of orchid that grow in Soroa is the Dendrobium fimbriatum, *a native of the tropics of Asia.*

The collection of ornamental plants in the orchid park also includes the Alpineae *and other* Zingiberaceae. *Pictured is an* Alpinea coccinea.

Zingiberacea, known in Cuba as lirio antorcha (Phaeomeria capitata). *Its flowers seem to be covered with wax.*

Cueva del Indio

The same limestone nature of the *mogotes* in the Valle de Viñales and water erosion led to the formation, during a distant geological age, of the large caverns found throughout the area, including that of Santo Tomás, which, with an extension of 47 kilometers, is the largest in Cuba. Many of these grottoes contain underground rivers, such the San Vicente, which runs through the so-called Cueva del Indio, one of the most explored and interesting caves.

There are several theories behind the origin of the name: one of them refers to the discovery of the remains of Guanahatabeyes Indian settlements inside of the cave; another refers to a stone found inside of the cavern that resembles a kneeling Indian who is about to smoke.

Discovered in 1920 by local farmers, the cave is today easily visited: a small motor boat runs for 250 meters along the river, with much of the route illuminated, allowing visitors to marvel at the curious shapes formed by the walls of the cavern, in which it is possible to make out a great variety of figures.

The Prehistory Mural

Painting on a canvas placed on a easel is not a risky endeavor for an artist. Under quite different conditions, Cuban painter Leovigildo González used a crag of one of the *mogotes* in the Valle de Dos Hermanas in Viñales to create a monumental wall painting measuring 180 meters in length and 120 meters in height. Visitors who come to see this work, in vivid colors and a markedly naive style, can admire depictions of the history of the world beginning from the age of dinosaurs and going through to the appearance of man on earth, or what is considered to have been the geological evolution of the Sierra de los Órganos, where this mural is located.

Inside many of the mogotes *of the Valle de Viñales are some of the largest caverns in the northern hemisphere. Flowing through one of them, the Cueva del Indio, are the waters of the San Vicente river.*

Some 300 meters of the Cueva del Indio are illuminated and more than half of it can be visited on a footpath and a ride in a small motor boat.

The sheer size of this naive painting on the side of this mogote *is one of the major attractions of the well-known Prehistory Mural.*

Growing tobacco demands a devotion very much like an art, developed by the Cubans over the centuries. One of the most delicate procedures consists of grading the mature leaves which go into the production of the most fragrant Havana cigars.

The production of Havana cigars has always been done mostly by hand. Today, thousands of young people are preparing to inherit this art of the old masters.

With this particular instrument resembling a spoon, called a chaveta, *the tobacco craftsmen cut the* capa, *the leaf which, previously selected for its moistness and softness, is used to "wrap" the cigar.*

Neither too tight nor too loose. In the production of cigars, each procedure must have an almost mathematical precision.

The final procedure consists of sealing the butt of the cigar with a piece of capa *cut with the* chaveta. *Each cigar produced by these expert hands has been made to please the most demanding consumer.*

The Best Tobacco in the World

For Cubans, the saying "to listen to the history of tobacco" means to suffer through a long tale on any topic that begins with the dawn of time and ends only with the exhaustion of the listener. The meaning of this unique saying probably refers to the fact that tobacco belongs to the most remote origins of the history of the inhabitants of the island.

According to the claims of brother Bartolomé de Las Casas, Columbus, upon arriving in Cuba, met "men holding in their hands a fire-brand and a certain grass and which, in order to inhale the fumes, they had wrapped this dried grass in a leaf, this also dry (...) and lit it on one end, while on the other they sucked, or sipped, and drew from it, inhaling the smoke from inside of it." He related that he later met some Spaniards who had also taken up the habit of smoking tobacco and that, "if they were reproached, told that it was a vice, they answered that they were incapable of resisting it."

Thus began the fame of Cuban to-

bacco, this aromatic plant which through a long and delicate growing and manufacturing process is transformed into the exquisite cigars that are famous throughout the world. The plantations of Vuelta Abajo, the older name of Pinar del Río, enjoy the best natural conditions for the cultivation of this refined product.

The drying rooms, which are always located near the vegas, or tobacco plantations, look like giant huts. They are built of wood and leaves from royal palm trees (yagua) and maintain a constant level of humidity and heat to preserve the leaves. Inside of these drying rooms, each stage follows a strict pre-set routine.

Before reaching production, the tobacco leaf receives the necessary care inside of the drying room. In this photo, an expert worker threads a bunch of leaves.

The levels of the drying room are filled with cujes (long poles of a special wood) which will hold the bunches of leaves for the time they need to dry until they are ready to be sent into production.

Pinar del Río is also known as the city of capitals. Most of the buildings are typical examples of the eclecticism in which Art Nouveau predominates.

Pinar del Río: the city of capitals

During the colonization of Cuba, the only area in which no settlements were established was the present province of Pinar del Río. One of the reasons for this was apparently the low level of development of the indigenous people who inhabited the area when the Spanish arrived. At least this was related in a letter sent in 1514 by Diego Velázquez to the King of Spain, Ferdinand the Catholic: " (...) and that their customs (...) are those of savages, as they possess neither houses nor villages, nor do they practice agriculture, but they feed from the meat of animals they hunt in the mountains, and of turtles and of fish (...) ." The long distances to the other areas of the country that were then under development, together with the difficulties in traveling to and from Pinar del Río, combined to keep the region from reaching a certain level of economic development until the middle of the 19th century, when the people there began to obtain positive results from the cultivation of tobacco, which had been promoted by the inhabitants of the area since the 17th century.

The territory of Pinar was governed by the Cabildo of Havana until 1774, when, by decree of the general captain, marquis De la Torre, the Tenecia de Gobierno de Filipinas was established, which in 1778 settled in the area where the city of Pinar del Río today stands. It was only later, in 1867, that the present provincial capital received the title of "city." It is for this reason that Pinar del Río, as opposed to other Cuban cities, has no colonial historical center. Nonetheless, it is possible to admire magnificent homes built during the 19th century and at the beginning of the 20th century, which give the city its own special architectural look, thanks especially to the beauty and variety of the columns and of the capitals that adorn them.

One of the most architecturally remarkable buildings, distinguished by a marked local eclecticism, is the famous Palacio de Guash, which today houses the Natural Science Museum of Tranquilino Sandalio de Noda, named after one of the most famous men of the Pinar region. The man was also a great lover of his native land, which, nearly ignored throughout its history until the triumph of the 1959 Revolution, was known as the "Cinderella of Cuba." This great thinker, poet, mathematician and self-taught naturalist, born in 1808, left in his "Letters to Silvia," published in the *Diario de La Habana*, one of the most suggestive descriptions of Pinar del Río ever written: "I will not paint for you the Vuelta Abajo with the dry and meager accounts of the geographers, nor with the fantastic and affected pretentiousness of the pseudo-romantics, but with its very colors, with the simplicity and clarity that are appropriate in speaking of this land that is so sublime and so terrible, so rich and so miserly, according to the passions that spring forth when one speaks of her." And again: "Follow me, if you will, and you shall see diverse habits and customs; you will see birds and insects that you have never seen, mountains, rivers, trees and flowers that you are not acquainted with, and in your enraptured soul, in contemplating for the first time nature in its lofty nakedness, there will exist no more memory of Havana."

Among the most illustrious sons of Pinar del Río is the father of the Cuban novel, Cirilo Villaverde, author of *Cecilia Valdés*, a literary monument of 19th-century Cuba. He also devoted his writing efforts to his native land, forever overlooked by everyone, by publishing in 1891, three years before his death, *Journey to Vuelta Abajo*, a travel book in which he describes with outstanding mastery the natural beauty of his province.

A majestic building that was once a hotel, in a city-center street.

One of the many architectural wonders of Pinar. This Neo-Classical house has columns with Corinthian capitals.

This house features both Classical and Neo-Classical styles. Note the elegance of its Ionic columns.

The Palacio de Guash, in an exquisitely eclectic style, today houses the Tranquilino Sandalio de Noda Natural History Museum.

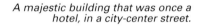

Mantanzas:
the Cuban Athens

A coastal highway leads to Mantanzas, whose province begins just before the highest bridge in Cuba, considered one of the seven engineering wonders of the island. From this bridge, called Bacunayagua, and even better from above at the vista point located on a nearby hill, it is possible to admire the impressive beauty of the Valle de Yumurí, which has inspired numerous poets, artists and singers.

Several kilometers down the road, travelers can gain a lofty view of the city of Matanzas, which extends around one of the most lovely bays of the entire country. Founded along several rivers in 1693, the city is especially known for its bridges. Matanzas began its development around the Plaza de la Vigía, the settlement's first plaza. Subsequently, in the 19th century, when the economy of the city reached its apex, the life and customs of the inhabitants found expression with the construction, on the same plaza, of the Teatro Sauto, built in an elegant Neo-Classical style with Neo-Renaissance influences, of the Provincial Museum and of the Hall of Justice. Notable buildings also rose around the second most important square of the city, the Plaza de Armas, which is today the Parque de la Libertad.

The cultural splendor of the city in the 19th century made it known as the Athens of Cuba.

The Bacunayagua bridge, at 110 meters in height, is the highest bridge in Cuba. It offers enchanting views of the Valle de Yumurí.

Declared a protected area, the Valle de Yumurí is one of the most beautiful valleys in the country.

The Parque de la Libertad, with the sculptural group in honor of José Martí by Italian artist S. Buemi placed at its center in 1909. Among the buildings ringing the park are the Municipality, the Casa de la Cultura, the Hotel Louvre, the French Pharmacy and the Provincial Library.

The French Pharmacy

Established in 1872 by Frenchman Ernest Troilet Lelièvre and Cuban Juan Fermín de Figueroa, this pharmacy is the only one of its kind that has been preserved nearly intact. It was continually operated as a pharmacy until 1964, when it was turned into a Pharmaceutical Museum.

The shop, with the image of the Immaculate Conception sculpted in white Carrara marble looking over it, still contains its original counters and shelves, all made of precious woods, and its columns carved out of single blocks of wood. The 193 Sévres porcelain jars are the pride of the museum.

In the backroom, where the medications were once prepared—most of them from medicinal plants—visitors can admire the dispensary and the books with the original formulas. The museum also houses a library preserving hundreds of unique books in Spanish, English, French and German dedicated to pharmacopoeia, medicine, chemistry and botany.

The central patio contains high shelves used to store glass cruets made exclusively for the pharmacy in a time when screw lids did not yet exist. Also worthy of note are the entrance, the storerooms and the laboratory, whose atmosphere seems to be suspended in time.

The glass cases and shelves of the French Pharmacy contain numerous apothecary jars in French porcelain, many of which are hand decorated.

The back room where the medications were prepared. The dispensary tables, in precious woods, were designed by Dr. Troilet.

The back room still holds books on pharmacopoeia in which more than a million formulas are collected as well as the Gold Medal awarded to one of them at the Paris Universal Exposition of 1900.

Varadero: the azure beach

In the 16th century, the narrow and long Hicacos peninsula, in the province of Matanzas, was a place where people went to collect the excellent saline, to cut timber from the forests near the beach and to catch the abundant fish. It was also a place where the ships of the Spanish fleet, as well as those of the corsairs and pirates that infested the surrounding seas, would anchor for repairs and to stock up on salt.

The beauty that nature endowed on this beach was not taken into account until the end of the 19th century, when writers and journalists began to use it as the setting for their tales of pirates and treasures, as well as for some indigenous legends.

A long strip of the finest sand stretching for 20 kilometers, along with a crystal clear sea whose waters maintain a constant year-round temperature and feature unsurpassable shades of blue that contrast with the verdant vegetation, attracted the first ten families to the area from the nearby city of Cárdenas. They established the village of Varadero in 1883, unknown at the time to the rest of the country.

The first inhabitants of this village, Creoles and Spaniards who had become rich in the vibrant economy of the area, built resort homes for themselves. But it was only starting in the 1920s that Varadero underwent a building boom, with the northern side of the peninsula lined with wealthy homes, many of them built of wood, which have been preserved to the present day. Many figures from the Cuban bourgeoisie and American millionaires also built fabulous homes, attracted by the splendid beach and attempting to make it a paradise for the rich, at a distance of only 140 kilometers from the capital.

Several years later, in 1961, these majestic buildings, abandoned for some time by their owners, became the training center for thousands of literacy teachers, who were at the forefront of one of the most ambitious projects of the young Cuban Revolution: to eradicate illiteracy from the entire country in just one year.

Of the three grandiose hotels that existed at the time of the triumph of the Revolution, Varadero has witnessed the addition of dozens of new hotels, restaurants, shops, nightspots and other services that make the beach the most important tourist destination of the entire island. This beach resort not only offers the chance to enjoy the fabulous sea with its fine sandy beaches, but it also features many recreational activities in its cultural centers, the numerous grottoes in the area, boating and water sports, fishing, diving, horse riding, and, more recently, an excellent 18-hole golf course.

Varadero, with 20 kilometers of the finest sand beaches, limpid skies and intensely azure and clam seas.

Tropical vines and coconut palms line the shores of one of the most beautiful beaches in Cuba.

Varadero is a very special place, with visitors coming from all over the world to relax at its resorts.

The Peninsula of Zapata

Whoever loves peace and quiet or wants to go trout fishing, or prefers to go diving in the deep marine grottoes or even birdwatching, will be certain to find the ideal spot to make their dreams come true in the Peninsula of Zapata, to the south of the province of Matanzas.

This peninsula, the largest of Cuba, boasts, along with the largest mangrove forests of the Antilles, a natural and human environment that is truly unique in the whole island. La Ciénaga, or wetlands, of Zapata, covers nearly the entire peninsula.

At the time of the triumph of the Revolution, the swamps were virtually isolated from the rest of the country, and the extremely poor population lived essentially off charcoal production and fishing. It was no doubt this isolation that made it possible for the peninsula to preserve its flora and fauna, which are still nearly intact.

The subsequent plans for the building of roads, schools, hospitals, housing and other services to improve the living conditions of the population were made with special consideration for conserving the environment, which is still today of great ecological value. Visitors can enjoy the marine grottoes, ideal for scubadiving, the endemic wildlife reserves (it is estimated that 80 percent of the island's bird species live in this area), and the legendary National Park of the Zapata Wetlands, the largest nature reserve in Cuba. However, when one thinks of the wetlands of Zapata, other things come to mind: first and foremost, crocodiles, those reptiles whose presence, once extremely abundant on the island, even surprised Christopher Columbus. The enormous crocodile breeding grounds of Boca de Guamá is considered one of the largest reserves of American crocodiles in the world. Then there is the Laguna del Tesoro, the largest in the country. According to experts, this fishing lagoon hosts the island's largest trout, which live

The Laguna del Tesoro, with its 16 square kilometers of surface area, is the largest natural lagoon in Cuba. The Guamá visitor center is located here.

The jicotea is one of the main breeds of endemic fauna in Cuba, perfectly preserved in the Ciénaga de Zapata, or wetlands.

The swamps of the Zapata Wetlands are an ideal habitat for crocodiles.

The crocodile breeding grounds of Boca de Guamá contain more than 10,000 specimens in different stages of growth.

Crocodile breeding is an important economic resource in the Zapata Wetlands.

there with bullfrogs, *jicotea, biajaca* and *manjuarí*, a sort of half-reptile, half-fish, living fossil. There is a legend that the lagoon owes its name to the fact that the indigenous people of the area, in facing the on-slaught of the colonizers, preferred to throw their wealth into these waters rather than give them up to the Spanish. Nevertheless, no treasures have ever been found in the depths of the lagoon.

The discovery of some wooden pylons, whose old age and symmetrical placement led experts to believe they were support poles of numerous raised dwellings belonging to the Taínos (one of the most evolved in-digenous groups), gave rise in the 1960s to the idea of building the tourist center of Guamá on ten islands that emerge from the lagoon. The islands were inter-connected by wooden bridges. Standing atop one of the islands is the Aldea Taína, which is composed of several wooden, thatched-roof dwellings. The com-plex, in a splendid natural setting, also features some 25 sculptures by the famous Cuban artist Rita Longa. These life-size sculptures depict indigenous Cubans carrying out their daily work.

Playa Larga and Playa Girón

Close to Boca de Guamá, in the Bay of Pigs, is the Playa Larga, a four-kilometer long deep-water beach, surrounded by lush vegetation and with an interna-tional birdwatching center. Playa Girón, which is smaller, is located at the end of the Bay of Pigs. Along with Playa Larga, this was the site of the 1961 mili-tary blunder of United States imperialism, when mer-cenary troops invaded the coast in an attempt to overthrow the young Cuban Revolution. The attack was repulsed. The Playa Girón Museum contains eye-witness accounts of the battle that took place here.

Playa Larga, today a center of tourism, was also one of the military objectives of the mercenary troops in 1961.

The small esplanade along Playa Girón hosts the tourist establishments.

The Playa Girón Museum displays the economic and social development of the Zapata Wetlands, the battle against the mercenary invasion, the arsenal captured from the enemy, and photos and accounts of the fallen heroes.

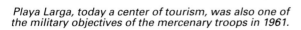

The Parque Martí, declared a National Monument and the former Plaza de Armas, is the exact spot in which Cienfuegos was founded in 1819. In the background is the Palacio de Gobierno.

Cienfuegos: the pearl of the South

The fear of a slave revolt similar to that of Haiti pushed the Spanish crown to try to increase the white population of the island. An infantry colonel born in New Orleans, Louis D'Clouet, made a proposal to the general captain, Don José Cienfuegos, for a "colonization contract" that called for the transfer of 46 French colonials from Burdeos to the Majagua peninsula.

Thus, in honor of Spanish monarch Ferdinand VII, on April 22, 1819, the village of Fernandina de Jagua was founded. The settlement would later become the town of Cienfuegos, in memory of the general captain who had accepted the idea of colonization.

Still preserved today are the original 25 city blocks, measuring 100 Castilian rods, which marked the beginning of Cienfuegos and which today form its historic center. It was in the Plaza de Armas, now Parque Martí, where the master-builders and architects set the exact center around which they would lay out the only Cuban city founded by the French. The development of livestock breeding, the cutting of timber from the forests, agriculture (especially the cultivation of sugarcane) and the port with its ever increasing traffic made Cienfuegos a wealthy city. By the end of the 19th century, there was a profusion of new buildings in the French Neo-Classical style, with friezes that were at times even too rich, and sumptuous gates and porticoes that were almost as wide as the streets. Eventually, however, the eclectic style won out in this city with its delectable atmosphere and its straight and broad streets, including the popular Paseo del Prado, the longest avenue in Cuba.

The Cathedral of Cienfuegos

This is, architecturally speaking, the most important religious building in the city of Cienfuegos as well as the first one built. Its sober Romantic facade seems to serve as an opening to Parque Martí. In this modest Cathedral, built with a nave and four aisles each 50 meters in length, and with a total width of 21 meters, the most outstanding feature is perhaps the glasswork of the 12 upper windows, on which the 12 apostles are depicted. According to experts, these represent the finest and most elaborate religious glass windows of this style in Cuba.

Teatro Tomás Terry

Facing the old Plaza de Armas, this building in the eclectic style houses the oldest theater of the city. The institution carries the name of one of the most eminent personages of Cienfuegos. Although it was built in 1890, it is still in excellent condition and can seat 1,200 spectators.

Original frescoes still adorn the ceiling, and even the curtain is decorated with oil paintings from the period. Taking the stage here have been such legendary figures as the Italian tenor Enrico Caruso and the no less talented Ricardo Stracciasi.

The Cemetery of Reina

Besides being one of the small jewels of Neo-Classical architecture in Cienfuegos, and in all of Cuba, the cemetery of Reina, inaugurated in 1839, is the only one of its kind left in Cuba, with burials that take place in niches, a typical custom of the 19th century. Especially of note are the elaborate cast metals in the perimeter ironwork of the chapels and the funerary monuments and the marble sculptures, among which is a *Sleeping Beauty*, considered the masterpiece of 19th-century Cuban funerary art.

Palacio de Valle

At the end of the Paseo del Prado, beyond the avenue lining the seafront of Cienfuegos, one arrives at the extremity of Punta Gorda, a small strip of land that the Spanish millionaire Acisclo del Valle chose in 1917 to build a gift to his wife, a truly unique palace in a magnificent natural setting.

The Palacio de Valle appears to be a sumptuous "birthday cake," an eclectic evocation of styles that are a completely incongruous mix, such as Neo-

Standing here since the founding of Cienfuegos, this modest cathedral in the Romantic style still preserves stained glass with religious subjects that are considered among the most beautiful in all of Cuba.

A simple triumphal arch at the edge of Parque Martí recalls the origins of this city, the only one in Cuba to be founded by the French.

Detail of the facade of the Teatro Tomás Terry. Three small murals embellished with polychrome mosaics, representing three arts, decorate this building, considered one of the most valuable examples of 19th-century Cuban architecture.

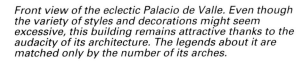

Front view of the eclectic Palacio de Valle. Even though the variety of styles and decorations might seem excessive, this building remains attractive thanks to the audacity of its architecture. The legends about it are matched only by the number of its arches.

A detail of the facade on the external portico surrounding the building. Here one can admire one of the bold Moorish arches and the meticulous and artistic works of the Catalan master-builders who directed its construction.

The sumptuous Moorish porch of the inner gallery with its stupendous ceramic decorations and rich mosaics seems to imitate the Salon of the Ambassadors of the Alcazar in Seville.

Detail of the iron spiral stairway that leads to the upper terrace. Note the elaborate design of the balustrade.

A turret in the Mozarabic style in one of the corners of the upper terrace. The Palacio de Valle now houses a cabaret-restaurant and a shop of Cuban crafts.

Gothic, Neo-Classic and Moorish. Despite its eccentricity, this building, designed by an Italian architect, possesses a certain grace.
After the collapse of the stock market in 1929, the owner, fallen into ruin, committed suicide. In 1958 the United States mafia bought the palace to make it into a casino, but the triumph of the Revolution did away with the money-making scheme.

Castillo de Jagua

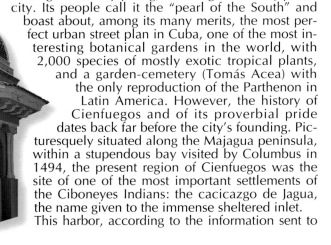

Although relatively young, Cienfuegos is a very proud city. Its people call it the "pearl of the South" and boast about, among its many merits, the most perfect urban street plan in Cuba, one of the most interesting botanical gardens in the world, with 2,000 species of mostly exotic tropical plants, and a garden-cemetery (Tomás Acea) with the only reproduction of the Parthenon in Latin America. However, the history of Cienfuegos and of its proverbial pride dates back far before the city's founding. Picturesquely situated along the Majagua peninsula, within a stupendous bay visited by Columbus in 1494, the present region of Cienfuegos was the site of one of the most important settlements of the Ciboneyes Indians: the cacicazgo de Jagua, the name given to the immense sheltered inlet. This harbor, according to the information sent to

the king in 1509 by the navigator Sebastián de Ocampo, "is the best and safest in the world, able to hold even one thousand ships," and was the scene of uneven battles between the natives and the Spaniards, especially in the areas of the present beach of Rancho Luna. In a short time, the sheltered harbor of Jagua became the favorite hiding place of corsairs, buccaneers and pirates. To fight the illegal trade carried out within the vast bay, the Spanish authorities chose the top of the hill that dominates the entry into the bay as the site to begin building in 1733 a fortress in ashlar, which was to be called Nuestra Señora de los Ángeles de Jagua.

Three quarters of a century before the founding of the city of Cienfuegos, in 1745, the Castillo de Jagua, as it is now called, was completed, thus becoming the first important colonial building in the area. Now a National Monument, the fortress possesses a single tower on a circular base with narrow emblasures. Still in a good state of repair are the original chapel, the deep moats that surround the fortress, the three strongholds each equipped with ten large canons, the drawbridge that permitted entry, the formidable red cupola atop the tower and the insalubrious cells where the prisoners in those days served their time.

At the foot of Castillo de Jagua is Perché, a picturesque fishing village with its houses built on wooden stilts. It was founded at the beginning of the 19th century by the French on the site of a previous pirate settlement.

Palacio Ferrer, today the municipal Casa de la Cultura, was built in 1918 on one of the corners of Parque Martí. Its late Neo-Classical style represents the good taste and refinement of the former bourgeoisie of Cienfuegos.

A typical home of Cienfuegos. Facades like this one, a classic example of the multi-colored eclecticism, are easy to find when walking through the streets of Cienfuegos.

The Castillo de Nuestra Señora de los Ángeles de Jagua, a robust fortress in stone ashlers finished in 1745, protected the bay from pirates well before the city of Cienfuegos was built.

Under this sculpture lie the remains of Che and of his guerrilla comrades who died in Bolivia. The high relief to the left of the sculpture depicts scenes from the life of the guerrilla Che.

Memorial to Ernesto Che Guevara

In the city of Santa Clara, situated in the center of the island, a column of hundreds of rebels led by commandant Ernesto Che Guevara carried out one of the most audacious moves of the war of national liberation. The battle, in December of 1958, led to the victory of the Cuban Revolution.

Forty years after, Fidel Castro recalled how the columns commanded by Che and Camilo Cienfuegos had marched westward "for more than 400 kilometers departing from the Sierra Maestra, after a hurricane, until Escambray, through unhealthy and swampy lands, infested with mosquitoes and enemy soldiers, under constant air attacks, without maps, without food (...) . Challenging the encirclements, the ambushes, the obstacles, the bombs, they finally reached their destination." And he concluded: "They were men of iron."

And it is in this city, liberated by Che and his men with the help of the population, which mostly backed the Rebel Army, that the Cubans have erected a monumental-sculptural complex in his honor: the Memorial to Ernesto Che Guevara.

Standing on a pedestal, a bronze sculpture some sev-

en meters tall and weighing 20 tons looks to the south towards Latin America. Sculpted by Cuban artist José Delarra, it represents Che during the trying battle of Santa Clara, with his arm in a sling and wearing his guerrilla uniform, looking as he did when he entered the city.

Within the monumental complex, inaugurated in 1988, are 16 other sculptured reliefs related to the figure of the heroic revolutionary. Built at the base of the monument in marble and precious domestic woods is the mausoleum which since October 17, 1997, has held the remains of the Heroic Guerrilla and those of his battle comrades who died in Bolivia. Inside of the mausoleum, a perennial flame placed within the center of the enclosure pays continuous homage to the heroes.

The mausoleum was also designed by Delarra, who in each of the 33 niches has modeled the faces of the guerrillas in cement.

The Memorial also houses a museum with photos, objects, documents and other testimonials (many of them little known) about the guerrilla actions of Che in Cuba, Congo and Bolivia.

Topes de Collantes

The province of Sancti Spíritus, whose capital of the same name is among the first seven cities founded by the colonizers, boasts of one of the most important mountain ranges of the country: the Escambray. In this *sierra*, several kilometers away from Trinidad, is the tourist resort of Topes de Collantes, which possesses a magnificent holiday center featuring health spas, whose efficacy is helped in large part by the unique climate of the area.

Along one of the red trails that depart from this center, one arrives at the Salto del Caburní, a suggestive waterfall at an altitude of 900 meters that spills the waters of the Caburní river some 75 meters. The strange geophysical and geological features and the exuberance of the vegetation make this trail particularly enchanting.

The fertile nature found in this geological fault transforms the Salto del Caburní into a kind of paradise. In the vicinity of the falls are a variety of ferns, including tree ferns, and colorful tropical butterflies. There are also endemic species of trees that provide precious woods.

At nearly 900 meters above sea level, in the mountainous area of Escambray, is the Salto del Caburní, a waterfall with a 75 meter drop in a paradise-like natural setting.

At Topes de Collantes it is possible to observe many freak geological formations. A view from the trail that leads to the Salto del Caburní.

The belltower of the since demolished church of San Francisco de Asís, built around 1813, is the ideal spot for taking a picture of Trinidad, the beautiful and well-preserved colonial Cuban outpost. Housed here is the Museo de la Lucha Clandestina.

Initially, the Plaza de Armas was the site chosen by Cortez for his encampment built in 1519, before leaving for the conquest of Mexico. At the end of the large Plaza Mayor are the church of the Santísima Trinidad and Palacio Brunet, today the Museum of the Romantic Age.

Trinidad: a colonial jewel

The colonial expedition of Diego Velázquez landed in the mountainous region of Guamuhaya (later called Escambray) on December 25, 1513. Under a leafy *jigüe* tree, these "white men" decided to build a small altar where a mass was celebrated for the first time in this region, with the people from the simple indigenous communities that populated the area looking on.

At the beginning of 1514 the third city of Cuba was established, la Santísima Trinidad, next to that *jigüe* tree where the Plazuela Real del Jigüe today stands.

Trinidad, whose major resource was livestock breeding, was, although wealthy, nothing more than a modest village of simple wooden, thatched-roof dwellings and with a no less simple little church. In 1527 a storm completely destroyed the new settlement, just when Pánfilo de Narváez was organizing his own journey of conquest—unsuccessful—to Florida. The devastated site, which only several years before had supplied men, munitions and arms for the enterprise of Hernán Cortés, remained almost unpopulated for a century. It is not known exactly when the Spanish started to live there again, although all signs seem to indicate that they returned there in the search for better coastal access for trade with smugglers.

In the 17th century, the city of la Santísima Trinidad had a second era of splendor. The exploitation of important crops in the surrounding area, such as sugarcane and tobacco, digging for minerals and livestock breeding furnished large amounts of capital that was put to immediate use in creating the architectural richness of the city, which appears today almost unchanged from its colonial past.

However, starting from the early 18th century, Trinidad suffered insistent attacks and sacks by corsairs and pirates, whose presence was a constant threat to the population, which was forced to arm ships and organize militias and groups of volunteers in order to fight off the incursions. When the English took control of Havana in 1762, they also attempted to conquer Trinidad, whose strenuous defense cost the invaders a terrible rout. During their retreat, the English were forced to leave behind a cannon, which is today symbolically reproduced on the city's coat of arms.

By 1797 Trinidad had reached such economic splendor that it was granted a Government Superintendency with political and military jurisdiction over the entire central territory.

Protected by the green mountains of the Escambray

The antique main altar of the church of the Santísima Trinidad, built from valuable Cuban woods. This church contains one of the most important collections of religious images in Cuba.

Near Trinidad is the tower built by the engineer Manaca-Iznaga in about 1820. This 85-meter tall tower, which was used to oversee the work of the slaves, is located in the Valle de los Ingenios, where visitors can see the machinery left by 43 antique sugar factories.

Entrance to the coach house of a home in Trinidad built in 1808. Its sober round-arched window-doors with grille work that run from the ground up are a typical feature of Trinidad. Note the Neo-Classical elements of the columns that set off the porch.

Calle Real in Jigüe. In Trinidad, the sidewalks are often very narrow or non-existent and the homes open directly to the streets paved with chinas pelonas, stones that were used for centuries as ballast in Spanish ships.

and designed to look eternally towards the Caribbean Sea, Trinidad today still possesses its picturesque appearance that dates from the last decades of the 17th century and the first half of the 19th century. Nevertheless, the major attraction of this city, declared, together with the nearby Valle de los Ingenios, a Heritage for Humanity by UNESCO in 1988, does not consist of impressive Baroque churches, elaborate palaces and historical monuments, as in other colonial cities of the Americas.

Although less sumptuous and varied than Havana, this is the Cuban city that has best preserved its colonial look and heritage, including its customs. This was especially helped by long periods of oblivion (particularly during the first part of the 20th century) that jealously fended off modernization. Its present appearance can be said to be the same one marveled over by the illustrious traveler Alexander von Humboldt, when at the beginning of the 19th century he visited Trinidad and described it in his famous *Political Essay on the Island of Cuba*.

There are many features that distinguish it: the large windows decorated with ironwork that adorn the houses and century-old buildings; the splendid doorways; the roofs covered with local red tiles; the streets and alleyways whose corners often end in cast iron sentry boxes; the cool shaded inner courtyards of its houses decorated with flowers and ferns; and the constant singing of canaries in cages, an antique custom of the festive and happy populace.

Palacio Brunet (Museum of the Romantic Age)

The historic center of Trinidad counts 55 city blocks and 1,211 buildings of great historical value, and, as in almost all colonial cities, the Plaza Mayor—originally the Plaza de Armas—marks the center of this unique city. All around it, the houses and dwellings conserve the typical colonial style of the 18th and 19th centuries; standing out among these is the palace of the count of Brunet, which now houses the Museum of the Romantic Age. This building, along with the Casa de Oritz, which is also on the square, is the only example of a two-storey construction in the central area and, together, two of the few houses with more than one storey in all of Trinidad.

The Palacio Brunet is the most typical example of a period home of the upper classes. The floors are marble, the central staircase is mahogany, the furniture consists of period pieces, the numerous utensils (many of them made of precious metals), and the canvasses of the 19th-century Cuban painter Esteban Chartrand set out in the 13 display rooms are some of the beautiful objects found in this house, which also features a pretty inner courtyard.

The main salon of the present Museum of the Romantic Age. One can admire furniture with decor inspired by the Imperial English style. The Bohemian crystal chandelier is from the 19th century. In the background, a portrait of the Duchess de La Torre, a member of an aristocratic family of Trinidad.

Spanish alcove in bronze and mother of pearl in the main Isabellan bedroom of the Palacio Brunet. Note the Carrara marble floor and the molding that decorate the walls of the room, all done by popular local painters. These wall paintings with floral and heraldic motifs are found throughout the house.

All of the decorative objects in the house were brought from Europe. This porcelain Spanish base, manufactured by Buen Retiro, now adorns the ante-chamber of the palace.

This Cuban dressing table in the Romantic style was made by a local woodworker using mahogany, one of the island's prized woods. This piece is found in the bathroom. The objects are in French porcelain with floral decorations.

The Ermita de la Popa, situated on the side of the hill of La Vigía, is the oldest hermitage in Trinidad. Built in the middle of the 18th century, the building features a simple but graceful Baroque facade.

An eloquent portrait of a Trinidad farmer.

The Hotel Ancón, on Playa Ancón, is located 12 kilometers from Trinidad.

Five kilometers of the finest coralline sand and shallow waters characterize Playa Ancón, the best beach on the southern coast of the island. It is located on the suggestive peninsula after which it is named.

Guamuhaya Archaeological Museum

One of the more surprising buildings in Trinidad, the Casa Padrón, the site of the Guamuhaya Archaeological Museum, displays its sumptuous style on one of the sides of the plaza. This museum, one of five in the city, holds a collection of findings that summarize the pre-Hispanic and colonial history of the region and includes objects and materials made from a wide variety of materials and methods of production.

Church of the Santísima Trinidad

The church of the Santísima Trinidad dominates the Plaza Mayor, built on the remains of the previous Main Parish. Although the Neo-Classical facade, showing the influence of later American-Baroque styles, has a certain charm, the church is not one of the more important religious buildings of Cuba. Nevertheless, the interior contains an interesting collection of holy images from the 17th to the 20th centuries, including the almost life-size *Cristo de la Vera Cruz*. This work is considered one of the best made effigies of Christ, with the most harmonious proportions, to be found in Cuba and one of the most important in all of the Americas.

The 13.6 kilometers of extraordinarily beautiful beaches make Cayo Coco a major center of tourism.

Cayo Coco

Built stone by stone, sprayed by the waves of the sea, the first Cuban road to allow a motorist to drive just above the surface of the water was finally completed in 1988, thus connecting the island of Cuba to that extraordinary isle (*cayo*) of 370 square kilometers, similar in size to such countries as Malta, Granada or the Seychelles.

Cayo Coco, in an area of the Sabana-Camagüey archipelago called Jardines del Rey, has been the "promised land" since the time of the Spanish conquest. Modern engineering has thus managed to end the numerous centuries of isolation known to this part of Cuba, whose only use had been mostly for smugglers and pirates.

In 1875, the isle was subdivided and sold in a public auction for 300 gold pesos to a Spaniard, who especially used it for another kind of illegal commerce, that of blacks taken into slavery from African. At the beginning of the 20th century, another man attempted to get economic advantage out of the isle: John Teophilus Hodge, of the United States, purchased the land with the absolute conviction of becoming rich by livestock breeding and planting citrus groves. He brought over the best specimens of the most productive strains of cattle and swine. He invested all of his money, but he was soon in store for a huge disappointment when he saw that oranges wouldn't grow and that his cows, in the semi-wild environment of the island, wouldn't obey the cowboys. The American returned to his country a poor man.

After that, the beaches received only sporadic visits from fishermen or the richest families of Morón, who sailed there to enjoy a day in the sun and who were surprised to be greeted by some of the docile cattle that Hedge had left on the island.

Eventually, the study of the island's environment and the accounts of another American, no less adventurous but more competent than Hodge, Ernest Hemingway, contributed to the growth of the fame of Cayo Coco and of other nearby islets such as Romano, Guillermo and Paredón Grande, which witnessed the hunt for German submarines and was the source of inspiration for Hemingway's novel *Islands in the Gulf*. From the sea, Hemingway observed those "dark hedges that rose from the water" and which, as he moved closer, increasingly "began to take on shape and color." But he especially observed a large number of white ibis, those little wading birds with their

89

Cayo Coco is an area of great naturalistic value, with dozens of protected species living there.

This tower marks the beginning of the land bridge to Cayo Coco, the first road of its kind built stone by stone over the seas of Cuba. The tower overlooks one of the main drawbridges of this magnificent work of engineering.

long, thin curved beaks that abounded on the coast of Cayo Coco and issued their characteristic call, *co-co*, giving the island its name.

The mere abundance of ibis, seagulls and especially the 30,000 pink flamingoes that live there—it is one of the largest reserves of this species in the entire hemisphere—was enough to make Cayo Coco considered an area of great naturalistic importance. Without a doubt, the reason consists plausibly in the fact that more than 80 percent of the isle's surface is covered with typical tropical forest vegetation—some areas are protected—in which dozens of animal species live. Today the isle has at least four trails for ecological tourism, while more and more people are scuba-diving off its coast to explore the great coral reef—the second largest in the world—that surrounds the entire Sabana-Camagüey archipelago, and where it is possible to encounter traces left by the pirates and corsairs, who for many years were the only observers of the beauty of Cayo Coco.

Camagüey: city of the Jars

The city of Santa María del Puerto del Príncipe was founded in 1514 as the political center of a vast region of savanna that extends over a large part of the center of the island, forming the passage to the extremely hot eastern part of the country. Its location was changed three times, until, in 1528, Camagüey—the name given to it by the indigenous people—was definitively built on the spot that it still occupies, between the Tínima and Hatibonico rivers.

Thanks to its broad plains, the site proved to be suitable for the development of livestock breeding, still a fundamental economic activity for the life of the region, later combined with the production of sugar.

Cattle breeding, which does not require a large amount of manpower, transformed Camagüey into a unique region, characterized by its low population density with an even smaller proportion of black people. The customs of the refined Creole aristocracy became dominant and the mulatto group that is characteristic in the rest of the country was less evident. The city's location halfway between Santiago de Cuba and Havana, the two most important cities of the island, led the region of Camagüey to benefit from the

smuggling that went around the commercial monopoly of the Spanish metropolis. That made it possible for Puerto Príncipe to undergo an economic growth that was already considerable by the middle of the 18th century. In those times, according to the description of Bishop Morelli of Santa Cruz, the settlement counted 1,506 houses, almost all of them one-storey high and well made. In 1817, Ferdinand VII granted the settlement the title of city and the right to have its own coat of arms.

Starting from this time, Camagüey also became known for its architecture. Even at its birth as a city, Camagüey's religious, military, governmental and public buildings appeared wealthy and noble. Among its most beautiful squares are Plaza de San Juan de Dios, Plaza del Carmen, Plaza del Cristo and the colonial Plaza de Armas. The church of Nuestra Señora del Carmen, Baroque in style and dating from 1825, the Palacio de Justicia, built in the middle of the 18th century, the seat of the Real Audiencia, and the Teatro Principal, inaugurated in 1850, are only some of the most important buildings that distinguish the urban profile of Camagüey. The historical center,

The construction of the church of Santo Cristo del Buen Viaje in Camagüey began in the early 19th century. It is a classic example of Colonial Creole architecture with reminders of Cuban Baroque. Near it is the city cemetery, the oldest one still in use in Cuba.

The former Plaza de Armas, in the historic center of
Camagüey, is the present Parque Ignacio Agramonte.
The statue of the hero of the Ten Year War portrays
him as a resolute fighter.

The winding streets of Camagüey still make the city a
true labyrinth.

which still preserves many of the original brick
homes with clay tile roofs that rise in the area of the
living room and then descend to the inner patio—the
so-called *colgadizos*—,was declared a National Monument in 1978. It is, in fact, along with Trinidad, one
of the Cuban cities that has best preserved its colonial
appearance.

Its distinctive mark, however, is represented by an exceptional trait. The shortage of water from which the
city has suffered over the centuries and the abundance of clay in the soil of the region led jarmakers to
devise a solution that in a short time was to become
the very symbol of Camagüey: the large clay jars normally used to store wine and oil became an indis-
pensable feature in the inner courtyards of the homes
of Camagüey. These jars were always poised to capture rainwater funneled off the roof from rain gutters.
This custom became so common that Camagüey
soon became known as the "city of the jars," an epi-
thet that the people of Camagüey accept with great
pride, as it is one of their most antique traditions.

The Camagüey jar is also found in the rural areas, with the typical farmers' homes made of wood and covered with yagua, *or royal palm, leaves.*

Nobody would be able to say when this jar was produced, nor when it ended up in this patio in Camagüey.

Another unique curiosity of Camagüey is the design of its narrow and winding streets. They were laid out in this fashion to make them difficult for pirates and pillagers to navigate. It is said that only the people who have lived there for many years are able wind their way through the city without getting lost. So-called *callejones*, or especially narrow streets, are common in Camagüey, and Funde del Catre, the tightest one of all, is the narrowest street in Cuba.

Today Camagüey continues to show off its history through not only the facades of its old colonial buildings or its parks, or its plazas or churches, but also through the behavior of its people, who have inherited that love that many illustrious men and women have shown towards Camagüey and Cuba. It is in this very land that the verses were written which today are recognized as the first Cuban literary work: the epic lyrical poem *Espejo de Paciencia* by Silverstre de Balboa. Also born here was Gertrudis Gómez Avellaneda, an important poetess who, with her refined and impassioned verse, gained fame as a great writer in 19th-century Cuba. Moreover, the vast savannas of Camagüey were the scene of the battles and of the glorious mission of independence of the patriot Ignacio Agramonte y Loynaz. Camagüey is also proud to have been the birthplace of Nicolás Guillén, the Cuban national poet.

The broad plain of Camagüey features especially beautiful sunrises and sunsets.

Located in the historic center of the city, the Iglesia de la Merced is, architecturally speaking, one of the most important of the island. It was completed in 1756.

Playa de Santa Lucía

Almost at the border with the province of Las Tunas, Camagüey reveals a natural treasure that represents one of its greatest attractions. Considered by many the second best beach in Cuba, Santa Lucía stretches eastwards for some 20 kilometers, running from the bay of Nuevitas, across the north coast and, like its "rival" Varadero, ending on a peninsula.

Besides its fine sand and its warm, transparent waters, Santa Lucía has the good fortune of being surrounded by other wonders that add to its fame. Since it is situated in front of the great 400-kilometer long coral reef sitting off the archipelago of Sabana-Camagüey, second only to the great barrier reef of Australia, it offers visitors the opportunity to enjoy both the magnificent beach and scubadiving. Moreover, the vicinity of the reef to the beach —barely two kilometers away—produces a strange natural phenomenon that makes the beach even better: the surf is slowed as it approaches the coast, which all but eliminates the waves. These conditions allow for bathing throughout the day, without any worries for the sudden caprices of the sea.

The vicinity of the islets of Sabinal and Romano, whose beaches are just as marvelous, has helped make Santa Lucía one of the most popular tourist destinations in the country.

In following rigorous guidelines for the preservation of the ecosystem and minimizing the environmental impact, the addition of new tourist facilities has greatly increased the prestige of Santa Lucía and made it one of the best beaches in Cuba.

Like almost all of the beaches of Cuba, Santa Lucía shows off its unspoiled shores.

These palm trees at the water's edge seem to have been placed there on purpose to let them sway in the breeze.

Today, Santa Lucía is one of the most attractive tourist spots in the country.

More than 200 years ago, from the summit of the Loma de la Cruz, a land surveyor looked out on the so-called Valle de las Delicias and traced the city of Holguín, today known in Cuba as the city of parks.

This view is enjoyed from the stairway that leads to the vista point on the top of this legendary hill. The locals say "who has not climbed Loma de la Cruz does not know Holguín."

Holguín: archaeological Capital

On the north coast of the province of Holguín, on the bay that the indigenous people called Bariay and which Columbus named San Salvador, the centuries-old history of the island of Cuba had its beginnings on October 28, 1492, almost as if the arrival of the "discoverers" had marked the beginning of life in the so-called New World. Found in this very region was instead the highest concentration of indigenous populations and cultures of pre-Columbian Cuba, as demonstrated by the important archaeological finds uncovered here over the years.

The first inhabitants of the area, looking out from the top of the hill that rises above the valley where the city today stands, were undoubtedly enchanted by the beauty of the landscape, by the softness of the breeze and by the sweetness of the climate, and decided to settle forever in that spot that would later be called the Valle de las Delicias.

A short time after that, at the conclusion of the terrible days of the Conquest of Mexico, the Spanish captain Francisco García Holguín received as an award for capturing the last Aztec emperor the title of marquis of the Valle and the lands spreading out northeastward from the town.

Founded in 1523, the settlement of Holguín did not have a stable location, at least until April 3, 1720, when it was moved to the valley which it now occupies, on the site of the property of one of the nephews of captain Holguín. Populated by farmers and ranchers, the settlement did not enjoy any particular economic prosperity until the beginning of the 19th century, with the development of the sugar and coffee industries and the increased cultivation of tobacco.

This fort with embrasures was built by the Spaniards on the top of this hill to allow them to sight troops of independence, whose presence would have been signaled by a heliograph. The tower was initially called Numancia, a symbolic name that was dropped during a battle with separatist rebels.

La Loma de la Cruz

On May 3, 1790, at the top of this small hill next to the city, a Franciscan father, prior Antonio de Alegrías, planted a wooden cross that marked the beginning of a religious-cultural tradition that the people of Holguín still celebrate with great devotion: the Romerías de Mayo, or May pilgrimage.

To climb and kiss the cross and be released from vows was, for 150 years, a true calvary for the many devout Catholics and followers of syncretistic cults. The construction of a 450-step stairway completed in 1950 made the processions and visits to this holy site easier. Some time later, a road was also built to provide access to this hill (*loma*), the real pride of the people of Holguín.

In 1872, because of continued attacks by separatists, the Cruz de Mayo lost its pre-eminence and was forced to share the top of the hill with a watchtower, which was later made into a small fort, still present, and inside of which the Spanish army had its heliograph.

La Periquera

Despite the prosperity reached by the 19th century, Holguín did not undergo significant architectural and urban development. Compared with other Cuban cities, there are very few important colonial buildings here, with the only concentration of them in the area of the Parque Calixto García, formerly the Plaza Isabel II.

Of the old buildings around the Parque Central Calixto García, named in honor of the general from Holguín who was a leader of the War of Independence, the most important is without a doubt La Periquera. Completed in 1862 as a home, this colonial building today houses the Municipal History Museum.

Although sober, this large building in a typical Neo-Classical style has considerable Moorish influence in the interior. The name of this colonial dwelling is the result of the spirit of independence of the people of Holguín. It is said, in fact, that during one of the battles of the fight for independence that took place in the city during the war of 1868, the frightened Spanish soldiers took refuge in the building. In those days,

Guardalavaca beach offers about 600 meters of one the finest sands in Cuba. Palms, tropical vines, flamboyanas *and* guanos *provide an exquisite entrance to the seashore, bathed by vibrant green and azure waters.*

the uniform of the crown army in Cuba was green, similar to that of a common bird on the island, the *periquito* (parakeet). Under siege by rebel troops, the Spanish soldiers shut themselves in the building, and from the grille work of the windows they seemed *periquitos en su periquera* (caged parakeets).

Guardalavaca

The northwest coast of Holguín, washed by the waters of the Atlantic, still maintains its rich natural heritage of great socio-cultural, economic, scientific and tourist value. With more than 110 kilometers of coast jutting into the sea and with 22 sandy beaches, the coast possesses a wealth of bays and coves, rich coastal flora and fauna, coral reefs and a narrow underwater shelf with a beautiful sea bottom, ideal for diving.

Located in Bariay, the spot where Columbus landed in his first journey, is the Bariay National Park, one of the best preserved and most unique natural areas in all of Cuba. Along with viewing the perfectly intact flora and the most varied marine and land fauna, visitors can enjoy beaches of the finest sand set here and there within the coves and inlets of the rocky north coast of the province.

The uneven outline of the coast has created magnificent natural beaches that combine for a total of almost 23 kilometers of sand, which only today, in virtue of the strong demand for tourism in the area, are beginning to become known. Among the beaches are Don Lino, Estero Ciego, Playa Blanca and others of great beauty.

The coast of Holguín is home to more than 23 magnificent natural beaches dotting the tranquil coastal bays and featuring the finest cream-colored sand.

The new hotels of Guardalavaca seem to be only slightly less impressive than the surrounding luxuriant vegetation.

To better protect the ecosystem, the original hotels have been carefully designed to be integrated in the physical environment of this unspoiled landscape.

The most famous, however, is the beach of Guardalavaca, on the coast of Banes, with its 1,700 meter strip of clean, cream-colored sand, punctuated by tropical vines and mangrove forests. A few meters from the shore is one of its major attractions: the coral reef that borders the coast and which, because of its vicinity, allows for the discovery of this marvelous seascape where a large variety of fish live. The reef rises from the water at low tide, creating a unique spectacle.

Chorro de Maíta Archaeological Museum

Thirty-three percent of the archaeological wealth of the country (more than 96 sites) are in the region of Holguín, considered the archaeological capital of Cuba. In the town of Banes, the Chorro de Maíta Archaeological Museum comprises the site of an Indo-Cuban cemetery that constitutes one of the most important archaeological finds of its kind in the entire Caribbean. Archaeologists have zealously preserved the position of 62 skeletons, thus enabling them to study the funerary ritual of the island's indigenous population. The museum also displays a wide range of objects in gold, shell, bone, flint and ceramic.

The remains of a man with a Caucasoid cranium confirm the presence of one of the Spanish *conquistadores*, who probably decided to mix his blood with that of the indigenous population.

Baní Indo-Cuban Museum

In the center of Banes is also the Baní Indo-Cuban Museum, which holds the most documented display of objects from the indigenous civilization. Among its hundreds of specimens (more than 14,000 are kept in the depository of the museum) is a gold idol holding a receptacle and depicting a woman with a plumed headdress. This statuette is the only one of its kind found in Cuba.

As can be seen in this photo, some of the bodies were buried in the fetal position. The finding of two skeletons of Taínos children wearing Spanish bracelets and necklaces seems to indicate that there were some pacific relations between Europeans and the natives.

The Chorro de Maíta Archaeological Museum was built on the site of the largest indigenous cemetery ever found in the Antilles. The display cases located in this 39-square-meter excavation contain objects made of gold, bone, flint and ceramics.

The excavations of Chorro de Maíta have allowed for the study of indigenous funerary rituals as well as of the culture and costumes of the pre-Columbian Antilles.

The bay of Santiago has always been the second most important port of Cuba. The city rises from here towards the east, like a sort of amphitheater built to admire the sea.

Santiago de Cuba: a terrace on the Caribbean

On June 28, 1515, captain Diego Velázquez de Cuéllar landed on the shores of a placid river in the south of the eastern region of the island that he was colonizing and decided to found a city there that he called Santiago, in honor of the patron saint of his Spanish majesty.

Living in the area, however, was an indigenous community belonging to the *cacicazgo* of Bayataquirí, a peaceful people who called the land in which they lived *Cuba*. Diego Valázquez, followed by his men, marched further south, perhaps to distance himself from the natives, but he could not keep the city that would rise there shortly afterwards from being known by the name that its primitive inhabitants had given to the spot.

The first concern of the new inhabitants was, as in all of the other recently established cities, to search for gold, which however they were able to find in only very small quantities.

The pioneers' disappointed dreams of riches nevertheless ended up coming true with the discovery and mining of copper deposits at some 25 kilometers to the northwest. But more than for its abundance of copper, this region owes its fame to the legend of the Virgen del Cobre, the most "national" of the Catholic traditions in Cuba and one of the highest expression of syncretism between Catholicism and the beliefs of African origin.

The settlement, then the capital of Cuba, received the title of city, while Havana instead had to wait several years to be granted that title.

Nevertheless, in 1549, the capital of the island was shifted to San Cristóbal de La Habana and from that time onwards Santiago de Cuba had to suffer the whims of the governors and functionaries of the Crown, whose interests would forever be directed towards the west of the country. There is no shadow of a doubt that the particular geography of the region of

Although built in the 1950s, this building in front of the Parque Céspedes was designed essentially following an 18th-century design. Today it hosts municipal offices. On the facade is the Gold Star that proclaims Santiago "Heroic City of the Cuban Republic."

Partial view of the Parque Céspedes. It was here that on January 1, 1959, a multitude of Santiago citizens heard the speech of Fidel Castro from the balcony on the day of the victory of the Revolution.

From the heights of the Loma del Intendente one can admire the old homes with their clay tiled roofs, typical of the historical center of the city. In the background are the towers of the Cathedral.

This extremely decorated balcony belongs to the house in which the conquistador *Diego Velázquez lived in the early decades of the 16th century. Today it houses the Historic Museum of Santiago de Cuba.*

The balcony at the main entrance of the Casa de Velázquez. Besides finding interest in the building itself, visitors can admire a remarkable example of Cuban civilization expressed in the architecture, furniture and the minor arts.

Popularly known as the Balcony of Velázquez, this blockhouse was originally built in the 1530s.

Santiago de Cuba, surrounded by mountains on one side and the sea on the other, its vicinity to the coasts of Haiti, Santo Domingo and Jamaica, the relative isolation in which the city was forced to live compared with the western part of the island, as well as the cultural and economic influence from the large emigration of French coffee growers who came fleeing from the Haitian Revolution at the beginning of the 19th century, have all generated and consolidated customs and ways that are exclusive to this part of the island.

To explain the peculiar personality of this population, one must also take into account the large-scale 19th-century immigration from Catalan, considered to be one of the regions of Spain with the most pronounced spirit of independence. It is therefore understandable how the ethnic composition of the population of Santiago is different from that of the rest of the country, as here the mixing among races is more marked.

Similar ingredients have made the *santiaguero* a different kind of Cuban, although they undoubtedly consider themselves the most strongly Cuban among all those who live on the island. The uniqueness of Santiago is reflected, for example, in the layout of the city, especially in the historical center, where, in addition to its particular architecture, the streets were adapted to the haphazard lay of the land. The terraces that top the houses and hang over the sidewalks, the streets, the alleyways, the Moorish facades and roofs all leave their imprint on the colonial architecture of Santiago.

Looking at the city from the bay, or better from the dockside avenue, or else from below towards its upper reaches, where the city begins to slowly climb as it moves away from the water, it can be seen how the houses, the warehouses, the industries, the schools, in short, the entire city, is built upon terraces, as if it were climbing one large natural staircase.

Santiago, as other Cuban coastal cities, had to suffer numerous incursions of corsairs and pirates starting from the moment of its very founding. In the course of its history it has been destroyed more than once by hurricanes and earthquakes. Epidemics of cholera,

In addition to the Cathedral, the seat of the Provincial Government and the Casa de Velázquez, other interesting buildings surround the Parque Céspedes.

From this terrace belonging to a hotel on Parque Céspedes, one can admire places that recall faraway times and lands. Only the unmistakably brilliant sunlight makes us understand that we are in Santiago de Cuba.

Calle Enramada, one of the main streets of the city center and without a doubt the most popular business street.

smallpox and yellow fever, aided perhaps by the hot climate, were time and again extremely hard hitting. During both the colonial era and the neo-colonial republic, many of the governors were seekers of fortune or corrupt, whose misdeeds were made possible by the recruitment of police and criminals. The fact that Santiago has been rightfully recognized as the cradle of the Revolution—the revolutionary movement saw its first light with the attack on the Moncada barracks on July 26, 1953—and as the Heroic City of the Republic of Cuba, and that the blood of rebels and patriots, of men and women, has many times flowed through its streets and plazas, can make those who come to the city for the first time believe they are in a place of great solemnity and nostalgia.

Despite this, the people of Santiago are not sad, untrusting or introverted. On the contrary, they are friendly, lively, music lovers, easy going and above all very hospitable. The *santiaguero* is famous in all of Cuba for his vocation as guide and host, amiably offering their house and food to every visitor without hesitation.

The characteristics of the population, made of restless and rebellious men and lovely and smiling women, its carnival of resounding liveliness, its ethnic roots and its location have made Santiago the most Caribbean city in all of Cuba. And when it is called the "terrace on the Caribbean" it is not a simple play on words, but a clear definition of a cultural and historical identity that does not require any academic proof.

Who meets a native of the Dominican Republic and sees him talk and gesture would have difficulty, at first, to distinguish him from a *santiaguero*. The fact is that the men and women who populate the Caribbean coast of the various countries in the region possess the same genes, giving them their extraordinary resemblance in temperament and personality. And in particular, Santiago is the point of convergence of all Caribbean civilization. Perhaps its mystery resides in this fact: the explanation to the poem by Federico García Lorca that obsessively repeats: "I will go to Santiago."

The Cathedral of Santiago was consecrated as the city's basilica by Pope Pius IX in 1879.

For the people of Santiago, the Cathedral is the symbol of the city as is Parque Céspedes, the site of the Plaza de Armas during the colonial era.

The Cathedral of Santiago

In the first centuries of the life of the city, earthquakes were particularly devastating to the Cathedral of Santiago, which had to be rebuilt several times when the modest and not very solid building could not withstand the violence of the quakes.

The bishops of the period knew very well that the church had to be improved, especially after the earthquake of 1770 almost completely destroyed it. But numerous arguments and disagreements, typical of the colonial era, over the design of the new building forced the city to wait 48 years before it would have a cathedral worthy of the name. It was finally built with the necessary mastery in 1818 and oriented on a north-south axis with the facade on the Plaza de Armas, which many years later would become the present Parque Céspedes.

The building, which was probably supposed to be definitive, was instead restructured twice, the first time in 1853 and the second in 1922, when it assumed its present highly eclectic appearance. The furnishing inside of its nave and four aisles are considered true decorative jewels, which count among them paintings and objects of great value. Within the basilica is also the seat of the Ecclesiastical Museum, which contains documents and objects of great historical importance.

The Archives of the Cathedral, besides holding precious historical documents pertaining to the Cabildo of Santiago de Cuba, also contain original musical scores of illustrious Cuban masters, such as Esteban Salas, who was the major American composer of choral music in his time, as well as works performed for the first time in Cuba. The church also contains the remains of the conquistador and colonizer of Cuba, Diego Velázquez, and of other important personages of the colonial era.

It is a building of great personality, characterized by belltowers and a cupola which stand out from a distance, as if they marked the exact center of Santiago de Cuba.

Whatever their religious beliefs, the people of Santiago consider the Cathedral the emblem of their city, just as they do the Parque Céspedes, a place where countless generations have met and relaxed since antique times, when the colonial Plaza de Armas stood there.

Inside of this building with its imposing Neo-Classic facade are the nine rooms of the Museo Bacardí, with its valuable historical and archaeological collections.

A typical street of Santiago: narrow, with an asymmetrical layout and an extremely varied and dynamic urban perspective.

Emilio Bacardí Museum

Cuba, whose national sentiment matured between 1868 and 1895, opened its first history museum on February 12, 1899, when the United States troops who were occupying the island had not yet left and Cuba was still not formally a republic.

In 1927, the original museum was transferred to the building where it is now housed, in the streets of Pío Rosado and Aguilera, and took the name of its illustrious founder, the patriot, journalist and writer Emilio Bacardí Moreau.

The museum preserves numerous accounts of José Martí, Antonio Maceo, Carlos Manuel de Céspedes and other important patriots, as well as historically important objects that reflect the tastes and lifestyles of famous Cubans.

Particularly noteworthy among the displayed objects is the collection of paintings from the Prado Museum of Madrid, the handmade arms of the fighters for independence, the throne of the black king that demonstrates the attributes of the African Cabildo of Santiago, which occurred in the 17th century, and a mummy and other archaeological discoveries from Egypt which have raised the curiosity of Cubans since 1912, when they were brought to Santiago from ancient Thebes.

The Moncada Barracks, a National Symbol

Located on one of the highest points of the city, the Moncada barracks are a place which more than any other has earned the title of National Monument.

The main objective of an attack carried out by Fidel Castro, at the head of about one hundred young men, on July 26, 1953, these barracks were assaulted with the purpose of inciting a national uprising against the Batista tyranny. The uneven fighting finished in a blood bath, with the killing of dozens of prisoners who had been captured from among the attackers. The heroic enterprise was not a military triumph, but it nevertheless served to open a five-and-a-half-year march culminating with the victory of the people's revolution, which would radically change the history of Cuba.

The Moncada barracks were transformed into the *Ciudad Escolar 26 de Julio*. The left wing of the main building, next to *Posta 3*, where the heroic battle took place, contains the rooms of the 26 July Historical Museum. The museum contains a reconstruction of the history of the struggle for independence of the Cuban people over the course of the centuries, from the colonial era until the overturning of the Batista dictatorship, including the preparations for the assault on the barracks, the battles in the Sierra Maestra, the invasions led by Camilo and Che, and the decisive battle of Santa Clara.

The Moncada barracks, the main bulwark of Batista in the eastern region of Cuba, and the second most important in the country, was attacked on July 26, 1953, by Fidel Castro and a valorous group of young revolutionaries.

The artist of the mural fragment that decorates the corner of Calle Aguilera and Padre Pico drew the face of a mulatto woman with typically mixed-blood traits and with a smile, a characteristic of the women of Santiago.

Artists of different nationalities have participated together with painters from Santiago in the INTER NOS cultural project. They left this beautiful mural on the corner of calles Heredia and Clarín (Padre Quiroga).

The Cradle of *Son* and *Trova*

In 1850, according to a well-known legend, Santiago already boasted of a band that had two pianos, a bass and two mandolins that were played by a black couple that had come to Santiago from Santo Domingo.

One of them, Teodora Ginés, became famous for having inspired the *Son de la Ma' Teodora*, the first example of *son*, the typical Afro-Caribbean rhythm that is the basis for much of the popular music that people throughout the world today dance to and sing.

Two centuries after the emigration of the French and of their slaves from Haiti, they gave Santiago a musical culture that would soon be assimilated and imitated.

Perhaps the custom brought by the French of having friends and relatives join together to listen to music in an intimate setting is at the origin of the *trova*, a way of conceiving of and performing songs characterized by the leading role that the *trovador* gives to the guitar and by the poetic quality of the words, almost always dedicated to love, women, nature and patriotic feelings. There have been four main figures in the history of traditional Cuban *trova*, which since the early 1900s has left us a large number of songs, *boleros, sones* and *guarachas*, still incredibly modern: Sindo Garay, Alberto Villalón, Rosendo Ruiz and Manuel Corona, three of whom were born in Santiago. Another key figure was José (Pepe) Sánchez, also born here in 1856, whose music was considered the precursor of the *trova*, and Trio Matamoros, a group that gave to Cuba and all of Latin America the Santiago style of performing the *son*.

In the late 1930s, the famous composers and performers Silvio Rodríguez and Pablo Milanés were able to create a musical movement called *Nueva Trova*, for the most part faithful to the tradition.

The Casa de la Trova, on Calle Heredia between calles Hartmann and Lacret, is an authentic temple of traditional Cuban music.

Older people frequently participate in the cultural days of Calle Heredia. These dance veterans faithfully follow the tradition of typical Cuban dances.

The patio of the Student House, on Calle Heredia. The orchestra playing traditional music was established in the early 1960s.

The house where the great Cuban poet and precursor of American Romanticism, José María Heredia, was born in 1803 is today an interesting museum.

Calle Heredia

Santiago, like any other city in the world, has streets that characterize it and whose very names are able to evoke the city. In speaking of Enramada, an exquisite pedestrian shopping street, one thinks immediately of Santiago. At the mere mention of Padre Pico, which suddenly becomes a long and steep stairway climbing among the houses, it is at once understood that the topic is Santiago. If you hear the sound of a *trompeta china* or the rhythm of the *conga* of the *tumbadoras*, you know that you're in Calle Trocha, an authentic symbol of the marvelous carnival of Santiago, the ideal place for dancing together in the most unbridled joy.

Who instead wishes to be immediately in touch with the soul of this Caribbean city must visit Calle Heredia, with its concentrated kaleidoscope of the city's cultural heritage.

One of the houses, which still preserves its characteristic architecture and its original antique furnishings, was the 1803 birthplace of the great poet José María Heredia, the first among the Cuban writers to have given a universal tone to the nation's letters, the precursor of American Romanticism and one of the first to have fully expressed through art the national spirit and yearning for independence. This colonial dwelling, now a museum, contains objects that belonged to the illustrious poet and, as a permanent exhibition, the published works of the greatest authors of Santiago. It is also a meeting place for literary conferences and other cultural activities.

Not far from here is the Casa de la Trova, a temple to traditional Cuban music, frequented night and day by new and old *trovadores*, professionals and amateurs, who perform their own pieces in a friendly and somewhat bohemian environment. The building that plays host to the *trovadores* is an important example of 19th-century Santiago colonial architecture, especially for its large and richly designed balcony.

Also in Calle Heredia is the eccentric Carnival Museum, a not-to-be-missed display of the traditional popular culture of Santiago, inaugurated in 1983. This institution is housed in an 18th-century colonial home, whose facade shows the typical use of *corredor*, a covered area used as a passage way between the outside and the actual house, with this example having richly worked railings and shutters made of precious woods. Among the various displays are interesting costumes and instruments used for the *congas*, the parades and masked processions that take place during the traditional carnival of Santiago.

109

The Carnival Museum provides a look at this festivity, whose origins go back three centuries. The collection of photographs, clothing, costumes, musical instruments and the numerous decorations covering various periods give an idea of the way Cuba's most famous popular festivals were and still are.

The museum also contains a section that displays the small and exotic instrument without which the *conga* of Santiago would lose much of its uniqueness and which constitutes the symbol of the carnival in the eastern part of Cuba: the *trompeta china*, a sort of cornet that plays five high-pitched notes and whose melody resembles that of bagpipes.

In this street, an emblem of the city's culture, is the Elvira Cape Library, named after the wife and collaborator of Emilio Bacardí Moreau, the first mayor of Santiago, who spread and promoted culture in his city. This provincial institution is one of the most important of the country. In addition to its specialized rooms and periodical library is the Music Archive, containing scores and works of the most important local composers.

These puppets in papier-mâché are both products of fine craftsmanship and aesthetically pleasing. The craftsmen put everything into them, even though they know that their works are ephemeral, destined each year to disappear at the end of carnival.

Also found in the Carnival Museum is el caballito, *a "festive" version of St. James the Apostle. This is not a form of irreverence, but rather a humanization of the figure of the saint that is closer to the earthly liveliness of the people of Santiago.*

One of the most prestigious choirs of the country, the Orfeón Santiago, also has its headquarters in this street. Here they organize concerts and recitals, which are always popular events among the public.

And only on such a street could there be the seat of the provincial delegation of the Union of Writers and Artists of Cuba (UNEAC), with daily encounters in which artists read their own works, sing their own songs and comment on the latest creations of the artists of Santiago, all taking place in a superb colonial-era home,

Among the other colonial buildings in Calle Heredia is the house of the Tejada brothers, talented painters who in lived in this building in the 18th century. Visitors can admire a typical inner patio of the same era with extremely elaborate wooden decorations. Its portico, with clear Baroque influence, is the only one of its kind in the city. It is presently the headquarters of an association that promotes and markets works of art and cultural events.

Calle Heredia, little more than one kilometer long, concentrates an important slice of the city's cultural life. It is an image that the people of Santiago hold dear to their hearts, as seen countless times in the works of the craftsmen and artists. And it could not be any other way, because Calle Heredia is at the same time history and legend, myth and reality, tradition and daily life.

The Mecca of Rum

Catalonian immigrants left their mark on the personality of Santiago. Facundo Bacardí y Mazó, a native of Sitges, near Barcelona, also left a great heritage: in around 1862, he discovered a formula for the production of Cuban rum, a beverage that would become famous throughout the world and that since the early 20th century has been one of the country's most important exports.

At the time that Bacardí was producing his light, delicate and full-bodied rum, but without the harshness of the famous Jamaican rum, there were only four other distilleries in Santiago and they produced a very strong liquor that was unable to compete with this new drink.

Don Facundo, however, with his great patience, did not aim at competitiveness, but instead invested his capital and time in the creation of five-, ten-, and fifteen-year-old reserves that would forever provide the basis for the blends of the best brands of Cuban rum. When in 1889 the founder died, he left his children not a great deal of money, but many barrels of reserve and his rum-making technique.

A short time after the end of the last War of Independence, the descendants of Facundo Bacardí possessed an inestimable wealth, a national beverage in Cuba and a prized liquor all over the world: an inimitable rum, even though the reason for its quality was no mystery, as it had been believed for many years.

The secret formula of this beverage was nothing more than an advertising ploy, since the enchantment of its quality consisted more than anything of the Cuban molasses produced from sugarcane grown in a unique climate and soil.

This uniqueness has been the reason behind the world's preference for

The Hotel Santiago stands out for its contradictory modern look within the colonial Caribbean environment. The architect José Antonio Choy intended to launch himself towards the future with his design, producing both a controversial and worthwhile manifest of the artistic Cuban avant-garde.

Santiago could not of course be without its Rum Museum. This very building was the birthplace of the well-known national beverage, now famous throughout the world.

Before the end of the 19th century, the liquor was distilled in primitive alembics like the one shown here.

The typical tile-covered roofs of Santiago can be admired from the heights of Calle Padre Pico

Calle Padre Pico suddenly turns into a steep staircase that climbs among the houses. It is one of the most characteristic spots of the city.

the different labels of Cuban rum: Havana Club, Caney, Legendario, Matusalén, Varadero, Caribbean Club, etc., of the different kinds of Carta Blanca (Light Dry) aged three years, as well as the "older" Carta Oro (Old Gold) aged five years and the Añejo (Extra Aged) aged seven years.

In Santiago, as in almost all of the other provinces of Cuba, the tradition of producing excellent rums of various brands continues. But what especially strikes the visitor is the preference given to this drink by the *santiagueros*, who seem to consume it non-stop and in greater amounts compared with the people living in other regions of the country.

That doesn't mean that they don't enjoy tasting the numerous drinks that are made with rum: the people of Santiago also love the famous Cuban cocktails that are famous all over the world, such as Daiquiris, Mojitos and Cuba Libres, a mix of rum and cola. And if in Santiago rum is drunk pure or mixed with other ingredients it is a matter of the occasion, even if, when all is said and done, drinking it straight has to do with the psychology of a people that love to be considered citizens of a *caliente* land.

The equestrian statue of Antonio Maceo rises in the enormous plaza, commemorating his memory with its height of 16 meters (22 meters including the base).

Plaza de la Revolución Antonio Maceo

Following the triumph of the Revolution on January 1, 1959, none of the numerous plazas and parks in the city of Santiago were able to hold the multitudes that wanted to celebrate the days dedicated to the patriotic events, most of them tied to the history of the city. Or at least not until the early 1990s, when the Plaza de la Revolución Antonio Maceo was built.

Able to hold about 200,000 people, this plaza of around 53,000 square meters contains the largest equestrian statue in the country, dedicated to the figure of Antonio Maceo, the illustrious patriot born in this city in 1845 and who went down in history known as the Bronze Titan.

In this effigy of Major General Antonio Maceo y Grajales, the valorous fighter keeps his hand open and his arm bent as if he were beckoning his followers.

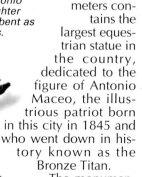

The monumental sculpture, 16 meters high and weighing 120 tons, was made by Santiago artist Alberto Lescay. It depicts the heroic personage in the act of opening his hand, as if it were a perennial call to battle and to follow his example of fidelity and dedication to the most noble ideals. The image of the extraordinary fighter shows a more markedly civic side to his historic personality, which he nevertheless possessed in good measure.

Accompanying it are 23 giant plates of steel, which steadily rise from the surface until they stand upright. These symbolize the use that the Cubans made of the machete, turning their working tools into effective weapons against the armies of colonialism, as well as the sublime gesture of Maceo when he led the insurrection of Baraguá, rejected the peace settlement of Zanjó, and then, on March 23, 1878, took up battle once again.

At the base of the monument, inside of a stairway that is also used as a speaking platform, is a room dedicated to the hero's historical memory that displays holographs depicting weapons and objects belonging to Maceo, including several pieces of family dinner ware, his marriage contract and his initiation ring for the freemasons. The historical events that marked the career and the military, political and patriotic thinking of the Bronze Titan are illustrated in this room.

114

This bulwark of the Castillo del Morro offers a sweeping view of the bay. It was from this very point in 1898 that the Spanish troops stationed in the fortress witnessed the uneven naval battle that brought about the United States victory over Spain and made it possible for the United States to exercise many years of control over Cuba.

The Castillo reflects the numerous introductions that the Antonelli dynasty brought to Caribbean military architecture. Housed here—and it couldn't have found a better home—is the Piracy Museum, a documentary account of the struggle between the colonial powers for the dominance of the lands and seas of the Caribbean.

The Morro de Santiago

Rising at the entry of the bay of Santiago de Cuba is one of the most interesting castles of the Americas, San Pedro de la Roca, more commonly known as the Morro de Santiago.

Because of its historical and architectural importance, UNESCO declared it a Heritage of Humanity in 1998, thus adding to the pride that the people of Santiago have always felt for their Castillo del Morro.

The growing audacity of English and French pirates from the middle of the 16th century, when they took important coastal cities such as Cartagena de India, Santo Domingo, Havana and Portobelo, induced Spain to create a continental system of defense.

Construction on the fortress of Santiago was initiated in 1643, but it was destroyed in 1662 during the attack of the famous English pirate Henry Morgan, and again in 1666 by an earthquake. It was finally completed in the early 1700s with the monumental form it still has today.

The castle reflects the fundamental principles used in the construction of such fortifications during the Middle Ages and the Renaissance, as well as the contributions of the Antonelli in the fortifications found in Havana and other places of the Caribbean.

Once finished, this fortress, rising 76 meters above sea level, was never taken by any of the city's attackers, even though very little could be done by the troops stationed here to prevent the destruction of the Spanish fleet by the United States navy in 1898. The soldiers could only look on futilely from the walls of the Morro as the squadron of admiral Cervera was annihilated, since the fortress possessed no long-range artillery and was incapable of countering the US battleships.

The Mausoleum and tomb of the National Hero José Martí in the Cemetery of Santa Ifigenia.

A front view of the Mausoleum of the Martyrs of the Revolution.

The Cemetery of Santa Ifigenia

This cemetery was declared a National Monument in 1937, as it was a burial grounds of many illustrious patriots and famous personalities from the world of art and culture. It can be said that the graves of Santa Ifigenia represent a true hall-of-fame in the history of Cuban heroism. Buried here are 29 generals from the War of Independence and the leader of the first armed uprising, Carlos Manuel de Céspedes, known as the *Padre de la Patria.*

There are a striking number of tombs and chapels topped by the Cuban flag and the red and black flag of the Movement of July the 26th, indicating the burial site of a murdered revolutionary or a war casualty. Also resting here are the remains of numerous martyrs from the attack on the Moncada barracks as well as the body of Frank País, the great hero of the underground struggle against the Batista tyranny.

But the symbolic encounter with history reaches its apex in front of the Mausoleum of José Martí, the most beloved and venerated hero of the Cubans. The hexagonal structure is 23 meters tall, with a crypt whose center contains a bronze tomb and a simple urn containing the remains of the hero, with the Cuban flag draped over it.

116

The National Sanctuary of Nuestra Señora de la Caridad del Cobre, founded in the 17th century. Since then, the faithful have come to pay homage to the Virgin.

The Cobre Sanctuary

The town of El Cobre, located a few kilometers from Santiago, awakened one morning in 1608 with the news that a miracle had occurred there. During a storm, three fishermen had spotted a strange sight in the middle of the furious waves of the bay of Nipe: a statuette inscribed with the words "I am the Virgin of Charity."

This supernatural event was confirmed, according to legend, when the effigy inexplicably vanished from the spot where it had been placed on three consecutive nights. These nighttime disappearances continued until the Virgin was taken to the Sanctuary of Cobre, as it was there she wished to take shelter and where, some 20 years later, she would take her place on the main altar of the church.

Popular imagination considerably enriched this legend, claiming that other apparitions had also taken place. But the truth is that the people identified with that image, whose face was, significantly, the color of copper, thus very similar to that of a mulatto woman.

In 1916, Pope Benedict XV named *Nuestra Señora de la Caridad del Cobre* the patron saintess of Cuba. Nevertheless, she had already been a national symbol for some time, not only for Catholics, but also for the syncretic religions of African origin that identified her with Ochún, one of the main goddesses of the Yorubá pantheon, venerated over time by African slaves and their descendants.

The National Sanctuary of *Nuestra Señora de la Caridad del Cobre*, founded in the 17th century, became a place of pilgrimage, where the faithful follow the tradition of bringing offerings to the Virgin. One of the best known offerings was that made by the famous novelist Ernest Hemingway, who donated the gold medal he received for winning the Nobel Prize for Literature in 1954.

The Caridad del Cobre, the only Cuban Virgin officially recognized as the national patron saintess in 1916. The crown and halo are made of gold and platinum with some 1,450 diamond, ruby and emerald inset stones.

The silver altar of the Capilla de los Milagros (the Chapel of Miracles) in the Cobre Sanctuary.

Parco Baconao

Declared a Natural Biosphere Reserve by UNESCO, this extraordinary park stretches for more than 50 kilometers along the southeast coast of Santiago de Cuba, extending inland until the mountains of the Sierra Maestra and containing about 80,000 hectares of stupendous landscapes and an invaluable wealth of flora and fauna.

In this land, in which hunting, fishing and timber harvesting are kept under strict control, an unusual growth and diversification has taken place in the forest zones and among the wildlife population.

Starting only a few kilometers from Santiago, Baconao offers visitors unique beaches and a large number of cultural attractions: from the most traditional peasant music to the surprising Prehistoric Valley, at Damajayabo, with some 196 prehistoric animals reproduced in stone.

Of the many cultural institutions spread throughout the park of Baconao, including museums, exhibit halls and art galleries, the La Isabelica Museum is of particular interest, housed in an old farm that belonged to French coffee growers in Gran Piedra. There, visitors can admire a rich collection of period tools and utensils.

Gran Piedra, a huge monolith forming an unusual crown on the top of a 1,200 meter high mountain—it seems that two completely different geological formations have come together—can be considered the vista point of all of Baconao. On the clearest nights, in fact, one can make out the lights of Santiago from here, and, under particular conditions, it is said also lights from Haiti and Jamaica.

A short distance to the east of the Prehistoric Valley, several kilometers from the coast in the Área de Barcos Hundidos, is the information center of La Punta, where visitors can find out more about the park, its attractions and its cultural sites.

The Parque Baconao possesses an incredible variety of places of interest that make the informative signposts mandatory reading for visitors.

The Valley of Prehistory contains 196 stone animals placed in an environment that is probably very similar to the one that existed during very remote times.

The beaches of Baconao are very close to the surrounding tall mountains covered with lush vegetation. This provides added enchantment to the clear and calm waters that characterize all of the magnificent beaches along the Cuban coast.

The road of La Farola, built in 1965, is the result of highly talented engineering and was the first road built to Baracoa.

Baracoa: the First City of Cuba

After several days spent navigating along the northwest coast of the island of Cuba—still certain of finding the continent described by Marco Polo—admiral Christopher Columbus ordered his crew on the morning of November 27, 1492, to dock the *Niña* and *Santa Maria* in an enchanting bay that he named Porto Santo.

He thus approached this verdant area, a natural harbor defended by a ring of high mountains. One of them particularly amazed Columbus because of its strange shape, with its perfectly flat top: "a promontory on which there is a high and square mountain that seems like an island" he wrote in his *Diario*. It was the second time that the navigator had touched Cuban soil.

Along the shore, many men and women with copper-colored skin and pure black hair looked on in amazement as the two caravels appeared, marking the encounter between two worlds. And, as if they presaged an omen of the future, those "Indians" fled hurriedly from the coast and hid in the mountains. The spot was known as Baracoa, named by the place's first inhabitants and main indigenous population, the

Taínos, and it possessed the richest and best cultivated land, the result of the high level of development of that people, who forever left their mark on it.

During the five days they spent at Baracoa, the Spanish *conquistadores* had time to realize that the place was suitable for "founding a village or a city and a fortress thanks to the presence of a good harbor, drinking water, fertile land, rich territories and much timber." This annotation, transcribed by brother Bartolomé de las Casas from the admiral's *Diario*, was evidently sufficient for captain Diego Valázquez to reach Baracoa some 20 years later and begin the process of the conquest of the Americas after founding the first city of Cuba, Nuestra Señora de la Asunción de Baracoa, the only one of the first seven cities to be preserved to the present time on the original site of its founding.

In February of 1512 Valázquez declared Baracoa the political capital of the island and set up his own household there. He then named a mayor and a justice official to exercise civil rule, established the municipality and asked the king to confer the title of city on the settlement, which it was soon given. The

119

monarch also gave precise guidelines for establishing the seat of the highest ecclesiastical authority there, making Baracoa from that moment the seat of the first bishopric of Cuba.

The scarce presence of gold that the conquistadors so desired and the scarce access to the rest of the island led to a very early halt in the development of Baracoa, and the city lost its preeminence over the other early settlements. Around 1533, the village was home to only 13 inhabitants, 26 soldiers, 212 natives and four blacks. Even Diego Velázquez had decided to go to Santiago de Cuba. However, Baracoa managed to hold on to all of its historical importance and natural beauty, still intact today.

The development of Baracoa between the 16th and 19th centuries was very much connected to the sea, not so much because it became a fishing community, but because its isolation from the rest of the country and the stupendous location of its harbor forced the city to form strong ties with pirates and smugglers. It is said that the inhabitants of Baracoa put up resistance to the fierce attacks leveled at them, but very soon, in order to survive, the people became used to systematically violating the absurd laws of the central government that brought them no advantage. They thus established an economy that would not, and could not, respect the ironclad commercial monopoly established by the central power.

This tight link with the sea represented the life of Baracoa and the main reason for the known events

In the language of the Taínos, Baracoa means "presence of water." The sea that bathes the city, and the numerous rivers in the area, such as the Toa, Miel, Yumurí, Duaba, to name a few, explain the name given to the place by its first inhabitants.

Baracoa still has its original layout nearly intact, with streets running towards the sea. In the background, square Yunque mountain dominates the city.

Bahía de Porto Santo, seen from the Castillo de Seboruco, today the Hotel El Castillo.

120

that took place there from the time Columbus first set foot on this land until 1965. In that year, five centuries after its discovery, Baracoa was connected via land with the rest of the country thanks to the monumental road that crosses the Sierra de las Cuchillas de Baracoa. The highway of La Farola is considered another of the seven wonders of Cuban engineering: 40 kilometers of road that crosses the mountains, conforming to the ruggedness and whims of nature, so much so that in 11 points the road leaps across the steep inclines, suspended in air on two columns.

The city spreads from the inlet of Porto Santo to the bay of Miel, bordered by the third longest seafront avenue in Cuba—only those of Havana and Cienfuegos are longer. At both ends of this avenue stand fortresses built between 1739 and 1742: that of Matachín, now the site of the Municipal Museum, and of La Punta. Together with the Castillo de Seboruco, rising on a 40-meter hill within the city, and now the Hotel El Castillo, these buildings represented the most important system of defense in the country after the fortifications of Havana.

The first city of Cuba and the second European settlement in the New World still shows its original street network. The city center also contains a unique triangular park. Among its architectural jewels are the fortifications, the Municipal building and the parish church of Nuestra Señora de la Asunción de Baracoa.

Cruz de la Parra

One of the oldest and most historically valuable objects jealously guarded in this city is the Cruz de la Parra, or Cross of the Arbor, held in the parish church.

The fame of this cross began with the discovery, subsequently proved through carbon-14 tests, of its place among the 29 crosses that Columbus planted during his voyages in the New World. It is, in fact, the only one of these crosses to have arrived to our times.

It was with this cross that brother Bartolomé officiated mass in his trips to Baracoa. Every time a

The city of Baracoa, with its three fortresses, was considered during colonial times the second best protected city of Cuba.

Matachín fort houses the Baracoa Municipal Museum, mainly dedicated to Indo-Cuban civilization.

The third longest seafront avenue of Cuba protects the city of Baracoa.

calamity took place, the people of the city carried the cross in a procession, certain that it was the most powerful religious object they possessed and the greatest show of adoration that they could make to God. Its name, according to the historical chronicles, derives from the story that it was once stolen by a fanatic, only to be found some time later entangled in the vines of an arbor.

The Spanish general Arsenio Martínez Campos, during an expedition of his army in the war of 1868, was left in awe before such an antique and venerated object, and he gave a description of the cross confirming the idea that it was produced in Europe before 1492: "It is of a strong rot-proof wood, sonorous to the touch, and examining the kind of wood from which it is made it is certain that the tree that produced it does not belong to the Cuban flora."

The Cruz de la Parra is one of the cultural symbols of Baracoa. This historical relic was placed in this case with reinforced metal to prevent the faithful from removing fragments and using them as amulets.

In protection of the city, surrounded by mountains, rises the effigy of the Indian rebel Hatuey, the cacique who led the first insurrection against the Spanish colonizers and who was accused of heresy and burned at the stake.

Traces of the Taínos

Among the almost 36,000 inhabitants of Baracoa, it is still possible to note a population with unique ethnic features, since the city is still home to the descendants of the Taínos indigenous group. As opposed to the rest of the country, where the natives of the island were exterminated, here some nuclei of this origin have survived, somehow isolating their characteristics without becoming part of the mix of races and cultures. Many faces of the people conserve the typical traits, and their dialect contains many words from their language that were never replaced by Spanish.

Numerous examples of their ways and customs remain preserved in the Municipal museum in the Fort of Matachín. Many of the most important objects of this indigenous culture have been excavated in the area: a wooden idol of *Guayacán* decorated with shells, and a seat, or *dujo*, in carved wood. Both of these objects are exhibited in the Montané Museum of Havana. Displayed in the American Indian Museum in New York since 1914 is a carved wooden oar that was found in Baracoa. The city, with its 65 archaeological sites, is one of the most important in Cuba for this kind of historical research.

The Traditional Cuisine of Baracoa

Many customs show how the Taína have preserved their traditions over the centuries. These are especially evident in their folklore and culinary habits, tightly linked to the production of coconut and cacao in the region.

Baracoa still maintains the cultural imprint of the Africans brought here in past times by the Spanish, French and Haitians, who, fleeing from the revolution, came to Cuba in the 18th century.

The Hotel Porto Santo, a colonial palace that has been perfectly restored and restructured in order to offer the comfort of a modern tourist center, is one of the three hotels of Baracoa.

From the Hotel Porto Santo, located on the bay and close to the airport, visitors can travel on the Toa river and to Baracoa to take in the city's major artistic and cultural sites.

Next to the seafront avenue is the Hotel La Rusa, the first hotel to be built in Baracoa. Opened by a strange immigrant who came to this remote Cuban city in the 1920s, it is considered a part of the city's historical heritage.

The marriage of these cultures has generated a typical cuisine with dishes such as *bacán*, a sort of pastiche made of *guineo*, or platano, pork, coconut milk, spices, chili pepper and salt, wrapped in platano leafs. Other popular dishes in Baracoa cooking include the *casabe* made by the indigenous population (a sort of flat bread made from cassava flour), and crab and fish cooked in coconut milk, just to mention a few.

There are also many sweets, in particular the inimitable coconut roll found throughout the city. In the 19th century, this typical sweet, which is wrapped in *yagua*, or the leaf of a royal palm tree, was produced in sugar mills. This handmade product, both functional and beautiful, is popular as a souvenir.

The Russian, the Legend

While the stock market crash of 1929 threw the rest of the world in disarray, Baracoa was experiencing a period of splendor due to its great banana production that had begun several years earlier. The world was on its knees, but, for the first time in its history, Baracoa was powerful. Along the Toa river, the largest in Cuba, sailing boats were laden with bananas. At Porto Santo, ships from all over the world loaded up the new "gold" of Baracoa.

One morning in that same year, a foreign woman, who had the look of an artist, arrived in the city. It was later discovered that she was born in Siberia and had grown up in Petrograd, now St. Petersburg, in faraway Russia, where the Revolution of 1917 forced her to set out on a journey with her husband, Albert. After marrying in Constantinople, the couple sought a place where they could settle down. They thus traveled first to France, then Java, and then to Italy, before coming to Baracoa, where they soon became celebrities, only to fade once again into oblivion.

At the end of the Second World War, the Cuban banana commerce faltered, with the market demanding

Finding it impossible to develop sugarcane or tobacco plantations because of its geo-physical attributes, Baracoa has instead promoted the production of cacao, coffee and coconut. The inhabitants still continue to grow these traditional crops, which are also used in the local cuisine.

This lush vegetation is typical of the river banks of Baracoa.

Many areas along the rivers of Baracoa are suitable for swimming.

increased amounts of bananas produced at lower and lower labor costs. Central America became the major exporter of bananas towards the United States and Europe and Baracoa thus slipped back into poverty and isolation. Nevertheless, the Russian, who spoke six languages and had a beautiful soprano singing voice, decided to stay here forever.

In the 1950s, Magdalena Menases—that was her name—sold her café, her belt factory and her small farm to build the Hotel Miramar, the first in Baracoa, and today known as the Hotel La Rusa. In the irony of ironies, the woman was destined to live through another revolution, in 1959. But this time she stayed and supported it. One of the most generous gestures she could make was to donate all of her jewelry to the national coffers, which Batista and his supporters had emptied before fleeing the country. Among the guests at her hotel were Fidel Castro, Raúl, Che and Celia Sánchez. The Russian died in 1976, after having become the symbol and legend of Baracoa.

Mountains, Rivers and the Sea

The Russian, as well as the landscape and places of Baracoa, inspired Cuban author Alejo Carpentier to write *La consagración de la primavera*. One can read a suggestive description of Yunque, of its "imposing and watchful presence (...) whose nearly flat summit rises from the background of the countryside, above a broad, dark green pedestal, spreading and dissolving into the green dusk of the surrounding mountains."

The square mountain described by Christopher Columbus and thus nicknamed by the Spanish was considered by the Taínos to be a sort of Olympus, the holy dwelling of their gods. The mountain is like a natural lighthouse that can be seen from a great distance, even out at sea, thus allowing navigators to recognize the port of Baracoa.

Heading west along the coast, one can discover, as Columbus did in 1492, some 14 kilometers of unspoiled beaches with crystal

Numerous unspoiled gray sand beaches lie east of Baracoa. One of these is Yumurí, where it is possible to gather the yellow, red and black seashells that are among the most beautiful in the world.

Following the coast northwards, one comes across enchanting Duaba beach, with its interesting history. It was here, in fact, that General Antonio Maceo landed, beginning the war of 1895.

waters. On one of these, Duaba beach, which is today a National Monument, General Antonio Maceo landed in 1895 with 22 men to start the War of Independence.

To the east, back towards the city, is the Miel river, which owes its name to the sweetness of its waters, which do not turn salty until the river meets the sea. There is a legend about the Miel that says whoever bathes in it at midnight will find love in Baracoa and stay there for the rest of his days.

2,000 years ago the Ciboneyes Indians already lived on the island. Their presence lasts until about 1515, when they were exterminated by the Spanish conquistadors.
Other indigenous groups of differing levels of development also populated the island before its discovery.

1492 (October 28) Christopher Columbus lands on the coast of Bariay, in the northeast of the island. He names the land Juana, in homage to the first child of the Catholic king and queen, Ferdinand and Isabella. Tobacco was already being cultivated by the natives.

1509 Sebastián de Ocampo charts the territory, demonstrating that it is an island.

COLONIAL ERA

1510 Diego Velázquez begins the conquest and colonialization that concludes in 1514. The Spanish bring cane sugar to cultivate.

1512 In the zone of Baracoa, the cacique Hatuey rebels.
After several months of resistance against the Spanish, he is captured and condemned to die, burned at the stake. This was the first show of struggle for freedom on Cuban territory.
Founding of the first village, which was named Nuestra Asunción de Baracoa. In the next two years, other villages were also founded: San Salvador de Bayamo, la Santísima Trinidad, Sancti Spíritus, San Cristóbal de La Habana, Santa María de Puerto Príncipe (Camagüey) and Santiago de Cuba. Each village had a governing organ know as Cabildo.

1526 One hundred and forty five African slaves are brought to Cuba. This barbarous and repugnant practice of human commerce continued until the 19th century, with the purpose especially of developing sugar production in the country.

1537 Starting from this date, corsairs and pirates attack Cuban villages. In 1555, the French corsair Jacques do Sores occupies, sacks and destroys Havana.

1558 The process of fortifying Havana begins, which will last until well into the 17th century.

1561 Spain organizes fleets of war ships to protect mercantile vessels sailing from the Americas towards the island. It also establishes Havana as the mandatory meeting place of these fleets, providing the city with an economic boom and transforming it into the exclusive center of legal commerce. The inland population is forced, for survival, to illegally trade with corsairs and pirates from England, France and Holland.

1608 The first work of Cuban literature is produced: the poem Espejo de paciencia, by Silvestre de Balboa, a native of the Canary Islands.

1701 From now until 1720, 100 factories for the production of sugar are established on the outskirts of Havana.
Others are also built in the center of the island. The production of tobacco also increases.

1728 The first University of Cuba is founded in Havana.

1762 The English take Havana on 12 August. Their rule lasts eleven months and has favorable repercussions on the economic life of the city.
Large quantities of English goods flow into the city, as do numerous slaves who are put to work in sugarcane plantations.
The islands grows wealthier thanks to the production of sugar and tobacco and other export products.

1763 With the Treaty of Versailles, England returns Havana to the Spanish, receiving Florida in exchange. The Spanish monarchy begins to practice illuminated despotism.

1781 Trade with North America is authorized on the condition that Spanish merchants do not participate. The United States gradually become the biggest purchaser of Cuban sugar.

1789 Free trade of slaves is established.

1790 The Papel Periódico de La Habana is founded, the first newspaper published in Cuba, for a reading audience of agriculturists, merchants and culture lovers.

1791 Cuba takes control of the sugar and coffee markets, which previously belonged to Haitian growers, whose plantations were destroyed by war.
The cultivation of sugarcane expands, becoming the most important Cuban export crop. Slavery increases.

1793 The Real Sociedad Económica de Amigos del País (The Royal Economic Society of Friends of the Country) is founded, with the goals of promoting the development of the island's main economic activities and increasing education and culture.

1810 The first independence conspiracy takes place under the direction of Román de la Luz and Joaquín Infante, who drafts the first project of a Cuban constitution. Among the most important independence conspiracies is that of the Soles y Rayos de Bolívar (1821-1828), in which the lawyer and first great Cuban poet José Maria Héredia was implicated and sent into exile.

1812 The abolition conspiracy movement led by the freed Negro slave José Antonio Aponte is discovered. The objectives of the movement are the abolition of slavery, social equality and the destruction of Spanish tyranny.

1824 From now until 1825, Félix Varela publishes in Philadelphia and New York "El Habanero," the first Cuban revolutionary newspaper. Because of his political ideology, Varela comes to be considered the precursor of ideas on independence, of love for the homeland and liberty.

1826 Alexander von Humboldt, the German scientist considered to be the second discoverer of Cuba, publishes the Political Essay on the Island of Cuba, the first scientific work on the geography of the country.

1837 The first railway in Cuba is built, before one is built in Spain, to transport sugar.

1838 The Tacón Theater is inaugurated in Havana. It is considered one of the most luxurious and important in the world at the time.

1850 Giuseppe Garibaldi arrives in Havana, remaining for several months.

1853 (28 January) José Martí is born in Havana. He becomes the founder of the Cuban Revolutionary Party and organizer of the War of Independence; poet, literary critic, journalist, diplomat and excellent writer.
He is considered the Cuban national hero. He dies in battle on 19 May 1895.

1868 (10 October) Carlos Manuel de Céspedes, recognized by Cubans as the "Father of the Nation," frees his slaves and sets off the first war against Spanish dominion. The war lasts ten years.
(20 October) What is to become the Cuban national anthem is sung for the first time in the city of Bayamo, taken by the patriots. National Culture Day is celebrated each year on this date.
(4 November) Spanish troops are charged by machete-armed patriots led by Máximo Gómez.

1869 The Assembly of Guáimaro gathers in April and approves the first Constitution.

1878 (10 February) The Zanjón Pact is signed: a group of military and civic leaders surrender to the commander of the Spanish troops.
(15 March) Major General Antonio Maceo refuses to accepts the Zanjón peace treaty, which he considers a "disgraceful surrender" that stains the dignity of the Cuban people. This act, of great revolutionary import, is historically known as the Protest of Baraguá.

1883 Investment of United States capital begins on the island, first in the industries of sugar and minerals, and then in other sectors. By now, control of the Cuban economy can be said to be in the hands of the United States.

1892 (10 April) José Martí founds the Cuban Revolutionary Party, which unites all the forces in the country to lead the winning struggle against Spanish domination.

1895 (24 February) The War of Independence begins, to whose organization were dedicated José Martí, Máximo Gómez and Antonio Maceo.
(19 May) José Martí, leader of the revolution, falls in uneven combat against the Spanish troops. His mortal remains are in the cemetery of Santa Ifigenia in Santiago de Cuba.

1896 (7 December) The lieutenant general of the Liberation Army Antonio Maceo, the "Bronze Titan," dies in combat at San Pedro, near Punta Brava in the province of Havana.

1898 (15 February) Spain has now virtually lost the war. In the harbor of Havana, the United States battleship, the Maine, explodes, giving the pretext to the Americans to militarily intervene in the conflict, with the objective of preventing the liberation of Cuba. In December, Spain and the United States, without the presence of the Cubans, stipulate a peace accord, signing the Treaty of Paris.
The United States military occupation of the island begins, lasting for about three years.

1901 The new Constitution is approved, in which the United States imposes an amendment, the Enmienda Platt, by virtue of which the United States denies the sovereignty and self-determination of the Cuban populus. In the same year, the National Library is founded.

NEO-COLONIAL REPUBLICAN ERA

1902 (20 May) The first Cuban president takes office. Cuba becomes a neo-colonial republic subordinated to the interests of the United States.

1906 (November) The second intervention of the United States takes place through 1909. Cuba's economic and political dependence on U.S. imperialism increases.

1921 Cuban José Raúl wins the title of world chess champion.

1924 With the painting Gitana Tropical by Victor Manuel, Cuban contemporary painting is born.

1925 The Cuban Communist Party is constituted. Among its founders is Carlos Baliño and Julio Antonio Mella. The dictator Gerardo Machado receives orders to repress the people's revolutionary movement.

1929 (10 January) Julio Antonio Mella is assassinated in Mexico by order of Machado.

1930 Nicolá Guillén, recognized as the national poet, publishes his first collection of verse: Motivos de son.

1933 (12 August) A general revolutionary strike brings about the fall of the Gerardo Machado dictatorship.
In the same year, the greatest Cuban novelist, Alejo Carpentier, author of, among his many works, El reino de este mundo, El siglo de las luces, Recurso del método, publishes ¡Ecué-Yamba-O!, his first novel.

1940 (5 July) The new constitution is approved, which, thanks to the participation of communist delegates, includes articles favorable to the interests of the Cuban populace. In the same year, Fulgencio Batista becomes president of the Republic.

1948 The National Ballet of Cuba is founded, whose most important member is the prima ballerina Alicia Alonso.

1952 (10 March) Batista attempts a military golpe supported by imperialists to destroy the government of Carlos Prío. Thus begins the bloodiest dictatorship suffered by the Cuban people.

1953 (26 July) Fidel Castro, at the head of a group of youths, assaults the Moncada barracks in Santiago de Cuba. At the trial, conducted behind closed doors, Castro delivers his self-defense, History will absolve me, which will become the political program of the Revolution.

1956 Fidel Castro and his comrades go into exile in Mexico to reorganize the struggle. There, Castro meets Ernesto Che Guevara. With 82 men, they return to Cuba aboard the boat Granma. The guerrilla war begins in the Sierra Maestra.

1958 The final battles of the War of Liberation take place. The dictator Batista flees the country on 31 December.

THE REVOLUTIONARY ERA

1959 (1 January) The Cuban Revolution triumphs. Fidel enters victoriously into Havana on 8 January.
(4 July) The Casa de las Américas is founded, a cultural institution that was to bring together the most important Latin American intellectuals. The literary award Casa de las Américas is considered to be among the most prestigious in international circles.

1960 (8 August) The nationalization of the country's economic resources begins.

1961 (3 January) The United States break diplomatic relations with Cuba, and the policy of economic embargo begins.
(16 April) The socialist character of the revolution is proclaimed.
(17 April) One thousand five hundred mercenaries of Cuban origin living in the United States land in the Bay of Pigs (Bahía de Cochinos) and attack the Playa Girón and Playa Larga. But the invasion is repulsed in only 72 hours.
(22 December) The literacy campaign reaches its apex, with a million

Cubans learning how to read and write. With an act celebrated in Plaza de la Revolución, Cuba is declared Illiteracy Free Territory.

1962 October Crisis. The president of the United States, John F. Kennedy, orders a naval blockade against Cuba and asks the USSR to remove the nuclear warheads placed in Cuban soil. Cuba maintains its intransigent stand during these events.

1963 (6 February) The government of the United States makes the naval blockade against Cuba official.

1965 (1 October) The Central Committee of the Cuban Communist Party is constituted. In occasion of this event, Fidel Castro reads the Leave of Absence extended to Che, in Congo to organize the guerrilla war.

1967 (8 October) Ernesto Che Guevara falls wounded in battle against the Bolivian army and is killed the following day.

1972 The Nueva Trova movement has its beginnings, led by songwriters and singers Silvio Rodríguez and Pablo Milanés.
In the same year, middleweight boxing champion Teófilo Stevenson wins his first Olympic gold medal, which he will also go on to win in the 1976 and 1980 Olympics.

1975 The first Congress of the Cuban Communist Party takes place in December.

1976 (15 February) The democratic-socialist Constitution of the Republic of Cuba is approved by popular referendum.
During the Pan-American Games of Montreal, runner Alberto Jantuorena wins two gold medals in the 400 and 800 meters.

1978 The 10th World Youth and Student Festival is held in Cuba.
Novelist Alejo Carpentier wins the important Miguel de Cervantes literary prize.

1979 (3 September) The 6th Conference of Non-Aligned Countries begins in the Palacio de Convenciones in Havana.
(3 December) The 1st International Festival of New Latin American Cinema is inaugurated.

1980 (4 April) The first Soviet-Cuban space flight takes place.

1990 Because of the fall of the blockade of socialist countries and the disintergration of the USSR, Cuba loses 85 percent of its foreign trade, to which the exacerbation of the U.S. embargo is added.
The country lives an economic crises which is followed by the so-called Período Especial.

1992 The crises worsens, especially after the U.S. government promulgates the Torricelli Law against those countries intending to break the economic blockade against Cuba.
Cuban poet Dulce María Loynaz wins the Miguel de Cervantes literary prize.

1993 Cuban poet and essayist Eliseo Diego wins the Juan Rulfo Prize in Mexico for his body of literary works.

1996 The government of the United States approves the Helms-Burton Law to destroy Cuba economically and re-establish a capitalist regime on the island.

1997 In the summer of this year, 11,000 young people from all over the world arrive in Cuba to celebrate the 14th World Festival of Youth and Students.
(14 October) After being found, the remains of Ernesto Che Guevara and his comrades depart from the airport of Valle Grande, in Bolivia, to return to Cuba and be laid to rest in Santa Clara.
The athlete Ana Fidelia Quirot, after numerous triumphs in international championships and after a period of recovery following an accident, becomes the world champion in the Athens Olympics in the 800 meters. In the same games, Javier Sotomayor, world record holder in Salamanca in 1993, wins the gold medal in the high jump.

1998 (21-25 January) The visit of Pope John Paul II is the first ever by a pope. His ecumenical mission includes the celebration of four masses in the cities of Santa Clara, Camagüy, Santiago de Cuba and in the Plaza de la Revolución in Havana.

Contents

"Crystal Clear is beyond 'Agile' since I think that Crystal Clear is Agile + Flexible + Practical. 'Flexible and Practical' is important for us. This is not theoretical methodology but practical methodology that lots of people are doing. When I read *Crystal Clear,* I felt that this was easy to understand. This book helps us from software process hell to successful software development through practical examples and useful samples."

—Basaki Satoshi, Schlumberger

"Alistair Cockburn shows how small teams can be highly effective at developing fit-for-purpose software by following a few basic software development practices and by creating proper team dynamics. These small teams can be much more effective and predictable than much larger teams that follow overly bureaucratic and prescriptive development processes."

—Todd Little, Sr. Development Manager, Landmark Graphics

"I find Cockburn's writings on agile methods enlightening: He describes 'how to do,' of course, but also how to tell whether you're doing it right, to reach into the feeling of the project. This particular book's value is that actual project experiences leading to and confirming the principles and practices are so...well...clearly presented."

—Scott Duncan, ASQ Software Division Standards Chair and representative to the US SC7 TAG and IEEE S2ESC Executive Committee and Management Board and Chair of IEEE Working Group 1648 on agile methods

"*Crystal Clear* identifies principles that work not only for software development, but also for any results-centric activities. Dr. Cockburn follows these principles with concrete, practical examples of how to apply the principles to real situations and roles and to resolve real issues."

—Niel Nickolaisen, COO, Deseret Book

"All the successful projects I've been involved with or have observed over the past 19 or so years have had many of the same characteristics as described in *Crystal Clear* (even the big projects). And many of the failed projects failed because they missed something—such as expert end-user involvement or accessibility throughout the project. The final story was a great read. Here was a project that in my opinion was an overwhelming success—high productivity, high quality, delivery, happy customer, and the fact that the team would do it again. The differing styles in each chapter kept it interesting. I started reading it and couldn't put it down, and by the end, I just had to say 'Wow!'"

—Ron Holliday, Director, Fidelity Management Research

"*Crystal Clear* gives me both essential and practical ways of creating and navigating motivated software development teams. At the same time, it increases the quality of engineering life!"

—Kenji Hiranabe, Project Manager, Eiwa System Management, Inc.

"Discussions around lightweight methods can become fairly esoteric and abstract, but finally, each development organization has to codify an approach that feels good, fits, and better yet, works. At Tomax we are still pursuing that goal, but we're getting much closer, in part based on the interplay between ideas and practices, philosophies, and methods that Alistair Cockburn so successfully connects. *Crystal Clear* is the perfect counterpoint to Alistair's earlier *Agile Software Development*, bringing some of the best thinking in the agile development community down to street-level in the form of implementable strategy and tactics. This book is essential reading for anyone who shares the passion for creating quality software."

—*Eric Olafson, CEO, Tomax Corp.*

"Imagine: Take a small group of developers, give them space, peace, tools, and access to their end users. And let them flourish, delivering valuable business software every few months. Efficiently, and without drama, Crystal Clear is the pragmatic way for small teams to deliver big results."

—*Dave Thomas, co-author of* The Pragmatic Programmer

"I like its emphasis on the human side of computing. I've never seen a book on software engineering talk about personal safety, and their discussion of easy access to expert users is very abstract . . . it explains much more about managing a project than any non-management book I have seen. You don't call it a management book—but topics like amity and burn charts are usually covered only in management books."

—*Ralph Johnson, Associate Professor, UIUC*

"This is the methodology I never knew I was already using. This book illuminates why the things I've been doing work, and also why some of the things I was doing didn't work."

—*Jeff Patton, ThoughtWorks*

"The Crystal Methodology System's biggest advantage is its flexibility. Crystal allows organizations to tailor the methodology to meet their needs—not the other way around—increasing your chances of getting everyone on board. As we have implemented Crystal Clear, I have found the Crystal Methodology System to be not only very people-oriented, but very result-oriented."

—*Jim Jorgensen, Project Manager, Web Services, Levi, Ray & Shoup, Inc.*

"Alistair Cockburn is creative, understandable, experienced, and wise. He speaks to the human side of process without discounting the technological detail. Starting from a small set of powerful concepts, *Crystal Clear* elaborates in various forms a rich collection of useful information. It captures experience, provides practical advice, and best of all, generates wonderful food for productive thought by managers and practitioners alike."

—*Richard Turner, author of CMMI Distilled, co-author of* Balancing Agility and Discipline

"*Crystal* brought me the closest rendition of what I see is the everyday life of a software development project: a community/group of people creating and inventing in a rather hostile/unfriendly/wild economical environment. All along their endeavor, people are struggling with a problem whose complexity is compounded by the puzzling but essential interactions of the human beings in the game. As I was myself stretching Crystal Clear to fit my particular projects, I had the chance to see the birth of this book. What I see now is a superb synthesis of the underlying principles and a clear description of the strategies and specific techniques that should be used to bring a fair number of software development projects in a safety zone while gaining both efficiency and quality of life."

—*Géry Derbier, Project Manager, Solistic*

"Once again, Alistair Cockburn has combined his highly developed sense of the problems that software teams face and his visionary and useful recommendations for how to improve software practices. This book provides fundamental principles, easy-to-adopt techniques, and stories from the trenches on human-powered approaches to develop quality software in response to customer needs. I strongly recommend this book to practitioners and students as a guide to build strong and effective software teams."

—*Lars Mathiassen, GRA Eminent Scholar, Center for Process Innovation,*
Georgia State University

"This is a great resource for any pragmatic programmer who needs to put together a full-fledged methodology for his team. Alistair is at his usual comprehensive and helpful best."

—*Andy Hunt, co-author of* The Pragmatic Programmer

"Alistair does a superb job of clearly and yet flexibly defining the least methodology that could possibly work for the safe delivery of software by small, co-located teams. Alistair exudes confidence in his methodology well beyond 'trust me, it works.' He does this by immediately establishing credibility in his extensive experience and by sharing details of experiences with real teams. You can't help but believe him! And you can't help but understand just how essential it is for small teams to practice Frequent Delivery, Reflective Improvement, and Osmotic Communication. He delivers a very powerful message in a variety of ways to touch the motivation and understanding of many points of view."

—*Laurie Williams, author of* Pair Programming Illuminated

"It's not 'just another methodology' that tells you what to do. Instead, it conveys a broader, richer, understanding of small-team software development. It includes clear, practical advice on how to tune the methodology to suit your team. This helps readers to make their own choices, appropriate to their own team, rather than just blindly following a 'recipe'-style methodology. Crystal Clear is not just a theory—it is based on the real-world experiences of successful teams."

—*John Rusk, www.agilekiwi.com*

"This book is just bursting with sound, practical advice described in a very accessible manner. Alistair perfects an incredible combination in giving clear how-to descriptions while simultaneously providing you with the underlying values and reflective discussions that stimulate your own thinking and creative adaptation of the techniques and practices. We recently applied the 'burn-down' charts with added scope—Wow!"

—Lise B. Hvatum, Product Development Manager, Schlumberger

"*Crystal Clear* is a must-read for anyone who expects a 'mature,' repeatable, and ever-shorter software development cycle. It changes the focus and attention from methodology, process, and measurement to the fundamental and foundational human behaviors and organizational dynamics played out in successful, reliable, and creative, software projects."

—David Spann, Organizational Development and Adaptive Project Management Consultant, and Adjunct Professor and former MBA Director, Westminster College

"*Crystal Clear* guided our development and user teams to focus on what could be done. As a result, we are finishing on time and under budget."

—Ernie Nielsen, Managing Director of Enterprise Project Management, Brigham Young University

"Many of the practices described in *Crystal Clear* can well be applied to large construction projects. Getting the "management team" together early, process planning by the team, communications and feedback, and the recognition of change are inherent in hard construction projects as well. . . . *Crystal Clear* brings to the reader a new perspective for the Project Management process. A must read for Project Managers."

—Joseph M. Wolfe, Jr., Senior Program Manager, Making Projects Work, Inc.

"*Crystal Clear* illuminates the basics, the fundamentals, of agile development. In sports we hear about coaches who stress fundamentals, the essential skills of the game. Teams that lose track of the fundamentals also fail to execute the complex. In talking about agile development, we often get caught up in the complex—large teams, distributed teams, embedded systems, and more. But even for these situations, learning the basics of agile development are essential, and that's what Alistair describes in vivid discussion, stories, and examples. Learn the fundamentals first—read *Crystal Clear*."

—Jim Highsmith, Director, Agile Software Development & Project Management Advisory Service, Cutter Consortium

Crystal Clear

The Agile Software Development Series

Alistair Cockburn and Jim Highsmith, Series Editors

Agile software development centers on four values identified in the Agile Alliance's Manifesto:

- Individuals and interactions over processes and tools

- Working software over comprehensive documentation

- Customer collaboration over contract negotiation

- Responding to change over following a plan

The development of Agile software requires innovation and responsiveness, based on generating and sharing knowledge within a development team and with the customer. Agile software developers draw on the strengths of customers, users, and developers, finding just enough process to balance quality and agility.

The books in The Agile Software Development Series focus on sharing the experiences of such Agile developers. Individual books address individual techniques (such as Use Cases), group techniques (such as collaborative decision making), and proven solutions to different problems from a variety of organizational cultures. The result is a core of Agile best practices that will enrich your experience and improve your work.

Titles in the Series:

Alistair Cockburn, *Surviving Object-Oriented Projects,* ISBN 0-201-49834-0

Alistair Cockburn, *Writing Effective Use Cases,* ISBN 0-201-70225-8

Lars Mathiassen, Jan Pries-Heje, and Ojelanki Ngwenyama, *Improving Software Organizations: From Principles to Practice,* ISBN 0-201-75820-2

Alistair Cockburn, *Agile Software Development,* ISBN 0-201-69969-9

Jim Highsmith, *Agile Software Development Ecosystems,* ISBN 0-201-76043-6

Steve Adolph, Paul Bramble, Alistair Cockburn, and Andy Pols, *Patterns for Effective Use Cases,* ISBN 0-201-72184-8

Anne Mette Jonassen Hass, *Configuration Management Principles and Practice,* ISBN 0-321-11766-2

DSDM Consortium and Jennifer Stapleton, *DSDM, Second Edition: Business Focused Development,* ISBN 0-321-11224-5

Mary Poppendieck and Tom Poppendieck, *Lean Software Development: An Agile Toolkit,* ISBN 0-321-15078-3

Craig Larman, *Agile and Iterative Development: A Manager's Guide,* ISBN 0-131-11155-8

Jim Highsmith, *Agile Project Management: Creating Innovative Products,* ISBN 0-321-21977-5

For more information visit www.awprofessional.com/series/agile

Crystal Clear

A Human-Powered Methodology
for Small Teams

Alistair Cockburn

Humans and Technology

✦ Addison-Wesley

Boston • San Francisco • New York • Toronto • Montreal
London • Munich • Paris • Madrid
Capetown • Sydney • Tokyo • Singapore • Mexico City

Publisher: John Wait
Editor in Chief: Don O'Hagan
Acquisitions Editor: Paul Petralia
Editorial Assistant: Michelle Vincenti
Marketing Manager: Chris Guzikowski
Cover Designer: Alan Clements
Managing Editor: Gina Kanouse
Senior Project Editor: Lori Lyons
Indexer: Larry Sweazy
Production: Jessica Balch and Pine Tree Composition, Inc.
Manufacturing Buyer: Dan Uhrig

The publisher offers excellent discounts on this book when ordered in quantity for bulk purchases or special sales, which may include electronic versions and/or custom covers and content particular to your business, training goals, marketing focus, and branding interests. For more information, please contact:

> U. S. Corporate and Government Sales
> (800) 382-3419
> corpsales@pearsontechgroup.com

For sales outside the U. S., please contact:

> International Sales
> international@pearsoned.com

Visit us on the Web: www.phptr.com

Library of Congress Cataloging-in-Publication Data:

20041096341

ISBN 0-201-69947-8

12 13 14 15 16 V036 14 13 12

Contents

Chapter 4 Explored (The Process) *111*

Crystal Clear uses nested cyclic processes of various lengths: the development episode, the iteration, the delivery period, and the full project. What people do at any moment depends on where they are in each of the cycles. This chapter linearizes the cycles to the extent possible and points out some of their interactions.

Chapter 5 Examined (The Work Products) *135*

This chapter describes team roles and the work products, showing examples of each work product. These particular work products are neither completely required nor completely optional. They are the ones I can vouch for, both one at a time and taken all together. Equivalent substitution is allowed, as is a fair amount of tailoring and variation. Although this is where the argument is most likely to occur, it is where the argument is least likely to affect the project's outcome.

You think you are using Crystal Clear, yet your project is not working. What's wrong? Crystal Clear can fail, but let's first double-check that you really are doing Crystal Clear. This chapter presents sample project situations. Some of them fulfill the intention of Crystal Clear, others violate it. The purpose here is to provide you with a personal warning system that you are or are not in tune with the intention of Clear.

Readers may be curious about how these ideas arose, how they compare with others in the industry, how far they can be stretched, and what to do when they don't seem to apply. The chapter is presented in question-and-answer form to allow for "talking about" the ideas, everything from philosophical foundations to "How do I get started?"

Chapter 8 Tested (A Case Study) *267*

Stephen Sykes of Thales Research and Technology in the United Kingdom experimented with an early version of this book and tried it out. Here is his report on the experience, along with the ISO 9001 auditor's recommendations. Many thanks to both Stephen and Thales.

Chapter 9 Distilled (The Short Version) *303*

At the end, it is time to roll it all back up again: What is the core of Crystal Clear, and what puts the team farther into the safety zone? This chapter is very short.

Preface

Crystal Clear: A few key rules to get a small project into its safety zone.

You have barely enough resources to get the system out. You don't want the team to write long documents, but they are forgetting things they are supposed to know about. You dislike heavy software development processes, but you want your team to work better than just randomly. You particularly want the software to come out the door successfully.

You considered sitting down and writing out the basic discussions the team should have and the work products they must be careful to attend to. You asked yourself:

What have other small, successful project teams done?

What practices do they use?

This book answers those questions. It is the result of ten years of debriefing successful small teams. Most of them repeated the same message:

- Seat people close together, communicating frequently and with goodwill.
- Get most of the bureaucracy out of their way and let them design.
- Get a real user directly involved.
- Have a good automated regression test suite available.
- Produce shippable functionality early and often.

Do all that, and most of the process details will take care of themselves.

This book sets out one of the most efficient and habitable methodologies you might hope to find: Crystal Clear. It is a *human-powered* methodology, most simply described as follows:

The lead designer and two to seven other developers in a large room or adjacent rooms, with information radiators such as whiteboards and flip charts on the wall, having access to key users, distractions kept away, delivering running, tested, usable code every month or two (okay, three at the most), periodically reflecting and adjusting on their working style.

This simple recommendation rests on both experience and theory. Software development can be characterized as an economically constrained *cooperative game* of invention and communication.[1] The way the team plays each game has everything to do with the project's outcome and the resulting software. Crystal Clear tackles the economic-cooperative game directly, addressing where to pay attention, where to simplify, and how to vary the rules. A number of teams have shared with me—and now with you, through this book—examples of their rules, work products, and even office layouts.

Many so-called "best" methodologies get rejected by a team as being too constraining, too invasive, or too difficult. Crystal Clear does not aspire to be a "best" methodology; it aspires to be "sufficient," in order that your team will shape it to itself and then actually use it.

ORIGIN OF THE MATERIAL IN THIS BOOK

The IBM Consulting Group asked me in 1991 to write a methodology for object-technology projects. Not knowing enough about methodologies at that time to make the crucial decisions, and at the suggestion of my boss, Kathy Ulisse,[2] I started interviewing project teams. What they told me was very different from what I had been reading in the books. In particular, they stressed aspects not covered in the methodology texts: close communication, morale, access to end users, and so on. It was not long before these issues separated in stark contrast the successful projects I visited from the failing ones. I came to see these issues, and not the design techniques, as the key to reaching a successful project outcome.

I got to try these ideas out as lead consultant on a $15 million, fixed-price, fixed-scope project of forty-five people. The ideas worked as advertised (coupled with a lot of creativity along the way), and showed themselves as core success factors. I wrote up the lessons learned from the project interviews and that project in *Surviving Object-Oriented Projects* (Cockburn 1998).[3]

One particular triplet showed up repeatedly: colocation of the team, frequent delivery, and access to an expert user. The differences in results between projects that

---

[1] Described at length in *Agile Software Development* (Cockburn 2002) and recapped in the first answer of Chapter 7.

[2] Thanks for the brilliant advice, Kathy!

[3] The project debriefings ended up as the basis for my doctoral dissertation, "People and Methodologies in Software Development" (Cockburn 2003a).

did and didn't do these far exceeded any other short list of practices. This book builds from that triplet.

The projects in my career have generally been of the fixed-price, fixed-scope variety. People usually underbid on these projects, which means that the only way the team can deliver on time is by being very creative with their development process. Unlike most of the other authors of the Agile Development Manifesto, I came to the agile principles through the need for efficiency, not the need to handle rapidly changing requirements.

As a result, Crystal Clear is well suited to the fixed-price context. If you are in such a situation, use the planning, communication, and reporting mechanisms I describe to meet your (probably unrealistic) deadline, and just be careful not to change the requirements at the start of every iteration. If you have an exploratory project in which the requirements are unknown or fluid, that is fine. Then allow the requirements to move at the start of each iteration.

CRYSTAL CLEAR IN THE CRYSTAL FAMILY

Crystal is a family of methodologies with a common genetic code, one that emphasizes frequent delivery, close communication and reflective improvement. There is no *one* Crystal methodology. There are different Crystal methodologies for different types of projects. Each project or organization uses the genetic code to generate new family members.

The name "Crystal" comes from my characterization of projects along two dimensions, size and criticality, matching that of minerals, color and hardness (see Figure 7-1).

Larger projects, which require more coordination and communication, map to darker *colors* (clear, yellow, orange, red, and so on). Projects for systems that can cause more damage need added *hardness* in the methodology, more validation and verification rules. A quartz methodology is suited to a few developers creating an invoicing system. The same team controlling the movement of boron rods in a nuclear reactor needs a diamond methodology—one calling for repeated checks on both the design and the implementation of their algorithms.

I characterize Crystal methodologies by color, according to the number of people being coordinated: Clear is for collocated teams of 8 or fewer people, Yellow is for teams of 10–20 people, Orange is for 20–50 people, Red is for 50–100 people, and so on, through Maroon, Blue, and Violet. Crystal Orange is described in *Surviving Object-Oriented Projects* (Cockburn 1998), and its variant Crystal Orange/Web is described in *Agile Software Development* (Cockburn 2002). I find that, except on life-critical projects, people can add in the verification activities through the methodology shaping and tuning workshops.[4]

Crystal's genetic code is made up of:

- The economic-cooperative game model
- Selected priorities
- Selected properties
- Selected principles
- Selected sample techniques
- Project examples

The economic-cooperative game model says that software development is a series of (typically resource limited) "games" whose moves consist of nothing else besides inventing and communicating. Each game in the series has two goals that compete for resources: to deliver the software in this game and to set up for the next game in the series. The game never repeats, so each project calls for strategies slightly different from all previous games. The economic-cooperative game model leads people on a project to think about their work in a very specific, focused, and effective way.

The priorities common to the Crystal family are

- *Safety* in the project outcome
- *Efficiency* in development
- *Habitability* of the conventions (the developers can live with them)

Crystal has the project team steer toward seven safety properties, the first three properties of which are core to Crystal. The others can be added in any order to increase safety margin. The properties are

- Frequent delivery
- Reflective improvement

---

[4]If your company develops FDA- or other life-critical "validated" systems, you may want to set up three base methodologies; one for a Clear (quartz) projects, one for Yellow or Orange, and a third for all of the validated systems. Those three should provide adequate basis for shaping to any of the projects in your company.

- Personal safety (the first step in trust)
- Focus
- Easy access to expert users
- Technical environment with automated testing, configuration management, and frequent integration

Crystal's principles are described in detail in *Agile Software Development* (Cockburn 2002). Among them are a few central ideas:

- The amount of detail needed in the requirements, design, and planning documents varies with the project circumstances, specifically the extent of damage that might be caused by undetected defects and the frequency of personal collaboration enjoyed by the team.
- It might not be possible to eliminate *all* intermediate work products and promissory notes such as requirements, design documents, and project plans; but they can be reduced to the extent that short, rich, informal communication paths are available to the team and working, tested software is delivered early and frequently.
- The team continually adjusts its working conventions to fit the particular personalities on the team, the current local working environment, and the peculiarities of the specific assignment.

Among the rest are trade-off curves that highlight the cost implications of different communication mechanisms, different project situations, and different strategies for concurrent development. I used the principles to derive Crystal Clear, but don't discuss them separately in this book.

The Crystal package includes selected sample techniques, including ones for methodology shaping, planning, and reflective improvement. Crystal does not require any specific technique to be used by any of the people on the project, so these techniques are included only as a starter set.

Each member of the Crystal family is generated at the start of a project by shaping a base methodology according to the genetic code. Since the situation changes over time, the methodology is retuned during the course of the project. Both shaping and tuning are performed fast enough that the time spent gets repaid within the project time frame.

Crystal Clear is an optimization of Crystal that can be applied when the team consists of two to eight people sitting in the same room or in adjacent offices. The property of close communication is strengthened to "osmotic" communication, meaning that the people overhear each other discussing project priorities, status, requirements, and design on a daily basis. This enhanced communication allows the team to work more from tacit communication and small notes than otherwise would be possible.

Because every company and project is slightly different, even Crystal Clear is not fully specified. The first steps in adopting Crystal Clear are to uncover your organization's strong points and weaknesses and to fit the recommendations of Crystal Clear around them to capitalize on the strong points and cover the weaknesses.

For some organizations, this is too much work. Crystal Clear is not for those organizations. It is for groups that want to build their own, personal, strong, and effective way to deliver software repeatedly.

Crystal Clear shares some characteristics with XP but is generally less demanding. You might think of it as a more laid-back alternative, a place to fall back to if XP isn't working for the group, or a springboard to get some agile practices in place before jumping into XP.

THIS BOOK IN THE AGILE DEVELOPMENT SERIES

This book is part of the Agile Software Development series edited by Jim Highsmith and myself. The series describes both theory and practice for software development.

The theoretical underpinnings are discussed in four books: *Agile Software Development* (Cockburn 2002), *Adaptive Software Development* (Highsmith 2000), *Agile Project Management* (Highsmith 2004), and *Lean Software Development* (Poppendieck 2003).

The other books in the series pick up the thread either by describing a technique for a particular individual or role, a technique set for the entire team, or a methodology sample.

- We find attention to the role of project manager in *Surviving Object-Oriented Projects* (Cockburn 1998) and *Agile Project Management* (Highsmith 2004), and attention to the role of requirements writer in *Writing Effective Use Cases* (Cockburn 2001b) and *Patterns for Effective Use Cases* (Adolph 2002).

- We find attention to the entire team in *Improving Software Organizations* (Mathiassen 2001) [OK] and *Configuration Management* (Haas 2003).

- Specific agile methodologies are described in *DSDM* (Stapleton 2003), *Agile Software Development Ecosystems* (Highsmith 2003), *Agile and Iterative Development: A Manager's Guide* (Larman 2003), and this book.

Future books will follow the theme, adding techniques for collaboration and team health.

Future books will follow the theme, adding techniques for collaboration and team health.

HOW TO READ THIS BOOK

Some people will read this book as an introduction to agile development techniques, and be relatively new to pair programming, test-driven development, osmotic communication, economic-cooperative game, continuous integration, and information radiators.

If that is you, then read this book pretty much straight through, because you are the person for whom I designed the chapter ordering.

- I wrote the Chapter 1, *Explained (View from the Outside)*, as an e-mail exchange between Crystal and myself to expose how these teams look to an outsider (remember, it was once all new to me, too).

- Chapter 2, *Applied (The Seven Properties)*, is the most important chapter. It describes what the team is aiming for, not the procedure it uses to get there.

- Chapter 3, *In Practice (Strategies and Techniques)*, should give you a handle on how some of this is done.

- Chapter 4, *Explored (The Process)*, describes the cyclical development processes core to all agile (indeed all modern) methodologies. It is something in which everyone should be fluent.

- Just scan Chapter 5, *Examined (The Work Products)*, on the first pass, since it is very detailed. Use it as an encyclopedia of work product samples when you get that far.

- Chapter 6, *Misunderstood (Common Mistakes)*, and Chapter 7, *Questioned (Frequently Asked)*, answer questions about what counts as okay and not-okay variations.

- Chapter 8, *Tested (A Case Study)*, gives you another chance to see the methodology from the outside, since it was written for people not familiar with Crystal Clear. It also contains an ISO 9001 auditor's analysis and recommendations, which shines light from a different angle.

- Read Chapter 9, *Distilled (The Short Version)*, to see if it makes sense at that point. If it doesn't, you may have to go back to Chapter 7 to see why such a simple recommendation works.

Some people are fully versed in modern agile development, including test-driven design and continuous integration. I suggest you go directly to Chapter 9. After that (when you are done snickering), read Chapter 2, probably the most important chapter in the book. My guess is that you will find some new ideas to try out in Chapter 3. After looking through those chapters, return to Chapter 9 to see if it all hangs together for you.

If you are giving this to your boss or manager, my hope is that the first chapter, with its e-mail format, is the kind of thing that can be read on the airplane or in the bathtub. A manager or executive should also read the Chapter 4, because learning how to fit a cyclical process into the organization is important.

Process or methodology designers are quite likely to turn straight to Chapter 5, because this is a standard way of evaluating methodologies (although in the case of Crystal Clear, quite insufficient). To complete the evaluation, though, you need also to read Chapter 7 to see the comparison with other methodology systems.

Finally, you will be ready to start. At this point, read the answer to the last question in Chapter 7, "How do I get started?", and work from there. That will take you back to the methodology shaping and reflection techniques, and Chapter 2.

I wrote each chapter in its own unique style and tone. There is a reason for this. People learning a methodology are in much the same situation as blind men trying to guess the shape of an elephant, each feeling a different part and coming up with a different answer. Each person's unique background causes that person to notice and look for different things. Therefore, the nine different chapters are written in quite different ways. I don't expect everyone to be happy with every chapter, but I do hope that everyone finds some chapter that addresses his and her individual background and interests.

ACKNOWLEDGMENTS

I am indebted to many more people for this book than for any of my previous ones: people who told me their stories, people who tried out the ideas, people who contributed samples, people who reviewed the text, and people who supported me emotionally.

Most of the people who told me their project stories during the last ten years don't know how much value they provided as they explained—even apologized for!— their ways of working. They often said, "We don't use a methodology here, we just . . .," or "I'm sorry, we don't bother to do [xyz], or maintain our documents, but we have found. . . ." It was only by comparing results across a number of projects that I discovered that in many of these instances no apology was ever needed and that there was a strength in the way they worked.

Certain people were pioneers in trying out these ideas out on their projects. Jens Coldewey was the first, back in 1998, Robert Volker in 1999, Géry Derbier in 2002, Stephen Sykes in 2003. Dr. Christopher Jones tried out an early version on his unsus-

Pete McBreen kept reminding me that *people* are also valuable carryovers from one project to the next (something I knew, but which kept slipping out of my descriptions until Pete reminded me again). Jeff Patton and Andy Pols were continual discussion partners on the topics.

Quite a number of people contributed office photos and work samples. Their names are listed separately in the permissions section and next to their contributions in the book, but I should like to highlight their importance here. For me as a writer intending to create something useful to you as a reader, it was important to have real work samples and not dummied up toy examples. These people recognized that importance and contributed what they had. I expect that all readers will appreciate their contributions.

Luke Hohmann and Tom Poppendieck read everything I wrote with astonishing thoroughness and caught errors of omission, commission, and even intention. Tom came up with the idea of dating the e-mails instead of numbering them. (Duh, why didn't I think of that? Thanks, Tom.)

Rich Turner is one of the people who could help me with the CMM(I) discussion in the context of Crystal Clear, and I'm thankful for his advice and review.

The Silicon Valley Patterns Group, and especially Russ Rufer and Chris Lopez, who read the manuscript carefully not just once, but twice, giving their usual thoughtful comments and pushing back on me when they felt I had gone off track. Russ argued me down relentlessly on some of sections until I finally got his point.

A few people read it from the Web and wrote in with corrections and improvements. Thank you, Marco Cova, Todd Little, Alan Griffiths, Howard Fear, Victoria Einarsson, Paul Chisholm, Pierce McMartin, Phillipe Back, Todd Jonker, Chris Matts, Gain Wong, Jeremy Brown, John Rusk, Johannes Brodwall, and Toby Kraft for your eagle eyesight.

The people in the Salt Lake Agile Group round table even ran through a "design the box" exercise for Crystal one day. The top quote from that day was,

"I've used Crystal all my life, and I've never been the same!"

Thanks to Jim Highsmith, discussion partner and series coeditor for the many illuminating discussions that shaped our ideas, our book series, and the wonderful Agile Development Conference in 2003.

Thanks to my new favorite coffee shop, the Salt Lake Coffee Break, which stays open until 2:00 A.M., has interesting clientele, power outlets that work, and baklava and Turkish coffee for those rare moments. Thanks to my family—to Deanna for checking in with me at the coffee shop at 1:00 A.M. to see how the typing was going (and then letting me sleep in in the morning), and to Kieran, Sean, and Cameron for their positive regard of my writing habit.

Chapter 1

Explained
(View from the Outside)

I distilled Crystal Clear by asking successful small teams what they would keep or change in the ways they worked. They responded with this deceptively simple set of rules. This chapter is written as an e-mail exchange between the fictitious Crystal and me. The e-mails let you encounter the rules from the outside, as I first did, and allow me to push back against Crystal's reports by asking questions.

The following e-mails are written to simulate what it is like to encounter for the first time a team doing Crystal Clear. While writing, I discovered that it was better to write as though Crystal were the one doing the project interviews and teaching Alistair-the-author, even though in real life Alistair did the interviewing. In what follows, Alistair gets to be the slowpoke, with Crystal pulling him reluctantly along, even scolding him on occasion.

Here is the office layout Crystal refers to:

Figure 1-1   *A work setting showing osmotic communication. (Courtesy of Tomax)*

June 1:   Dear Alistair,

Just getting back from my trip to Cryogenic Commerce, and I have to tell you what I saw. This must be the dozenth time I have visited a successful software group, and there is great similarity between the really productive ones. I know many organizations want to work in an extremely fast, productive way, so I am going to capture this one for the others who want to do so, too. The folks at C.C. were articulate about what they did, so I think I can answer your questions.

The project consists of three people, Kim, Pat and Chris. Kim is the team leader and lead designer.

Kim says that they run all projects with two to four people if possible, because that is how many they can coordinate easily. They run six people on occasion, but that is a stretch and they refuse to go larger than that. They say that if they need more than six people, they haven't set up their project scope correctly.

They all sit in one room, as in the photo. They do this whenever they can, but if, for some reason, they have to use separate offices, they arrange for them to be next to each other.

Very close contact is one of the most important things to their way of working. They want communicating to be as easy as calling across the room. There is just too much happening for them to have to pick up the phone or walk down the hall. They can get away with adjacent offices, but only barely.

I asked what they use for their requirements and design medium. They pointed to the whiteboard and said, "There is our design medium."

Using the whiteboard as the primary design medium is one of the things I have found over and over. One project manager told me, and it was on a much larger project, that he was so pressed for time that they just photographed the whiteboard as their design documentation! Another time the team leader showed me the tables, lines, and scribbles on his whiteboard and said, "I defy you to tell me what published methodology supports THIS notation!"

I have to agree. I have seen many sketches on whiteboards around the world. I can hardly think of a better medium. The only thing is that you can't fold it up and take it with you! Thank goodness there are printing whiteboards and PC-attached whiteboards, the Mimio radio device for ordinary whiteboards, and digital cameras.[1] I could easily cost justify any of those on saved communication time.

Kim said they use very light use cases as a basis for requirements. I'll send you an example of their two-paragraph use cases later on.

On occasion they find they can live with even briefer requirements. They have very good links to their users, so the lighter stories are mostly just a

---

[1]The software product Pixid removes glares from digital whiteboard photos.

reminder of what must be developed. The continuous conversations with the users keep the requirements accurate.

Once they collect their use cases and other requirements, they don't create many other archived deliverables except the final commented code and the user help text. I know this may sound incredible, but I have seen it over and over and over again, in the highest productivity groups I have found, and I don't think it can be ignored.

They hold design reviews at the whiteboard. There is no formal writing for these, most of the information is conveyed in the talking and hand movements, with some instance diagrams and interaction diagrams drawn along the way, and some other diagrams.[2] Some of these do not match any published drawing standard—but why should they, if everyone in the room understands what they mean?

What else is there to say?

They look over each other shoulders a lot, sometimes doing *side-by-side programming,*[3] so they get a lot of code reviewing done on a continuous basis. They like this, calling it "peer code peering." I have run into some form or another of this in many places.

Extreme Programming (XP) people take the idea the farthest, programming in pairs. XPers say they catch more mistakes this way, sooner, than they would ever have imagined, and the resulting designs are better. It also gives them some intellectual backup. There is always someone else who understands a bit of how each person's code is built, and they also learn programming tricks from each other.

I did ask Kim and company whether they used ROOM or DOOM or UML or OML or any of the other published methodology things. They were not at all shy on this one! Pat said, "Our job is to get software out, not spend our time drawing pictures!" Chris said, "Who should we draw them for and why? Our users see the results so quickly, and we all understand the insides thoroughly. You've seen our whiteboards." Kim added, "We tried them for a while, but we are so closely linked that they don't add anything."

This was a very outspoken group, but I have encountered this reaction from other teams, and not just small ones. Most small teams are a little apologetic about not using the drawing notations and tools, as though they are doing something wrong. On the other hand, an architect on a 150-person project said he doubts that graphical techniques scale and so on his large project they kept all their design information in text.

Well, there you have it. No doubt you have some questions, so fire away and I'll see what I can answer.

Cheerily, Crystal

---

[2]See Chapter 5.

[3]Placing their screens about 18 inches apart, they each work on their own programming tasks.

Dear Crystal,

Thanks for the description. I guess I do have one question to start with. Did you get enough detail to describe their process? What happened and what did they do, and what happened then and what did they do?

Best regards, Alistair

June 2:   Dear Alistair,

Yes and no. I stuck around for several days, so I could see them in action. What I would say is this, and you can do with it what you want. . . .

Their minute-to-minute process was so complicated that I couldn't possibly write it all down, and if I could, you couldn't possibly follow it, let alone install it on another team.

What I would say is that they strive to develop a community mind. They sat down at the beginning and understood the problem they were solving, worked out how they were going to go about it, and then started working. They are in close enough communication that they know what is important and what is happening. That is enough to keep them in step with each other, and they let the dance, as it were, improvise itself around them.

Here's what I can offer:

First, they interview their users and their sponsoring executive. Pat also went and watched the users at work, so Pat became the local expert on user actions. They collected requirements as two-paragraph use cases, you recall. They prioritized these with the users, so they knew which ones delivered the greatest value and which ones were needed first.

Then they got their technology requirements straight, what they had to use and what they could use. Kim is the technical leader, so Kim pretty much decided on the technology and laid out the basic architecture.

Third, they made a delivery plan, which included a delivery every two months.

Within each delivery, they first discuss the purpose of screens and screen sequences with users, using either just words or pencil and paper, until they are pretty clear on the user requirements. They discuss how to set up the core business objects and who gets what parts of the system.

Typically, Kim takes the infrastructure, Pat takes the user interface, and Chris takes the business objects. They are not hung up on this. There have been times when Pat and Chris each took both business objects and user interface objects, and they shared frameworks.

There is an initial demo to the user, after a couple of days or a couple of weeks, using just the screen and some dummied up data. A fully functional demo comes after perhaps a month. Everyone learns something from these, even though they have been in discussion quite closely.

I'll tell you what happened one time, just so you understand.

Chris had gotten all the user screens pretty much right and all, but the first prototype took seven seconds round-trip for a transaction. The user looked at the screen and asked, "Uh, is that the way it is going to perform in real life?" Chris said, "Well, we have some performance tuning to do, but more or less, yes. Why?" The user replied that she gets sent a fax with hundreds of lines on it, and she simply types from the fax, "heads down," as it were, never looking at the screen, but just touch typing the hundreds of entries. She couldn't possibly wait seven seconds between each line.

Chris was dumbfounded. "But what do you do if there is a typing error?" "Oh, well this is all recorded just for tax deduction purposes, so actually we don't much care if there is an error. It isn't worth the time to correct it," answered the user.

Chris was quite shaken up by how badly they had misunderstood the requirements, even after interviewing the user and showing drafts of the screens and all. I guess it just goes to show you the difference between a mockup and real usage.

That's most of their "process."

Cheers, Crystal

Dear Crystal,

Thanks for the field notes. I look forward to your next installment. Tell me about testing. Do they have test tools, regression tests, external testers, what do they do?

Thanks, Alistair

June 3:   Dear Alistair,

Yes, I meant to get to testing sooner or later. First let me finish off the process, and the testing will show up.

Imagine they have a delivery period lasting 2 months. They go over the requirements with the users, and start drafting their design. Here is where the process gets fuzzy.

Some of the people at C.C. are "thinkers," others are "typers."

The thinkers sit down and think about the problem, designing on paper or whiteboard for as long as they can stand, until they either have a design they believe in or else they have to start programming to work out their confusion. This thinking sometimes takes a few minutes, other times it takes hours, or even a couple of days in the worst case. After they program some real code, they learn more about how their design is working, and they either continue with it, or think and draw some more on how it needs to be changed.

The "typers" just start typing right away. At least, that's how it looks. What they really do is think about a tiny piece of functionality, write a unit test if they're doing test-driven development, and then get that tiny section of code working. When they add the next section, they refactor the two together to improve the design. These people spend more time typing and less staring than the others, but I can't particularly tell that it makes any real difference in the long run. It seems to be more a personality thing.

Constant testing. The best groups, and C.C. is one of them, deliberately design an architecture that supports fully automated regression testing. Some groups run their tests from the workspace window, then stick them right into the class system with the rest of the production code. Other groups stick them into files and run batch jobs against their code, pulling the test cases out of the files.

Kim said that it is hard to convince even experienced people to bother setting up a system architecture that supports regression testing and to build test cases as they go. However, once they experience the pleasure of developing with automated regression tests at their fingertips, they never go back. The regression tests and batch test architecture give them a freedom to make changes and a feeling of security they never had before. They make some changes, then push the test button, and find out if they messed up something that was working before.

Let's see, process. . . . They have a number of small design reviews within the team, they demo the system to the users a couple of times, build regression tests, and at some point they declare they are done. They write the user manual or help text, create a production build, run the tests again, and then deliver the system to some friendly users

How am I doing?

Crystal

Dear Crystal,

Doing fine. Now, every methodology must announce its tolerances. You are saying that Crystal Clear has tolerances like this:

- ♦ Coding style has great tolerance, being a matter for the team to decide.
- ♦ On the other hand, regression testing, peer code peering, user links, and short releases are matters with very little tolerance.
- ♦ Team size has some tolerance, the range being 2–8 people.
- ♦ Release length has some tolerance, the range being 1–3 months.

I am with you on those things. I am still stuck on the process, though. It seems that they just "run around and do *stuff*." I sort of get the idea, but I can't think of how to describe it to someone else.

What do you think we should do about this lack of description?

Trusting you, but still confused,

Alistair

June 4: Dear Alistair,

Get serious, Alistair, these are grown people, and they have normal mental equipment. What do they do? They look around, they think, they talk to each other, that's what they do.

One note about the team lead or lead designer, though:

Kim said that they always have one experienced person on the team. They often have one novice. If they have two rank novices, the team lead must be particularly experienced and good.

I recall you told me about your first job fresh out of college, and it wasn't much different. You were on a team of three designing a hardware subsystem of a flight simulator. You were the novice. You shared the office with your boss, the team leader, and the lead designer. The other designer sat in the office across from you. Your boss designed the subsystem's architecture and you other two contributed design and ideas.

Your team leader had been through it before, and his boss had been through more. You lived it and learned it. And that was on a project with 26 designers total. It is much easier if the entire project is only three to five people.

Are you willing to trust that three intelligent trained people can use their common sense?

The main thing is that the overall process delivers releases often enough that there is little time for the project to go far off track.

So there.

You talk about techniques. Well, these people use every technique known to computer science, and a bunch of stuff never described. That is why this methodology has to have a lot of tolerance. They care about how the end result looks, not what sequence someone went through to invent it.

Cheers as always, Crystal

Dear Crystal,

Uh, thanks for that, I think I needed it. Somehow it is just so easy to forget about people thinking and talking to each other when doing this process stuff. :-(

Actually, I *am* wondering how to make this ISO/CMM(I) certifiable,[4] but let's leave that for a while and figure out what else there is to say.

Okay, you've talked about team setup, user connections, incremental iterative development, use cases, deliverables, testing, what else is there to cover?

Regards, Alistair

June 5: Dear Alistair,

You forgot to mention something critically important in a methodology: team values. That drives the rest of the methodology.

The key phrase here is "light on work products, strong on communications," with *reflective improvement*. They work on developing a community mind, with constant linkage to the users and frequent demonstrations and deliveries. The favored milestone is delivered functionality, and with that they can correct almost any problem.

By staying light on the work products, they move much faster, and they change directions faster. Since they can move faster, they can deliver something useful in less time, thus making their

---

[4]See the auditor's analysis in Chapter 8.

milestones. Since they deliver in less time, they need fewer intermediate work products. It is self-reinforcing, as you see.

They view developing software as an evolving conversation—an economic-cooperative game, actually. In any one move they go forward and create reminders for each other.

Is that enough to satisfy you?

Cheerily, Crystal

Dear Crystal,

That's great, thanks. I'll see if I can capture what you have said in some sort of closed format so someone can walk away with it on paper.

Shall I use the list of methodology elements I use in my other books, with roles, deliverables, teams, skills, standards, and all that? I'm afraid I'll have trouble with all this tolerance you want me to stick in there.

What really strikes me about this is that when you write down how an organization works, even a small group with a light methodology and small set of deliverables, it really looks complicated!

Best regards, Alistair

June 6:   Dear Alistair,

I'll propose something shorter, more stable and easier to remember than your tables and tuples. I think that some of the items in your tuples aren't really critical, and there are multiple pathways that work.

How about focusing on the key *properties* they set into place, and let different teams to follow their own preferred paths, just as long as they establish the properties.

For example: *Frequent Delivery* as a property. How frequent is *frequent*, and just exactly what counts as a *delivery*? How do they do the delivery? I propose we leave the answers up to the team to decide, as long as *frequent deliveries* of some sort are happening. Some of the others would be:

Reflective Improvement
Osmotic Communication
Personal Safety
Focus
Easy Access to Expert Users

and don't forget their

Technical Environment, with automated testing, configuration management, frequent integration.

For the work products, provide *samples*. They will be much more useful than templates. Get whiteboard photos, sketches, whatever, from real teams.

Yes, even a small methodology is a complex thing, but what do you expect? It is the encoding of a culture, and of a successful culture which produces serious software. Crystal Clear is as simple and short as I can keep it, but I can't make it simpler than it is.

Just let go of the techniques.

Cheerily, Crystal

> Dear Crystal,
>
> Got it. We'll consider techniques a "local matter" then.
>
> Here's the next question. Many people will think that Crystal Clear will only work with all expert developers.
>
> What do you have to say about this?
>
> Best regards, Alistair

June 7:   Dear Alistair,

Relevant question. Long answer. . . .

People learning a new skill pass through three quite different stages of behavior, known as *following, detaching,* and *fluency.* We can call them levels 1, 2, and 3. These stages of learning are well known in *aikido,* where they are called *Shu, Ha,* and *Ri,* which translate roughly to *follow, break, leave.* It is probably not an accident that craft houses in the Middle Ages also had three levels: apprentice, journeyman, and master.

This is all described in *Agile Software Development,* but it may be a good idea to summarize here, also.

In Japan, they draw Shu-Ha-Ri with the characters:[5]

Figure 1-2   *Shu, Ha, Ri.*

---

[5]These date back to the early days of Japanese Noh theater.

A person just starting can't learn multiple methods at once, even if there are ten that could work. So in Level 1, the *following* stage, people look for *one* procedure that works. They copy it. They learn it. They measure success by how well they can follow it. In fact, they take for granted that it works, and can get very upset if it fails on them.

The *Shu* stage manifests itself in software development methodologies as thick, detailed manuals.

This book is an example. Crystal Clear can be described in one sentence (as in Chapter 9). To an experienced software developer, this one sentence is adequate guidance.

That sentence is not enough for a Level 1 practitioner. He wants details of what to do. When I expand a particular technique, process or work product, I am writing to readers at Level 1 on that particular item.

Everyone is Level 1 on a new skill. Even advanced developers work at Level 1 the first time they try a Reflection Workshop.

Eventually, they recognize that the technique won't serve all situations.

In the *detaching,* or Level 2 stage, they look for rules about when the procedure breaks down. Let me give you two examples.

In the 1990s, organizations that had become highly tuned to Information Engineering (IE) architectures suddenly had to deliver object-oriented software. They first tried to adapt the IE methods, then they developed completely new development methodologies. Along the way, they often regressed through totally *ad hoc* techniques before discovering new structures to support the OO projects.

A second shift happened after the Agile Development Manifesto was published in 2001.[6] Many groups trying it out found a mismatch between agile and their standard organizational practices. So they experimented with alternative ideas.

Eventually, people become fluent in enough situations that they stop paying attention to which technique they are using at any moment. They invent, blend, and adapt everything they know faster than they can even describe.

This is the *fluency*, or Level 3 stage.

Level 3 developers don't pay huge attention to the methodology formula. They pay attention to what is happening on the project and make process adjustments on the fly. They understand the desired end effect and simply make their way to that end. Simply stating the desired *Properties* of the project suffices for them.

Discussions among Level 3 people sound distressingly Zen:

> *"Use a technique so long as it is doing some good."*
> *"Do whatever works."*
> *"When you are really doing it, you are unaware that you are doing it."*

---

[6]http://AgileManifesto.org

To someone at the fluency level, this is all true. To someone still detaching, it is confusing. To someone looking for a procedure to follow, it is useless.

The one-sentence description of Crystal Clear is enough for the Level 3 developer. That description has been used directly by several project leaders, one of whom reported back later, "We did what you said, and it worked!" (which, to a Level 1 audience, doesn't communicate very much).

Try being aware of these levels the next time you are in a meeting. You are quite likely to find two people stuck in an argument, and notice that they are at different levels on the current topic. What is a natural set of variations for one person seems bewilderingly vague to the other. If you identify the level difference, the two can negotiate the level of the discussion, or at least be more patient with each other.

All of this applies to Crystal Clear.

I don't think that Crystal Clear can be run by a team of all Level 1 practitioners. I doubt that these 300 pages of description are explicit enough.

Tom Poppendieck describes the paradox neatly: Level 1 people need the detail, but can't handle its complexity. Level 3 people can handle the complexity, but have little use for the detail.

To deal with that paradox, I have in Crystal Clear that any one project needs at least one Level 3 developer or two Level 2 developers. That *lead designer* expands the information on the fly.

These pages support him or her in doing that.

In practice, the lead designer more or less runs the project. Often there is one other fairly experienced person, but the rest are all at various stages of beginning or middling (some young, inexperienced, and bright, some older and tired or just at their maximum level of capability).

So finally I can answer your question: No, it is not the case that Crystal Clear will only work with all expert developers. But at least one of them needs to be a Level 3 developer.

I have in mind that the project sponsor will be hiring according to that staffing pattern.

What is your next question?

Crystal

Dear Crystal,

Thanks, and yes, I can already tell where I can use those levels to defuse some meetings.

It strikes me, suddenly, that you have not said much about tools up to now. I sense there is more here than you have let on, and that it is actually rather important.

Regards, Alistair

June 8:   Dear Alistair,

Yes, tooling deserves special mention[7].

---

[7]Tools deserve a complete article (Cockburn 2004e).

Clear does not *mandate* any particular tools, just as it does not mandate any specific technique. That is because the tools differ in various technologies.

That having been said, there is one tool that gets mentioned by almost every team I visit, including even the smallest teams of three people: the configuration management tool.

A startling number of teams I visit don't have any configuration management system in place at all. Those are not the successful teams I am documenting, however. The absence of configuration management doesn't imply the project will fail, but successful teams almost unanimously name their configuration management tool as the single most important tool they possess.

Crystal

Dear Crystal,

Last hard question—What would it mean for a group to say they are "in compliance" with this methodology?

Alistair

June 9:   Dear Alistair,

Compliance is a funny thing. On the one hand, we want enough compliance that the project is safe, and not so much that people get uptight about the details, as well as guidance to teams interested in setting up their projects to succeed, work efficiently, and be "habitable" at the same time.

Compliance to methodologies is a graduated incline. Imagine, if you will, a *mesa*, a flat plateau above some plains. But imagine that instead of a cliff from the plains to the mesa, there is a sloped incline.

The mesa at the top is "obviously compliant." There is a certain amount of room for movement, all safely within both the letter and intention of the methodology.

The slope is the transition zone, the gray area of compliance, "Are we compliant? It's not the letter of the methodology, but is it in the intention?"

A methodology description should say something about the transition zone, otherwise there will be incessant bickering about the letter versus the intention of the methodology. It should say something about, "Here's what it takes to say you are safe; here are some things you can do and still say you're doing (or sort of doing) it; do these and you are definitely out."

The dividing line on the sloping part will never be perfectly clear, but there should be some way of telling the shift between the three zones. This allows people to say, "Gee, we are doing everything just as described, and it's still not working" or "Oh, I see. We forgot *that* critical part. Let's try that and see if it all works better."

Accordingly, here is what it takes to say you are using Crystal Clear. Because these are great, I start each with a smiley face :-)

1. **:-) You have short, rich communication paths.** You are sitting very close together, preferably in one big room. You might be sitting in adjacent rooms if there are really only 4–6 of you and you visit each other a lot. Recognize that the quality of communication drops the moment you have to pick up the phone or walk out the door.

2. **:-) You deliver increments monthly or every other month, absolutely no longer than three months apart.** You schedule and track code execution milestones, and not by document completion milestones.

3. **:-) You have a real user on the project, even if only part time.** Your user helps you construct your screen sketches and both validates and breaks your UI designs. You get the system reviewed by real users at least once per increment prior to delivering it.

4. **:-) You have a project mission statement.** You use one of a wide variety of requirements formats. You have a description of the system design (using one of the many description techniques you can invent).

5. **:-) You have a clear ownership model for your work products.** For each class, module, or use case, you know who it is that can change or, more importantly, delete parts of it. The answer may be either a single person, anyone

in a given subteam, or even anyone on the team (this is the rule in XP projects). You should never have to have the whole team sit around the screen and ask, "Who put this in here? What is it doing there? Can we delete it?" If you have to do this, you know you have a breakdown in the ownership model.

Here are some things you can vary and still say you are doing Clear. Because these are still okay, I start each with a neutral face :-|

1. :-| **You sit in adjacent rooms,** if there are really only 4–6 of you and you visit each other a lot. Recognize that the quality of communication drops the moment you have to pick up the phone or walk out the door.

2. :-| **You use the Scrum backlog technique or XP's planning game** for prioritizing and scheduling your work (Schwaber 2002; Beck 2000). I personally like to use the *blitz-planning* (also known as the project-planning jam session) technique. The point I wish to make here is that Crystal Clear allows borrowing from other methodologies. Using XP's *planning game* does not mean you are not doing Crystal Clear. It only means that incorporating elements of other methodologies is a natural part of Crystal Clear.

3. :-| **There is only one iteration per delivery, but you arrange several user viewings.** When the users see the system, they will comment, which will generate new work to be put into the delivery cycle. That feedback is crucial to product success. "Iterations" provide closure and velocity information, but so do short delivery cycles. Nothing replaces the user viewings, though.

4. :-| Your users cannot accept operational increments as often as you produce them, or they can't accept partial functionality. So, **you deliver tested, delivery-ready code to a "staging station"** where the increments are added together over time until it is suitable to deliver them to the end users.

5. :-| **You describe your design using hypertext documents and technical memos** and avoid UML drawings, or you describe classes using UML or one of the -OOM notations, and avoid responsibility statements. **You document your system using videos** of the designers walking through the design. There are lots of variations for how to describe the design (we aren't even close to figuring out the best way). If you **don't like my use case format, you can come up with your own** requirements format (possibly user stories or feature lists). With

most of the work products, equivalent substitution is permitted as long as the intention of the item is preserved and the project's safety properties are not in jeopardy.

Here are some things that, if you are doing them, you are definitely outside of Clear. Your rule set might work for you, but it is not Crystal Clear. I start each with a frowny face :-(

1. :-(**You work in different buildings or different cities.** This means your communications paths are long and thin, that you must communicate by phone, e-mail, or occasional visits. You cannot fulfill the requirements of Crystal Clear, which requires that team members be able to initiate and carry person-to-person conversations many times a day with little effort. Longer distances raise the barrier to conversation, the form of communication is inferior, and you cannot rely on the common shared memory of the group. (I note, as you probably do, that working on different floors of the same building falls in a gray zone in these descriptions. I doubt you can make Clear work properly across floors. I think you can't make it work properly even down a corridor. But I leave myself open to disproof-by-example.)

2. :-(**Your increments are longer than four months.** Your feedback path is too long. You can no longer avoid "promissory notes" types of documents because you are not delivering often enough to demonstrate the progress you are making. Shorter increments is a critical success factor to your project (see *Surviving Object Oriented Projects*), no matter what methodology you are using.

3. :-(**There is no user viewing prior to delivery.** My experience is that this means the users will be given something that doesn't meet their needs, too late to make changes. Even projects doing everything else on the Crystal Clear list, who miss this, end up in trouble when the users finally do see the system.

4. :-(**There are no real users available** to your team. The hazard being addressed here is that the user requirements are coming from some sort of intermediary, a marketing representative or executive who promises they are telling you what the users "really" want. Research indicates that this sort of user input is unreliable, and direct links to real users are needed.

There is one part of Clear that is between optional and mandatory: use of a fully automated regression test harness and test suites for unit and acceptance tests. It gets the question mark (?) symbol.

1. **? There are no automated test suites.** Many systems have successfully shipped without automatic test suites. Really successful people, on the other hand, repeatedly say that the test suites give them speed and comfort in improving and debugging the system, and are high on their priority list. These days, speed in altering code is dependent on having automated test suites available, and more teams are using test-driven development (Beck 2003) to do even better.

   Teams using automated tests find they can update the design of the code with great freedom: They retest their work at the push of a button, discovering whether they introduced a new bug. Avoiding introducing new bugs when removing old ones is one of the best ways to improve and shorten project delivery times.

   Without regression testing, making changes to the system becomes tedious and unreliable, unreliable enough that one of two bad things happen: the team makes the change and introduces new errors, or they don't make the change, and allows the code to grow unnaturally complex ("crufty" is a word often used for such code).

   Why is automated regression testing optional in Crystal Clear if it is so great?

The answer is that automated regression tests are not actually required to have a project success. It makes the team's life easier and it makes the code more malleable, but I have seen and participated in many projects that succeeded without using fully automated regression test suites.

Since Crystal Clear is proposed as a high-tolerance methodology, I have to leave automated regression testing as optional. At a personal level, I can say that the best programmers I have met use them, and recommend them highly . . . but not using them does not mean the project will fail, and so is not a basis for saying a group is not using Crystal Clear.

So there you have it. What it takes to be safely inside Clear, what you can vary, and what it takes to be outside.

Whew, I'm exhausted! How much more do you want from me?

Crystal

Dear Crystal,

   I promise this is the last question—refresh for me what Crystal Clear is trying to be and why it works?

   Alistair

June 10: Dear Alistair,

   Summarizing . . .

   Crystal Clear aims to be a simple and tolerant set of rules that puts the project into the safety zone. It is, if you will, *the least methodology that could possibly work*, because it contains so much tolerance.

The entire Crystal family has been described as consisting of

♦ Frequent Deliveries
♦ Reflective Improvement
♦ Close Communication

Crystal Clear pushes that last one up to Osmotic Communication.

Core to all of the Crystal family are a couple of ideas. One is that intermediate work products and "promissory notes" such as detailed requirements documents, design documents, and project plans might not be eliminated, but they can be reduced to the extent that

♦ Short, rich, informal communication paths are available to the team.
♦ Working, tested software is delivered early and frequently.

Another is that the amount of detail needed in the requirements, design, and planning documents varies with the project circumstances, specifically

♦ The extent of damage that might be caused by undetected defects
♦ The frequency of personal collaboration

Finally, the team reflects and adjusts its working conventions on the fly to fit

♦ The personalities on the team
♦ The local working environment
♦ The current assignment

The reason Crystal Clear works is that the people involved are professionals led by someone who is supposed to be a Level-3 developer. With rich, low-cost communications between them, the team members will diagnose most of their own problems. If they are given access to users and deliver running code every month or two, they get feedback on what they are doing. If they are not interrupted too often, they will make progress. In other words, the project is likely to work.

Note that Crystal Clear does not aim be the most productive, rigorous, or scalable methodology in addition to its goal of being simple, tolerant, and successful. People are welcome to adopt more disciplined development habits as they choose, including a full-time user, pair programming, test-driven development, and fully automated regression tests.

They are, however, unlikely to be able to drop any of the rules of Crystal Clear and still be safe.

Crystal Clear comes with an important truth-in-advertising clause: Eight people or less, collocated, not a life-critical system. Distributed teams need other forms of communication, larger teams need more coordination, and teams working on life-critical systems need more verification procedures in place. Those teams will have to find another methodology, or tune Crystal Clear upward to fit their needs.

I think this closes off our discussion.
Best wishes,
Crystal

Chapter 2

Applied (The Seven Properties)

Reading how Crystal Clear works raises two particular questions:

"What are these people concentrating on while they work?"
"Can we get farther into the safety zone?"

This chapter describes seven properties set up by the best teams. Crystal Clear requires the first three. Better teams use the other four properties to get farther into the safety zone. All of the properties aside from Osmotic Communication apply to projects of all sizes.

I only recently awoke to the realization that top consultants trade notes about the *properties* of a project rather than on the procedures followed. They inquire after the health of the project: Is there a mission statement and a project plan? Do they deliver frequently? Are the sponsor and various expert users in close contact with the team?

Consequently, and in a departure from the way in which a methodology is usually described, I ask Crystal Clear teams to target key properties for the project. "Doing Crystal Clear" becomes achieving the properties rather than following procedures. Two motives drive this shift from procedures to properties:

◆ The procedures may not produce the properties. Of the two, the properties are the more important.

◆ Other procedures than the ones I choose may produce the properties for your particular team.

The Crystal family focuses on the three properties *Frequent Delivery, Close Communication,* and *Reflective Improvement*[1] because they should be found on all projects. Crystal Clear takes advantage of small team size and proximity to strengthen close communication into the more powerful osmotic communication. Aside from that one shift, experienced developers will notice that all the properties I outline in this chapter apply to every project, not just small-team projects.

By describing Crystal Clear as a set of properties, I hope to reach into the *feeling* of the project. Most methodology descriptions miss the critical feeling that separates a successful team from an unsuccessful one. The Crystal Clear team measures its condition by the team's mood and the communication patterns as much as by the rate of delivery. Naming the properties also provides the team with catch phrases to measure their situation by: "We haven't done any reflective improvement for a while." "Can we get more easy access to expert users?" The property names themselves help people diagnose and discuss ways to fix their current situation.

---

[1] Thanks to Jens Coldewey of Germany for pointing this out to me!

PROPERTY 1.   FREQUENT DELIVERY

The single most important property of any project, large or small, agile or not, is that of delivering running, tested code to real users every few months. The advantages are so numerous that it is astonishing that any team doesn't do it:

◆ The sponsors get critical feedback on the rate of progress of the team.

◆ Users get a chance to discover whether their original request was for what they actually need and to get their discoveries fed back into development.

◆ Developers keep their focus, breaking deadlocks of indecision.

◆ The team gets to debug their development and deployment processes and gets a morale boost through accomplishments.

All of these advantages come from one single property: frequent delivery. In my interviews, I have not seen any period longer than four months that still offers this safety. Two months is safer. Teams deploying to the Web may deliver weekly.

Have you delivered running, tested, and usable code
at least twice to your user community in the last six months?

*   *   *

Just what does "delivery" mean?

Sometimes it means that the software is deployed to the full set of users at the end of each iteration for production use. This may be practical with Web-deployed software or when the user group is relatively small.

When the users cannot accept software updates that often, the team finds itself in a quandary. If they deliver the system frequently, the user community will get annoyed with them. If they don't deliver frequently, they may miss a real problem with integration or deployment. They will encounter that problem when it is very late, that is, at the moment of deploying the system.

The best strategy I know of in this situation is to find a friendly user who doesn't mind trying out the software, either as a courtesy or out of curiosity. Deploy to that one workstation, for *trial* (not production) usage. This allows the team to practice deployment and get useful feedback from at least one user.

If you cannot find a friendly user to deliver to, at least perform a full integration and test as though you were going to. This leaves only deployment with a potential flaw.

*   *   *

The terms *integration, iteration, user viewing,* and *release* get mixed together these days. They have different effects on development and should be considered separately.

Frequent integration should be the norm, happening every hour, every day, or, at the worst, every week. The better teams these days have continuously running automated build-and-test scripts, so there is never more than 30 minutes from a check-in until the automated test results are posted.

Simply performing a system integration doesn't constitute an *iteration,* since an integration is often performed after any single person or subteam completes as a fragment of a programming assignment. The term *iteration* refers to the team completing a section of work, integrating the system, reporting the outcome up the management chain, doing their periodic reflective improvement (I wish), and, very importantly, getting emotional closure on having completed the work. The closure following an iteration is important because it sets up an emotional rhythm, something that is important to us as human beings.

In principle, an iteration can be anywhere from an hour to three months. In practice, they are usually two weeks to two months long.

The end date of an iteration is usually considered immovable, a practice called "time boxing." People encounter a natural temptation to extend an iteration when the team falls behind. This has generally shown itself to be a bad strategy, as it leads to longer and longer extensions to the iteration, jeopardizing the schedule and demotivating the team. Many well-intentioned managers damage a team by extending the iteration indefinitely, robbing the team of the joy and celebration around completion.

A better strategy is to fix the end date and have the team deliver whatever they have completed at the end of the time box. With this strategy, the team learns what it can complete in that amount of time, useful feedback to the project plan. It also supplies the team with an early victory.

Fixed-length iterations allow the team to measure their speed of movement—the project's *velocity*. Fixed lengths iterations give that rhythm to the project that people describe as the project's "heartbeat."

Some people lock the requirements during an iteration or time box. This gives the team peace of mind while they develop, assuring them they will not have to change directions, but can complete *something* at least. I once encountered a group trying out XP where the customer didn't want the trial to succeed. This customer changed the requirements priorities every few days so that after several iterations the team still had not managed to complete any one user story. In such hostile environments, both the requirements locking and the peace-of-mind are critical. Requirements locking is rarely needed in well-behaved environments.

The results of an iteration may or may not get released. Just how often the software should be sent out to real users is a topic for the whole team, including the sponsor, to deliberate. They may find it practical to deliver after every iteration, they may deliver every few iterations, or they may match deliveries to specific calendar dates.

Frequent delivery is about delivering the software to users, not merely iterating. One nervous project team I visited had been iterating monthly for almost a year, but not yet delivered any release. The people were getting pretty nervous, because *the customer hadn't seen what they had been working on for the last year!* This constitutes a violation of frequent delivery.

If the team cannot deliver the system to the full user base every few months, *user viewings* become all the more critical. The team needs to arrange for users to visit the team and see the software in action, or at least one user to install and test the software. Failure to hold these user viewings easily correlates to end failure of the project, when the users finally, and too late, identify that the software does not meet their needs.

For the best effect, exercise both packaging and deployment. Install the system in as close to a real situation as possible.

PROPERTY 2.   REFLECTIVE IMPROVEMENT

The discovery that took me completely by surprise was that a project can reverse its fortunes from catastrophic failure to success if the team will get together, list what both is and isn't working, discuss what might work better, *and make those changes* in the next iteration. In other words, reflect and improve. The team does not have to spend a great deal of time doing this work—an hour every few weeks or month will do. Just the fact of taking time out of the helter-skelter of daily development to think about what could work better is already effective.

*Did you get together at least once within the last three months
for a half hour, hour, or half day to compare notes, reflect,
discuss your group's working habits, and discover what speeds you up,
what slows you down, and what you might be able to improve?*

*   *   *   *

The project that gave me the surprise was *Project Ingrid* (described in *Surviving Object-Oriented Projects* (Cockburn 1998)). At the end of the first iteration—which was supposed to be four months long, but they had extended—they were far behind schedule, demoralized, and with what they recognized as an unacceptable design. It was what they did next that surprised me: They released twenty-three of the twenty-four client-side programmers to go back to their old jobs, hired twenty-three new people, changed the team and management structures, paid for several weeks of programmer training, and started over, requiring the new group to redo the work of the first team and make additional progress.

At the end of the second iteration, they again were behind schedule but had a design that would hold, and the team structure and programmers were functioning. They held another reflection workshop, made additional changes, and continued.

When I interviewed them, they were in their fourth iteration, ahead of schedule and content with their design and their work practices.

Since that interview, I have noticed that most of the projects I have visited got off to a rough start or encountered a catastrophe early on. This is so common that I have come to expect, almost even welcome it: from that first catastrophe come all sorts of new and important information about the project's working environment, which would be deadly, but hidden.

On *Project Winifred* we managed at the end of the first three-month delivery cycle what I called a "bubble-gum" release (the system was just barely held together by the software equivalent of bubble-gum). However, we delivered something every three months, getting better and better each time until we finally delivered the contracted function on time.

After each delivery, a few of us got together. We identified what wasn't working and discussed ways to fix it. We kept trying new strategies until we found ones that worked. Frequent delivery and reflective improvement became critical success factors to us as they are to so many projects.

*   *   *

The people, the technology, and the assignment change over the course of a project. The conventions the team uses need to change to match.

The people on the team are the best equipped to say what is best suited to their situation, which is why Crystal Clear leaves so many details unstated, but for the team to finalize. The reflective improvement mechanism allows them to make those adjustments.

Every few weeks, once a month, or twice per delivery cycle, the people get together in a reflection workshop or iteration retrospective to discuss how things are working. They note the conventions they will keep and the ones they want to alter for the next period, *and they post those two lists prominently for the team members to see while working in the next iteration.*

Whatever the frequency, meeting format, and technique used, successful teams hold this discussion periodically and try out new ideas. Teams may try, in various forms: pair programming, unit testing, test-driven-development, single-room versus multiple room seating, various levels of customer involvement, and even differing iteration lengths. These are all proper variations within Crystal Clear.

For people to say they are using Crystal Clear, it is not necessary that they continue to use the starter conventions. In fact, it is expected that they will try new ideas. In a Crystal user group meeting, people discuss what they had experimented with, how they felt about those experiments, and how they evolved their working conventions. One team may report moving the meetings from every two weeks to every month, another moving from the format I describe in Chapter 3 to a straight discussion of people's values while developing.

I like to use the reflection workshop described in Chapter 3. Norm Kerth's (2001) book, *Project Retrospectives*, presents an extended format, along with many activities to try within the workshop. The specifics of the workshop format aren't nearly as significant as the fact that the team is holding one.

PROPERTY 3.   OSMOTIC COMMUNICATION

Osmotic communication means that information flows into the background hearing of members of the team, so that they pick up relevant information as though by osmosis. This is normally accomplished by seating them in the same room. Then, when one person asks a question, others in the room can either tune in or tune out, contributing to the discussion or continuing with their work. Several people have related their experience of it much as this person did:

> We had four people doing pair programming. The boss walked in and asked my partner a question. I started answering it, but gave the wrong name of a module. Nancy, programming with Neil, corrected me, without Neil ever noticing that she had spoken or that a question had been asked.

When osmotic communication is in place, questions and answers flow naturally and with surprisingly little disturbance among the team.

Osmotic communication and frequent delivery facilitate such rapid and rich feedback that the project can operate with very little other structure.

Does it take you 30 seconds or less to get your question to the eyes or ears of the person who might have the answer? Do you overhear something relevant from a conversation among other team members at least every few days?

*   *   *

Osmotic communication is the more powerful version that small projects can attain of close communication, a property core to the entire Crystal family. Osmotic communication makes the cost of communications low and the feedback rate high, so that errors are corrected extremely quickly and knowledge is disseminated quickly. People learn the project priorities and who holds what information. They pick up new programming, design, testing, and tool handling tricks. They catch and correct small errors before they grow into larger ones.

Although osmotic communication is valuable for larger projects, it is, of course, increasingly difficult to attain as the team size grows.

It is hard to simulate osmotic communication without having the people in the same room; however, adjacent rooms with two or three people in each confers many of the benefits. Herring (2001) reported the use of high-speed intranet with Web cameras, microphones, and chat sessions to trade questions and code, to simulate the single room to (some) extent. With good technology, teams can achieve some approximation of close communication for some purposes, but I have yet to see osmotic communication achieved with other than physical proximity between team members.

*   *   *

Discussion of osmotic communication inevitably leads to discussion about office lay-out and office furniture.

Crystal Clear needs people to be very close to each other so that they overhear useful information and get questions answered quickly. The obvious way to do this is to put everyone into a single room ("war room"; see Figure 2-1), repeatedly shown as being very effective (Olson 2000).

Many people who have private offices resist moving into a group space. However, you can sometimes turn lemons into lemonade (so to speak) with this move:

> Lise was informed by her management that her department would have to reduce the number of square feet they used. This meant giving up private offices. She suggested that her people work together and design their own office spaces, three to five people in a combined area. The groups put fewer square feet around each work table so they could allocate space for additional areas with chairs, a sofa, or, in some cases, their own meeting rooms.

Figures 2-2 and 2-3 show what one group came up with. Note that although they had fewer square feet per person than before, they ended up with longer sight lines and a conversation area with soft chairs.

Figure 2-4 shows the small meeting room one group put on the side of their shared office. They used it to talk without disturbing whoever was still programming, and also to leave their design notes and plans up on the wall.

Figure 2-1   *Osmotic communication. (Courtesy of Tomax)*

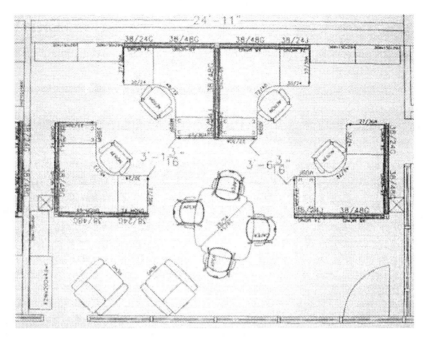

Figure 2-2   *Floor plan. (Courtesy of Schlumberger)*

Figure 2-3   *Photo of same office. (Courtesy of Schlumberger)*

Figure 2-4   *Group work room attached to shared office. (Courtesy of Schlumberger)*

Lise's group used the usual office furniture: concave, designed to have the fat CRT back into the corner. This sort of table presents a disadvantage to an agile development team, because it is hard for a second or third person to see the screen. The war room in Figure 2-1 may look less glamorous, but there is a utility in those ugly tables: People can congregate around a screen; pairs of people can work together easily. It is for this reason that agile development teams prefer straight tables, or even better, tables that bulge outward toward the typist.

If you set up a war room work area, be sure to arrange another place for people to go to unwind and do their private e-mail. This allows people to focus when they step into the common area and find a bit of relief from the pressure by stepping out. Such an arrangement is referred to as a "caves and common" arrangement.

One project team got permission to set up a common discussion area with soft chairs and sofa (Figure 2-5). On the wall in front of the chairs is the ever-present whiteboard with whiteboard capture device. This is where the team adjourned to hold their group design discussions, iteration planning meetings, and reflection workshops.

Agile Software Development (Cockburn 2002) contains additional information on "convection currents" of information flow within a group, osmotic communication, the value of colocation, and examples of office layout.

*   *   *

Figure 2-5   *Group discussion area. (Courtesy of Darin Cummins and ADP's Dealer Services)*

Osmotic communication generates its own hazards, most commonly noise and a flow of questions to the team's most expert developer. People usually self-regulate here and request less idle chit-chat or more respect for think time.

Attempting to "protect" the lead designer with a private office usually backfires. That person really needs to be sitting in the middle of the development team. The lead designer is often the technology expert, a domain expert, and the best programmer, and so is necessarily in high demand. When she is taken away, the younger developers miss the chance to develop good development habits, miss growing in the domain and the technology, and make mistakes that otherwise would get caught very quickly. The cost to the project ends up being greater than the benefit of quiet time to the lead designer. Having the lead designer in the same room as the rest of the team is a strategy called *Expert in Earshot* (Cockburn url eie), a special use of osmotic communication. (Andrews url) has a blog entry about creating such a seating arrangement accommodating twenty people.

Even the best success property is unsuitable under certain circumstances. Osmotic communication is no exception. If the lead designer gets so overloaded and so frequently interrupted as to be unable to make progress on anything, the lead designer needs a workplace with no interruptions at all and extremely limited communications with the team, a *Cone of Silence,* I call it. Many lead designers use the hours from 6:00 P.M. to 2:00 A.M. as their cone of silence, but it is better for all involved if an acceptable cone of silence can be set up within normal working hours. The cone of silence strategy is described in detail in (Cockburn 2003b).

PROPERTY 4.   PERSONAL SAFETY

Personal safety is being able to speak when something is bothering you, without fear of reprisal. It may involve telling the manager that the schedule is unrealistic, a colleague that her design needs improvement, or even letting a colleague know that she needs to take a shower more often. Personal safety is important, because with it the team can discover and repair its weaknesses. Without it, people won't speak up, and the weaknesses will continue to damage the team.

Personal safety is an early step toward **trust**. Trust, which involves giving someone else power over oneself, with accompanying risk of personal damage, is the extent to which one is comfortable with handing that person the power. Some people trust others by default, and wait to be hurt before withdrawing the trust. Others are disinclined to trust others, and wait until they see evidence that they won't be hurt before they give the trust. Presence of trust is positively correlated with team performance (Costa 2002).

The different ways in which one can be hurt lead to different forms of trust and distrust (Mishra 1996). A person lacking open honesty might lie or conceal. One who lacks congruence in actions will be inconsistent. A person lacking either competence or reliability will fail to complete assignments. A person lacking concern for others may act to damage them, including giving away sensitive information.

Accepting exposure to these varied potential damages is using different forms of trust. It is neither realistic nor necessary to ask everyone on a project to trust each other in all forms. It is important that people can speak and act freely—they need to trust each other with respect to damaging actions and betrayal.

When there is no evidence of betrayal or damage, people will reveal information more freely, which will speed the project. Therefore, personal safety is the critical property to attain.

> *Can you tell your boss you mis-estimated by more than 50 percent,*
> *or that you just received a tempting job offer? Can you disagree*
> *with your boss about the schedule in a team meeting? Can people*
> *end long debates about each other's designs with friendly disagreement?*

*   *   *

Establishing trust involves being in a situation where one of those dangers is present and seeing that the other people do not hurt you. In other words, to build trust, there must be exposure.

Three particular exposures are relevant in software development:

◆ Revealing one's ignorance
◆ Revealing a mistake
◆ Revealing one's incapability on an assignment

Skillful leaders expose their team members (and themselves!) to these situations early, and then demonstrate with speed and authenticity that not only will damage not accrue, but also that the leader and the team as a whole will act to support the person.

> One project leader[2] told me that when a new person joined her team, she would visit that person privately to discuss his work and progress, and wait for the inevitable moment when he had to admit he hadn't done or didn't know something.
>
> This was the crucial moment to her, because until he revealed a weakness, she couldn't demonstrate to him that she would cover for him or get him assistance. She knew she was not going to get both reliable information and full cooperation from him until he understood properly that when he revealed a weakness or mistake, he would actually get assistance. She said that some people got the message after her first visit, while others needed several demonstrations before opening up.

Another project leader told of building cohesion and safety in the team by having the group work together to solve a difficult problem they were facing. In solving the problem together, they learned several things:

◆ First, they wouldn't get hurt if they admitted ignorance, even in their own area.
◆ Second, they learned how to interpret each other's mannerisms as nonthreatening, even in heavy argument.
◆ Finally, they learned that together they could solve things they couldn't solve alone.

Trust is enhanced with frequent delivery. When the software is delivered, people recognize who did their share of the work and who shirked, who told the truth, who damaged or protected whom, and who, despite their superficial manners, could be trusted along which dimensions. With personal safety, they speak from their heart during the reflective improvement sessions.

*   *   *

---

2   Thanks to Victoria Einarsson in Sweden.

Personal safety goes hand in hand with *amicability*, the willingness to listen with goodwill. The project suffers when any one person on the team stops listening with goodwill, or loses the inclination to pass along possibly important information. In addition to personal skill, a project's forward progress relies only on the speed of movement of information across people ("meme-meters per minute," if you will).

Usually one person on the team sets the lead in amicability. On a larger project, it is often crucially the project manager. On a Crystal Clear project, it can be anyone on the team. Unless there is a specific reason countering it, amicability spreads quickly and makes the team more comfortable in exchanging information quickly. Personal safety and amicability together help lead to collaboration across organizational boundaries, the establishment of global lifelines for the project. I set amicability as significant management element on a project, partly as evidence for personal safety.

Once personal safety and amicability are established, a useful, playful dynamic may emerge. People may wage competition with each other. They may argue loudly, even to the verge of fighting, without taking it personally. In the case where someone does take it personally, they sort it out and set things straight again.

Be careful, though, not to confuse personal safety with politeness. Some teams appear to have personal safety in place, but actually are just being polite because they are unwilling to show disagreement.[3] Covering their disagreements with politeness and conciliation, they don't detect and repair mistakes that are present. This damages the project in the end, as in the case of overamicability described in *Agile Software Development* (Cockburn 2002, p. 101).

There is a fair amount of literature on the subject of trust, some of which you may find applicable to your situation. Read more in Hohmann (1997), Kramer (1996), Costa (2002), and Adams (2002).

---

[3]   Thanks to Kay Johanssen for this distinction.

PROPERTY 5.   FOCUS

Focus is first knowing what to work on, and then having time and peace of mind to work on it. Knowing what to work on comes from communication about goal direction and priorities, typically from the executive sponsor. Time and peace of mind come from an environment where people are not taken away from their task to work on other, incompatible things.

> *Do all the people know what their top two priority items to work on are?*
> *Are they guaranteed at least two days in a row and two uninterrupted*
> *hours each day to work on them?*

*   *   *

Even with the best of intentions, developers will work on things that only randomly bring business value if they are not told what will provide business value. It is the job of the executive sponsor, starting from the project chartering activity and running continuously throughout the project, to make it clear to everyone where the organization's priorities lie.

The vice president of a fifty-person company sat down one night, prioritized the seventy pending company initiatives, and announced the results to her managers the following day. She went around to each developer individually and made sure they each knew the top two items for them.

One lead designer I met kept the project's mission statement and priorities posted on the wall and referred to them regularly.

Just knowing what is important isn't enough. Developers regularly report that meetings, requests to give demos, and demands to fix run-time bugs keep them from completing their work. It quite typically takes a person about twenty minutes and considerable mental energy to regain her train of thought after one of these interruptions. When the interruptions happen three or four times a day, it is not uncommon for the person to simply idle between interruptions, feeling that it is not worth the energy to get deeply into a train of thought when the next distraction will just show up in the middle of it.

People asked to work on two or three projects at the same time regularly report that they are unable to make progress on any one project. It seems to take an hour and a half for a person to regain the train of thought after working on a different project.

Among the experienced project managers that I interview, the consensus is that about one and one-half projects is the most that a person can be on and stay effective. By the time a third project is added, the developer becomes ineffective on all three.

Contrast this with the inexperienced managers who, underestimating the cost of switching between projects, assign developers to work on three to five projects at the same time. I encountered one developer assigned to seventeen projects simultaneously! You can imagine that he barely had time to report at the various meetings his ongoing lack of progress on all fronts.

The repair is simple, though uncomfortable. The sponsor makes it clear which projects and work items are top priority for each person, and arranges for the top two items to be distinctly higher in priority than all the rest.

The team should then adopt conventions that provide focus time for the team members. One such convention is that once a person starts working on a project, that person is guaranteed at least two full days before having to switch to a second project. This allows for some project switching, while guaranteeing the person enough time to make actual progress instead of using all the time just to get back up to speed on each project before leaving it again.

The next convention to adopt may be to localize distracting interruptions. My experience is that it is generally impractical to bottle up interruptions to something so neat and tidy as "mornings only" or "between 1 and 3 in the afternoon." It is in the nature of interruptions to come sporadically and with high priority. What the team can do is to create a two-hour time window during which interruptions are blocked. There are very few interruptions that can't wait for two hours. Some teams use from 10:00 to noon as a time when meetings, phone calls, and demos are not allowed.

With two hours of guaranteed focus time each day, and two days in a row on the same project, a developer who otherwise is being driven to distraction may get four full hours of work done in a week. One developer who adopted these reported after a few weeks that he had gotten more done in those few weeks than in the several months before that.

PROPERTY 6.   EASY ACCESS TO EXPERT USERS

Continued access to expert user(s) provides the team with

- ◆ A place to deploy and test the frequent deliveries
- ◆ Rapid feedback on the quality of their finished product
- ◆ Rapid feedback on their design decisions
- ◆ Up-to-date requirements

Researchers Keil and Carmel published results showing how critical it is to have direct links to expert users (Keil 1995). Surveying managers who had worked both with and without easy access to real users, they write

> . . . in 11 of the 14 paired cases, the more successful project involved a greater number of links than the less successful project. . . . This difference was found to be statistically significant in a paired t-test ($p < 0.01$).

Their research led them to a specific recommendation: "Reduce Reliance on Indirect Links." In other words, get real access to real users.

Does it take less than three days, on the average, from the time you come up with a question about system usage to when an expert user answers the question? Can you get the answer in a few hours?

*   *   *

All very nice, but how many users, and how much time?

Even one hour a week of access to a real and expert user is immensely valuable. The more hours each week that an expert user is available to a team, the more advantage they can take of that proximity. The first hour, however, is the most crucial.

The other thing that is important is the length of time until a question gets answered. If a question won't be answered for another three days, the programmers are likely to put into the code their best current guess, and may forget to recheck their decision when they are with the users again. Therefore, they should have telephone access to the expert user during the week.

Here are the three user access methods I hear about most often:

- ◆ *Weekly or semiweekly user meetings with additional phone calls.* You may find that the user loads the team with information in the first weeks. Over time, the developers need less time from the user(s), as they develop code. Eventually, a natural rhythm forms, as the user provides new requirements information and also reviews draft software. This natural rhythm might involve one, two, or three hours a week per expert user. If you add a few phone calls during the week, then questions get answered quickly enough to keep the development team from going off in a false direction.

◆ *One or more experienced users directly on the development team.* This is only rarely possible, but don't discount it. I periodically find a team located inside the user community or is in some way collocated with an expert user.

◆ *Send the developers to become trainee users for a period.* Odd though this may sound, some development teams send the developers to either shadow users or become apprentice users themselves. While I don't have a very large base of stories to draw from, I have not yet heard a negative story related to using this strategy. The developers return with a respect for the users and an appreciation for the way their new software can change the working lives of the users.

Keil and Carmel name additional user links, including facilitated teams, user-interface prototyping, interviews, tests, bulletin boards, usability labs, observational study, and focus groups. In a quick search on the Internet, I turned up a number of companies that specialize in finding subjects and testing software with real users.

I distinguish between the *expert user* and the *business expert,* because they are often different people. The business expert knows the business policies, including which are fixed, which are likely to change, and the dependencies between them. Users generally don't know this information. On the other hand, the expert user knows which operations are common and which are rare, what shortcuts are needed, what information doesn't really have to be entered, and what information needs to be visible at the same time. The business expert won't know this information, since it comes only from continuous daily operation.

The development team will contain a business expert (see Roles in Chapter 5). That person may be the sponsor, or the expert user, or it may be the lead designer. Such a person is almost always available to a project, and so I don't fuss about it so much. The expert user, on the other hand, is usually missing, to the detriment of the project, which is why I fuss about it so much here. Easy access to expert users provides a safety net for the team, as well as being a competitive advantage. It is likely to be a critical success factor for a small team.

*   *   *

"Okay, we've got the users—now what do we do with them?"

You need to know what they want, what their sponsors are willing to pay for, where their fast and rare-but-significant usage patterns lie, whether you have overlooked something critical. You need the users before, during, and after design.

Before you get too far into designing the system, you need to identify the user roles that the sponsors consider the most important people to fit the application. These are the *focal roles*. The system will present different "personalities" (e.g., fast and efficient or warm and friendly) to each different role. The designers will accentuate one personality over others, and you want to make sure they accentuate the most important one(s).

The technique described in a section of the next chapter, Essential Interaction Design, is one way to identify the focal roles and personalities to develop. The attraction of this workshop technique is that you can gather the information in just a few days.

During design, you will need answers to many small questions. For this you need easy access to expert users on an ongoing basis as described in this section.

After design, when you think you are done, you need users again, to evaluate your results. If the system will go to a few, local users, simply invite them in for a test drive. If, on the other hand, you have a large number of geographically dispersed users, then the cost of evaluation is greater. I don't know of any special efficiencies for this situation. Techniques for usability evaluation have been described for decades (customer focus groups and usability samples being the prime examples).

Before I leave this property, I ask you to read again the last paragraphs of the frequent delivery, in which I describe the troubles arising from not arranging for *real* user feedback. Even teams that do every other practice in agile development find themselves facing catastrophic bad news at the end of the project if they neglect such feedback during the project.

PROPERTY 7. TECHNICAL ENVIRONMENT WITH AUTOMATED TESTS, CONFIGURATION MANAGEMENT, AND FREQUENT INTEGRATION

The elements I highlight in this property are such well-established core elements that it is embarrassing to have to mention them at all. Let us consider them one at a time and all together.

Automated Testing. Teams do deliver successfully using manual tests, so this can't be considered a *critical* success factor. However, every programmer I've interviewed who once moved to automated tests swore *never to work without them again*. I find this nothing short of astonishing.

Their reason has to do with improved quality of life. During the week, they revise sections of code knowing they can quickly check that they hadn't inadvertently broken something along the way. When they get code working on Friday, they go home knowing that they will be able on Monday to detect whether anyone had broken it over the weekend—they simply rerun the tests on Monday morning. The tests give them freedom of movement during the day and peace of mind at night.

Configuration Management. The configuration management system allows people to check in their work asynchronously, back changes out, wrap up a particular configuration for release, and roll back to that configuration later on when trouble arises. It lets the developers develop their code both *separately* and *together*. It is steadily cited by teams as their most critical noncompiler tool.

Frequent Integration. Many teams integrate the system multiple times a day. If they can't manage that, they do it daily, or, in the worst case, every other day. The more frequently they integrate, the more quickly they detect mistakes, the fewer additional errors that pile up, the fresher their thoughts, and the smaller the region of code that has to be searched for the miscommunication.

The best teams combine all three into **continuous integration-with-test.** They catch integration-level errors within minutes.

Can you run the system tests to completion without having to be physically present?
Do all your developers check their code into the configuration management system?
Do they put in a useful note about it as they check it in?
Is the system integrated at least twice a week?

*　　　*　　　*

How frequent should frequent integration be? There is no fixed answer to this any more than to the question of how long a development iteration should be.

One lead designer reported to me that he was unable to convince anyone on his team to run the build more than three times a week. While he did not find this comfortable, it worked for that project. The team used one-month-long iterations, had osmotic communications, reflective improvement, configuration management, and some automated testing in place. Having those properties in place made the frequency of their frequent integration less critical.

The most advanced teams use a build-and-test machine such as Cruise Control[4] to integrate and test nonstop (note: having this machine running is not yet sufficient . . . the developers have to actually check in their code to the main line code base multiple times a day!). The machine posts the test results to a Web page that team members leave open on their screens at all times. One internationally distributed development team (obviously not using Crystal Clear!) reports that this use of Cruise Control allows the developers to keep abreast of the changing code base, which to some extent mitigates their being in different time zones.

Experiment with different integration frequency, and find the pace that works for your team. Include this topic as part of your reflective improvement. For more on configuration management, I refer you to *Configuration Management Principles and Practice* (Hass 2003) *Configuration Management Patterns* (Berczuk 2003), and *Pragmatic Version Control using CVS* by the Pragmatic Programmers (Thomas 2003). You may need to hire a consultant to come in for a few days, help set up the configuration management system, and tutor the team on how to use it.

*   *   *

Automated testing means that the person can start the tests running, go away, not having to intervene in or look at the screens, and then come back to find the test results waiting. No human eyes and no fingers are needed in the process. Each person's test suites can be combined into a very large one that can, if needed, be run over the weekend (still needing no human eyes or fingers).

Three questions immediately arise about automated testing:

◆ At what level should they be written?
◆ How automated do they have to be?
◆ How quickly should they run?

---

[4]   http://cruisecontrol.sourceforge.net/

Besides *usability tests,* which are best performed by people outside the project,[5] I find three levels of tests hotly discussed:

◆ *Customer-oriented acceptance tests running in front of the GUI* and relying on mouse and keyboard movements

◆ *Customer-oriented acceptance tests running just behind the GUI,* testing the actions of the system without needing a mouse or keyboard simulator

◆ *Programmer-oriented function, class, and module tests* (commonly called unit tests)

The automated tests that my interviewees are so enthusiastic over are from the latter two of those categories. Automating unit tests allow the programmers to check that their code hasn't accidentally broken out from under them while they are adding new code or improving old code (*refactoring*). The GUI-less acceptance tests do the same for the integrated system, and are stable over many changes in the system's internal design. Although GUI-less acceptance tests are highly recommended, I rarely find teams using them, for the reason that they require the system architecture to carefully separate the GUI from the function. This is a separation that has been recommended for decades, but few teams manage.

Automated GUI-driven system tests are not in the highly recommended short list because they are costly to automate and must be rebuilt with every change of the GUI. This difficulty makes it all the more important that the development team creates an architecture that supports GUI-less acceptance tests.

A programmer's unit tests need to execute in seconds, not minutes. Running that fast, the programmer will not lose her concentration while they run, which means that the tests are actually run as the programmer works. If the tests take several minutes to run, she is unlikely to rerun the tests after typing in just a few lines of new code or moving two lines of code to a new function or class.

Tests may take longer when the code is checked into the configuration management system. At this point, the programmer has completed a sequence of design actions, and can afford to walk away for a few minutes while the tests run.

The acceptance tests can take a long time to run, if needed. I write this sentence advisedly: The reason the tests run a long time should be because there are so many tests or there is a complicated timing sequence involved, not because the test harness is sloppy. Once again, if the tests run quickly, they will get run more often. For some systems, though, the acceptance tests do need to run over the weekend.

---

[5] Google even has a category for it: Computers > Human-Computer Interaction > Companies and Consultants > Usability Testing.

Crystal Clear does not mandate when the tests get written. Traditionally, programmers and testers write the tests after the code is written. Also traditionally, they don't have much energy to write tests after they write code. Partially for this reason, more and more developers are adopting test-driven development (Beck 2003).

The best way I know to get started with automated testing is to download a language-specific copy of the *X-unit* test framework (where *X* is replaced by the language name), invented by Kent Beck. There is *JUnit* for Java programmers, *CppUnit* for C++ programmers, and so on for Visual Basic, Scheme, C, and even PHP. Then get one of the books on test-driven development (Beck 2003, Astels 2003) and work through the examples. A Web search will turn up more resources on *X-unit*.

Both *httpUnit* and Ward Cunningham's FIT (Framework for Integrated Tests) help with GUI-less acceptance tests. The former is for testing HTML streams of Web-based systems, the latter to allow the business expert to create her own test suites without needing to know about programming. Robert Martin integrated FIT with Ward's Wiki technology to create FITnesse.[6] Many teams use spreadsheets to allow the business experts to easily type in scenario data for these system-function tests.

There are, sadly, no good books on designing the system for easy GUI-less acceptance testing. The Mac made the idea of scriptable interfaces mainstream for a short while (Simone url) and scripting is standard with Microsoft Office. In general, however, the practice has submerged and is used by a relatively small number of outstanding developers. The few people I know who could write these books are too busy programming.

*   *   *

I end this section with a small testimonial to test-driven development that I hope will sway one or two readers. Thanks to David Brady for this note:

> Yesterday I wrote a function that takes a variable argument, like printf(). That function decomposes the list arguments, and drops the whole mess onto a function pointer. The pointer points to a function on either the console message sink object or a kernel-side memory buffer message sink object. (This is just basic inheritance, but it's all gooky because I'm writing it in C.)
>
> Anyway, in the past I would expect a problem of that complexity to stall me for an indefinite amount of time while I tried to debug all the bizarre and fascinating things that can go wrong with a setup like that.

---

[6]   http://fit.c2.com and http://fitnesse.org respectively.

It took me less than an hour to write the test and the code using test-first.

My test was pretty simple, but coming up with it was probably the hardest part of the whole process. I finally decided that if my function returned the correct number of characters written (same as printf), that I would infer that the function was working.

With the test in place, I had an incredible amount of focus. I knew what I had to make the code do, and there was no need to wander around aimlessly in the code trying to support every possible case. No, it was just "get this test to run." When I had the test running, I was surprised to realize that I was indeed finished. There wasn't anything extra to add; I was actually done!

I usually cut 350–400 lines of production-grade code on a good day. Yesterday I didn't feel like I had a particularly good day, but I cut 184 test LOC and 529 production LOC, pLOC that I *know* works, because the tests tell me so, pLOC that includes one of the top-10 trickiest things I've ever done in C (that went from "no idea" to "fully functional" in under 60 minutes).

Wow. I'm sold.

Test infection. Give it a warm, damp place to start, and it'll do the rest. . . .

David Brady

EVIDENCE: COLLABORATION ACROSS ORGANIZATIONAL BOUNDARIES

There is a side-effect from attending to personal safety, amicability within the team, and easy access to expert users: it becomes natural to include other stakeholders into the project, as well.

Géry Derbier, working with the French postal service (*La Poste*) to build software to run a new facility to handle all the mail going into and out of northern France, reported on his use of Crystal. With twenty-five people, his was a project in the Crystal Yellow category. However, he knew the principles of the Crystal methodologies family, particularly the "stretch to fit" principle, and therefore chose to extend Crystal Clear to his larger setting wherever possible.

> We discussed his project, and at one point covered their project's linkage to the integration testing team located 30 km away and to the business and usage expert working for *La Poste*. I asked questions of the sort: "How often did that person visit the team? How did he feel about that? How did his manager feel about his coming over so often?" Géry's answers were, for both external groups: "One day a week; comfortable; happy to be involved so early."

After our discussion, I realized that Géry had built the additional safety of collaboration across organizational boundaries into his project. His project was happily linked into both the customer and integration environments with a colleague on each end. *La Poste's* contract measured and paid according to integrated test results every few months (frequent delivery). The *La Poste* executives got software delivered in growing increments and paid accordingly. Géry's bosses, who had no previous experience with incremental delivery, were happy about this also, since they saw regular delivery turn into regular payments. Géry had a support structure on all sides.

Collaboration across organizational boundaries is not a given result on any project. It results from working with honesty amicability and integrity within and outside the team. It is hard to achieve if the team does not itself have personal safety and, to a lesser extent, frequent delivery. I consider the presence of good collaboration across organizational boundaries as partial evidence that some of the top seven safety properties are being achieved.

REFLECTION ON THE PROPERTIES

I don't believe any prescribed procedures exist that can assure that projects land in the safety zone every time. Nor, with the exception of incremental development, do I show up on a project with any particular set of rules in hand, even though I have my favorites. This is why Crystal Clear is built around critical properties instead of specification of procedures.

A Crystal team works to set the seven properties into place, using whatever group conventions, techniques, and standards fit their situation. The conventions may vary by project and by month. New techniques get invented with each new technology (and usually go out of style again a few years later). These seven properties, on the other hand, have been applied on good projects for decades.

My intention with Crystal is to not invade the natural workings of individuals on the project where possible, and to allow the most possible variation across different teams, while still getting those diverse projects into the safety zone. To allow variation, I must remove constraints. Removing constraints means finding broader mechanisms that provide a safety net. The ones I choose to rely on are these:

◆ People are by nature good at looking around and communicating.

◆ They take initiative when provided with information.

◆ They do better in an environment that is safe with respect to personal and emotional safety and particularly freedom from personal attacks.

◆ They do their best work if they can satisfy their need for contribution, accomplishment, and pride-in-work.

The Crystal Clear safety net is built on those things. Personal safety gives people the personal courage to share whatever they discover. Osmotic communication gives them the greatest chance to discover important information from each other and does so with very low communication cost. Reflective improvement gives them a channel to apply feedback to their working process. Easy access to expert users gives them the opportunity to quickly discover relevant information from the user(s). Frequent delivery creates feedback to the system's requirements and the development process. The technical development environment including automated tests, configuration management, and frequent integration allows people to safely make changes to the system, synchronize the multiple minds that are in motion at the same time, and get feedback on the system's intermediate stages quickly. Focus allows the team to spend their energy well on the most important things.

Ron Jeffries once characterized Crystal Clear as, "Have a few developers come together in peace, love and understanding, ship code every other month, and think about it periodically, and good software will emerge." He is close.

*   *   *

You should be asking at this point, "But what is special in all this about small projects? Shouldn't *all* project teams set these properties in place?"

The answer—with two side notes—is, "Of course." The properties that make a small-team project successful *should* be very similar to making any project successful, but should be optimized for the small-project situation.

The first note is that the properties are easier to reach on a small project. Personal safety is easier, since the people interact with each other more often and come to know each other sooner. The feedback loops are much smaller, and the rest of the properties follow accordingly.

The second note is that osmotic communication, which lives from background hearing and communication along lines-of-sight, really only works with small teams. Larger teams will set up osmotic communication within subteams and close communication across subteams.

Chapter 3

In Practice (Strategies and Techniques)

Crystal Clear does not require any one strategy or technique. It is good to have a set in hand to get started, however. This chapter presents a few of the less well-documented and more significant ones used by modern agile development teams.

Many useful strategies and techniques have been named in the last decade, from XP's "planning game" to Dave Thomas and Andy Hunt's "tracer bullets." The *Pragmatic Programmer* (Hunt 1999), *Extreme Programming Explained* (Beck 1999), and *Refactoring* (Fowler 1999) are particularly rich in ideas.

There are strategies and techniques not in those books that are useful to the Crystal Clear team, particularly through the early months of the project. I include ones that make a good starter set, are recommended by experienced developers, few people seem to know, are simple, and, most of all, are useful.

THE STRATEGIES

The strategies I have selected to outline are

1. *Exploratory 360°,* part of project chartering
2. *Early Victory,* a project management strategy
3. *Walking Skeleton,* a joint architecture/project management strategy
4. *Incremental Rearchitecture,* a strategy related to *Walking Skeleton*
5. *Information Radiators,* a strategy for communication

Strategy 1.   Exploratory 360°

At the start of a new project, usually during the *chartering* activity, the team needs to establish that the project is both meaningful and that they can deliver it using the intended technology. They look around them in all directions, sampling the project's

◆ Business value
◆ Requirements
◆ Domain model
◆ Technology plans
◆ Project plan
◆ Team makeup
◆ Methodology or working conventions

They may check other aspects of the project, but these are the usual.

The entire *Exploratory 360°* for a Crystal Clear project takes a few days up to a week or two if some new and peculiar technology is to be used. Based on what they learn, the team decides whether it makes sense to proceed.

*   *   *

Business-value sampling consists of capturing, with key stakeholders, what the system should do for its users and their organization(s). This should result in the names of the key use cases for the system, along with the focal roles the system should serve and the personalities and functions it should present to the world.

Requirements sampling consists of low-precision use cases that show what the system must do, and with what other people and systems it will have to interact. Often that drafting exercise turns up interfaces between organizations or technology systems that had not formerly been identified.

Concurrently or from the use case drafts, the developers sample the *domain model*. This sample serves to highlight the key concepts they will be working with, the core of the business, the programming, and the discursive vocabulary. It also helps the team to estimate the size and difficulty of the problem at hand.

The developers create a *technology* sampling, running a few experiments with the technology. Ward Cunningham and Kent Beck call these *spikes* (see http://c2.com/cgi/wiki?SpikeSolution). The assignment is to ask: Can we really connect these technologies? Will they withstand the intended loads? Can our developers master the technologies in time? The programmers perform the smallest programming assignment needed to make it clear the project is not running down a blind alley. The experiments establish the technical plausibility of the project.

The team creates a coarse-grained *project plan*, possibly from the project map or a set of stories and releases. It might be done using the blitz-planning technique described later in this chapter, or XP's planning game. This plan is reviewed by the lead designer, the executive sponsor, and the expert user to make sure the project is delivering suitable business value for suitable expense in a suitable time period.

Finally, the developers discuss their process, either in a *Reflection Workshop* or a *Process Miniature*.

*   *   *

Here is the story of one project that failed three elements of the *Exploratory 360°*:

> During the technology sample, the developers found, much to their surprise, that they could not connect the organization's email system to their intranet and browser system. It was not clear how they could actually deliver the software services they had envisioned.
>
> The project planning sample showed the cost to be about three times higher than the executive sponsor was interested in spending.
>
> The business value sample showed that the organization should not allocate very many developer resources to this problem; it would be better outsourced (or simply bought), and the development team allocated to a more significant business problem.

You would think that canceling or outsourcing such a project would be obvious to all involved. However, the developers were keen to experiment with the new technology, and therefore kept the project alive, under the guise that this project would serve as a good learning vehicle. Fortunately, the executive sponsors paid attention to the exploratory 360° results, stopped the programmers, outsourced the project, and put these key developers on a project of much greater value to the organization (which, I am happy to add, they enjoyed much more).

Strategy 2. Early Victory

Winning is a force that binds a team and contributes to the self-confidence of its members. Sociologist Karl Weick (1979) found that *small wins* helps a group develop strength and confidence. Happily, these can be arranged relatively early in the project, when the team badly needs them. This is the *Early Victory* strategy.

On software projects, the early victory to seek is the first piece of visibly running, tested code. This is usually the walking skeleton (a tiny piece of usable system function, very often not much more than the ability to add an item to the system database and then look at it). Although this may not sound like much, team members learn each others' working styles from this small win, users get an early view of the system, and the sponsors see the team delivering.

*　　*　　*

Project teams often argue over the sequence in which to attack their problem. An often-mentioned strategy is *Worst Thing First*. The reasoning is that once that worst thing is out of the way, everything will be easier.

The problem with worst-thing-first is that if the team fails to deliver, the sponsor has no idea where the failure lies: Is the team not good enough to pull off this project? Is the technology wrong, or is the process wrong? In addition, the team members may get depressed or start to argue with each other.

Since I often join teams that haven't worked together before and are tackling a new problem with new technology, I prefer *Easiest Thing First, Hardest Second*. The team members get to debug their communication and their process on a relatively simple assignment. They and the sponsors get the confidence of an early victory. If the most difficult problem is still outside the team's capabilities, I look for the *hardest thing the team can succeed with* as the second task.

Once the risk of team and technical failure abates, a good strategy is *Highest Business Value First*. This strategy not only generates maximum financial returns for the project (Denne 2003) but also maps well to earned-value charts.[1] You can *show* everyone you are delivering business value and not just work hours. If the project should run out of time, it will be abundantly clear to the sponsors that they got the best value for money in the time spent, useful in both friendly and hostile circumstances.[2]

---

[1]   See p. 98.
[2]   See badly formed fixed-price project bids, on p. 301 and also (Patton 2003).

Strategy 3.   *Walking Skeleton*

A walking skeleton is a tiny implementation of the system that performs a small end-to-end function. It need not use the final architecture, but it should link together the main architectural components. The architecture and the functionality can then evolve in parallel.

*   *   *

I first learned of the walking skeleton idea when a project's lead designer approached me for a conversation and described a project of his. He said (approximately):

> We had a large project to do, consisting of systems passing messages around a ring to each other. The other technical lead and I decided that we should, within the first week, connect the systems together so they could pass a single null message around the ring. This way we at least had the ring working.
>
> We then required that at the end of every week, no matter what new messages and message processing was developed during the week, the ring had to be intact, passing all of the previous weeks' messages without failure. This way we could grow the system in a controlled manner and keep the different teams in sync.
>
> It worked wonderfully, and we would do it again.

I had the opportunity to apply this idea on a client-server system on my first large project.

> We were moving frighteningly slowly. Our first three-month delivery was scheduled to deliver only a small set of functionality that might be considered interesting to the end users. We had to cut scope to meet even this mild ambition, and in the end delivered what I refer to as "read a number, write a number."
>
> Much to my surprise, the system went live on schedule, the sponsors threw a big party, and the users started putting numbers into the system.
>
> The system's design and code was not pretty, but we had connected the server-side software to the database system and could write functions on top of that architecture. Having the architectural elements connected and a sample piece of function running on it, we were able to develop more functionality in parallel with revising the architecture to be more robust (the *Incremental Rearchitecture* strategy).
>
> Our sponsors were happy with this early victory. We tested the team, the process, the technologies, and the architecture at a very early point in the project.

Other authors have other names for similar sorts of ideas. The Poppendiecks (2003) write about a "spanning application"; Dave Thomas and Andy Hunt use what they call "tracer bullets" (Hunt 1999).

What constitutes a walking skeleton varies with the system being designed. For a client-server system, it would be a single screen-to-database-and-back capability. For a multi-tier or multi-platform system, it is a working connection between the tiers or platforms. For a compiler, it consists of compilation of the simplest element of the language, possibly just a single token. For a business process, it is walking through a single and simple business transaction (as Jeff Patton describes in the technique *Essential Interaction Design*, later in this chapter).

Note that each subsystem is incomplete, but they are hooked together, and will stay hooked together from this point on.

The walking skeleton is not complete or robust (it only *walks*, pardon the phrase), and it is missing the flesh of the application functionality. Incrementally, over time, the infrastructure will be completed and full functionality will be added.

A walking skeleton is different from a *spike*.[3] A spike is "the smallest implementation that demonstrates plausible technical success." The spike typically takes between a few hours and a few days to complete, and is thrown away afterward, since it was built with nonproduction coding habits. A spike serves to answer the question: Are we headed in the *wrong* direction?

A walking skeleton, on the other hand, is permanent code, built with production coding habits, regression tests, and is intended to grow with the system. Once the system is up and running, it will stay up and running for the rest of the project, despite the incremental rearchitecture that is quite likely to occur.

---

[3]   http://c2.com/cgi/wiki?SpikeSolution.

Strategy 4. Incremental Rearchitecture

The system architecture will need to evolve from the walking skeleton and handle changes in technology and business requirements over time. It is rarely effective to shut down development to perform an architectural revision, so the team evolves the architecture in stages, keeping the system running as they do so.

The team applies the idea of incremental development to revising the infrastructure or architecture as well as the system's end functionality.

*   *   *

The question naturally arises: How completely designed should the system architecture and infrastructure be during the early stages of the project?

Any one person has his personal "thought horizon," how much complexity he can keep in his head for several days in a row, how much he can foresee from his experience and knowledge of the situation. An architect who has done similar systems in the same domain using similar technologies can think through to a farther horizon than one just getting started.

Some people keep the thought horizon down to a few days. They get started immediately with an initial design, and learn from that early version in which direction they should push the design. Others like to think longer and consider more contingencies before committing to an initial architecture.

The thought horizon on a Crystal Clear project is almost certainly reached within a week or two. At that point, the designers are probably speculating beyond their thought horizon, and would be better setting up the walking skeleton. They should use that to get to the first of their frequent deliveries, and use the feedback to improve the architecture. "Don't overdrive your headlights" is how some people phrase it.

Here is a story about the use of incremental rearchitecture from my first large project.

> The infrastructure team found after the second delivery that the object-to-relational database mapping they had planned to use would require an ever-increasing amount of programming as new functionality was added; in other words, it wouldn't scale. Being under heavy time pressure on a fixed-price contract, pressure was on them to simply keep plowing forward and just work harder and faster to keep up with the increasing work load.
>
> The team lead decided, however, that an architectural redesign was needed. His team continued to support the old design for one more increment, while the system's delivered functionality was still small, and at the same time started their redesign.

They slipped the new architecture into the third delivery cycle, coaching the function-development teams on how to write to the new interfaces, and supporting them with some number of automatic code-generation mechanisms. In the fourth delivery cycle, they ripped out all of the uses of the initial architecture.

On the fourth delivery cycle, the infrastructure architect breathed a sigh of relief: they could finally keep up with the now rapidly growing system functionality.

The converse also applies. Here is the unhappy story of a team that did not apply incremental rearchitecture when they should have.

The architects promised their executives that their radically new architecture would allow direct translation from use cases to running Java code, making the product incredibly responsive to changing business needs. This approach was, of course, a risky proposition, since no one had accomplished this before.

Recognizing this risk, I suggested to the project manager that their project use the exact strategy we had used in the story just above: create a simple, straightforward architecture that could be delivered on time, and swap in the new architecture if and when it proved itself.

The project manager said she had great confidence in the lead architects and didn't want the extra rework, so she chose to hang all hopes on the new architecture. Unhappily, the problem of going from use cases to running code turned out to be insoluble to those people. In the end, the project was left with no running architecture at all, and no product was ever shipped.

Developers in the last decade have shown that tidy, simple architectures are reasonably straightforward to upgrade to their next stage of complexity and performance. The business consequence of this is that, very often, a company can create an early version to demonstrate function and possibly even generate revenue, and then use the incremental rearchitecture strategy to revamp the infrastructure under the running system.

Starting from a simple working architecture and applying incremental rearchitecture is a winning strategy for most, though not all, systems.[4] It provides a number of advantages when it can be used:

◆ The architecture is easier to modify when modifications are needed.
◆ The function and infrastructure teams get to work in parallel, advancing the moment at which usable function becomes available, or at least visible.

---

[4]   It would, for example, probably be a bad idea to ask all cell phone users to take their phones back to the supplier so that a new software architecture could be downloaded!

- The end users can view the system's proposed functionality early, and correct its fundamental fitness for business use.
- The running system might reveal shortcomings in the architecture that the early thought experiments didn't catch.
- The system can sometimes be deployed to a limited market, in which case the business will start earning revenue to help pay for ongoing development.

In deciding when to apply the strategy, ask

- whether the system can, in fact, be developed in two streams, with the infrastructure or architecture evolving in parallel with the system functionality (the answer is usually yes)
- whether, by first creating a fallback, simple architecture and testing the system in live use, the business might catch an unpredicted architectural mistake (the answer is often yes);
- whether the business can earn early revenue on deployment of a version with limited functionality to a limited market (the answer is surprisingly often yes)

Incremental rearchitecture is further discussed at length in the article "Extending an Architecture as It Earns Business Value" (Cockburn 2004a).

Strategy 5.   Information Radiators

An information radiator is a display posted in a place where people can see it as they work or walk by. It shows readers information they care about, without their having to ask anyone a question. This means more communication with fewer interruptions.

A good information radiator

- Is large and easily visible to the casual, interested observer
- Is understood at a glance
- Changes periodically, so that it is worth visiting
- Is easily kept up to date

Typically, it is on paper, posted in the team room or in the hallway. In a few exceptional circumstances, it is on a Web page that people refer to frequently. Unusual examples of information radiators include a (real!) traffic light, a colored orb, and a computer monitor hung outside a cubicle's partition in the hallway.

Todd Little of Landmark Graphics made the interesting observation that information radiators generally serve to inform people *outside* the project team. The people on the project team generally know the information posted, because of their close communications with each other. It is the people outside the team who want or need to know that information in order to make their own decisions, and otherwise would interrupt the team to get that information, or would simply guess at it (often incorrectly).

*   *   *

Information radiators can be used on any project, large or small. A small team can use them very conveniently to maintain information that they otherwise would have to maintain on the computer (which is both slower and less visible).

Information radiators are typically used to show status information, such as:

- the current iteration's work set (use cases or stories)
- the current work assignments
- the number of tests written (or passed)
- the number of use cases (or stories) delivered
- the status of key servers (up, down, in maintenance)
- the core of the domain model
- the results of the last reflection workshop

Online files and Web pages generally do not make good information radiators, because an information radiator needs to be visible without significant effort on the part of the viewer. I have, of course, run into exceptions to this rule. One was the team performing continuous integration with CruiseControl, a dedicated server running a build-and-test script and posting the test results to a Web page. The programmers tended to leave that Web page visible at all times on their screens, so they could respond to failing integration tests immediately. The other exception was the monitor hung over a cubicle wall into the hallway (see Figure 3-5), displaying current run time measurements of the system in use.

Freeman-Benson and Borning wrote an experience report on a methodology they call YP (Borning 2003). They report on the effect of using a real traffic light:

Actually there are several: one in the hallway of our laboratory, two more in developer offices, and one virtual traffic light on the web. We use four color combinations:

◆ green when the build and all the tests have succeeded,

◆ yellow when the build and tests are in progress,

◆ yellow and green together when the build has passed the point where it is likely to fail (in practice, this means that all the tests have passed and that the final installer and distribution are being produced), and

◆ red if any part of the build or tests has failed.

The traffic light is a powerful symbol of the current state of the software. The web version at www.urbansim.org/fireman makes the status visible to anyone else who might be interested (including you, Gentle Reader, if you wish), and in particular for our customers, although in a less compelling way than the physical device.

The first author has used the traffic light as part of applying YP in four other development projects as well. Interestingly, only one team in addition to ours is still using the light—the other teams disconnected their lights because they didn't like them being red all the time. Rather than fixing the underlying problem (that their system was sufficiently unstable that their regression tests would not pass reliably), they chose to "eliminate the messenger." Only one of the teams acknowledged this decision explicitly.

In conversations with other team leads and software managers, we learned that a number of them had tried "failure indicators" such as sirens, flashing lights, red lights, and so forth, and that each had cancelled the experiment after a few days. Apparently the use of negative reinforcement (a red light) without the corresponding positive reinforcement (a green light) was too damaging to morale. Our experience with the traffic light is quite the opposite: everyone who joins a YP team immediately reports a

Figure 3-1   Development status of the user stories. (Courtesy of ThoughtWorks)

sense of comfort at the large (8–12") green light glowing its message of "all is well with the build." Or on the rare occasions when the software has failed the nightly build tests, as the staff arrives in the morning, in the winter's gloom, with the lab hallway illuminated by the red glow of the traffic light, it's clear that a) something has gone wrong, and b) it should get fixed as soon as possible.

Figures 3-1 to 3-5 are photographs of different information radiators.

Figure 3-2   Charts of the code base kept near the programmers. Notice the code size going down in the last two deliveries! (Courtesy of Randy Stafford, IQNavigator)

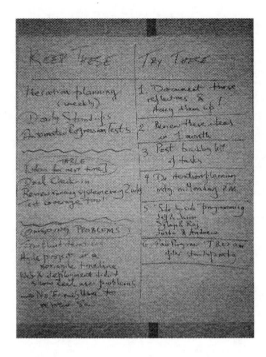

Figure 3-3   *The results of a reflection work-shop. (Courtesy of Jeff Patton and Tomax)*

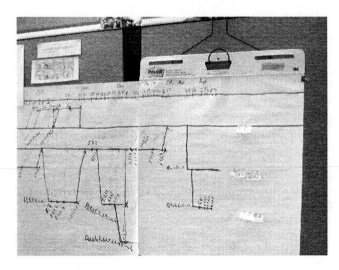

Figure 3-4   *Keeping track of the CVS branches. I like the creative use of hangers, pads and cubicle parti-tions. (Courtesy of John Bullock, IQNavigator)*

Figure 3-5 A monitor hung over the cubicle wall to show real-time measurements of the system in operation. (Courtesy of Randy Stafford, IQNavigator)

THE TECHNIQUES

The techniques I have selected are

1. *Methodology Shaping,* gathering information about prior experiences and using it to come up with the starter conventions
2. *Reflection Workshop,* a particular workshop format for *Reflective Improvement*
3. *Blitz Planning,* which I also sometimes refer to as a project planning "jam session" (as in jazz) to emphasize its collaborative nature, a quick and collaborating project planning technique
4. *Delphi Estimation,* a way to come up with a starter estimate for the total project
5. *Daily Stand-ups,* a quick and efficient way to pass information around the team on a daily basis
6. *Essential Interaction Design,* a fast version of usage-centered design
7. *Process Miniature,* a learning technique
8. *Side-by-Side Programming,* a less intense alternative to pair programming
9. *Burn Charts,* an efficient way to planning and reporting progress, particularly suited for use on *Information Radiators*

As described in the e-mail series between Crystal and Alistair (see Chapter 1), no single specific technique is mandated by Crystal. These particular strategies provide a good starting point, particularly the methodology shaping and reflection workshops, since those are most likely to be new to the group. Burn charts have become an interesting topic in their own right, since they have a natural match to the earned-value charts used in systems engineering project management.

Technique 1.   Methodology Shaping

Establish the starter methodology in two steps:

1. Project interviews
2. Methodology shaping workshop

The information from the first feeds into the second.

Project Interviews

With this little technique, you will build a small library of experiences in your organization that shows the strengths, weaknesses, and themes of your organization. When you go into the methodology shaping workshop, you will examine them and discuss how to take advantage of the strengths and how to compensate for, or avoid, the weaknesses.

> We found in one organization a theme that projects that had good internal and external communication went well, but when they didn't have that communication, the teams had a bad time and the outcome was negative.
>
> Seeing this in front of us, I made extra effort to bring our project experiences to the directors of development and the requesting division. We wrote a one-page summary after every iteration, summarized our costs, accomplishments, frustrations, and lessons learned. We arranged for these two people to meet for an hour and review the project using the report as a base for their discussion. They actually talked about many other things during that hour, but they both commented on the positive effects of allocating time for discussion and beginning by going through the report.
>
> At the end of that year, the director of development commented, somewhat quizzically, that we had had a fairly similar project assignment as two other groups, but those other two projects failed, while ours succeeded. Looking at the projects, we noticed that ours was the only project that took time to attend to communication paths both within and external to the project. The theme we had found in our project interviews had played out once more, true to form.

Technique Variant 1

Start with yourselves, but also include other people from a few other projects in your organization. Have several people on your team interview people on other projects. Start your collection with four to ten interview reports. It is useful (but not critical) that each of your people interview more than one person on one project. You might talk to any two of the following: the project manager, the team lead, a user interface designer, and a programmer. Their different perspectives on the same project will prove informative. Even more informative, however, will be the common responses across multiple projects.

Keep in mind is that whatever the interviewee says is relevant. During an interview, don't offer your own opinions about any matter but use your judgment to select the next question to ask.

The following steps summarize how I have worked over the years in doing my own project interviews (Cockburn 2003a).

Step 1. I ask to see one sample of each work product produced. Looking at these, I detect how much ceremony was likely to be on the project and think about what questions I should ask about the work products. I look for duplicated work, places where they might have been difficult to keep up to date. I ask whether iterative development was in use, and, if so, how the documents were updated in following iterations. I look, in particular, for ways in which informal communication was used to patch over inconsistencies in the paperwork.

> On one project, the team lead showed me twenty-three work products. I noticed a fair degree of overlap among them, and so I asked if the later ones were generated by tools from the earlier ones. The team lead said no, the people had to reenter them from scratch. So I followed up by asking how the people felt about this. He said they really hated it, but he made them do it anyway.

You can guess that that last piece of information is very useful in the methodology shaping workshop.

Step 2. I ask for a short history of the project. This history includes date started, staff changes (growing and shrinking), team structure, and the emotionally high and low points of the project life. I do this to calibrate the size and type of the project and to detect where there may be other interesting questions to ask.

Step 3. I ask, *"What were the key things you did wrong that you wouldn't want to repeat on your next project?"* I write down whatever they say, and I fish around for related issues to investigate.

Step 4. I ask, *"What were the key things you did right that you would certainly like to preserve in your next project?"* In response to this question, people have named everything from where they sit, to having food in the refrigerator, to social activities, communication channels, software tools, software architecture, and domain modeling. Whatever you hear, write it down.

Step 5. I revisit the issues, *"What are your priorities with respect to the things you liked on the project? What is most critical to keep, and what is most negotiable?"*

This is redundant, technically speaking, but my experience is that people come up with slightly different answers. I write those down. It is useful to ask at this point, *"Was there anything that surprised you about the project?"*

Step 6. Finally, I ask whether there is anything else I should hear about. I see where the question goes.

You may find it useful to construct an interview template on which to write the results, so you can exchange them easily. The time that we did this, our template was two pages long (to control the amount of writing the interviewer does) and contained the following sections.

1. Project name, job of person interviewed
2. Project data (start/end dates, staff size, domain, technology).
3. Project history
4. Did wrong/would not repeat
5. Did right/would preserve
6. Priorities
7. Other

Technique Variant 2

Jens Coldewey, in Germany, used a different technique to get the information he sought for his methodology shaping workshop. He sent to each member of his upcoming group a short questionnaire, asking what they had liked about their previous projects and wanted to retain on the new project, and what they had not liked about their previous projects and would want to set up differently on the new project. He took those answers straight into the methodology shaping workshop.

Technique Variant 3

Following Jens's lead, I have also run a facilitated workshop to come up with the same information. You can do this workshop in groups of any size, from a Crystal Clear project of just four people, to an organization of several dozen people. Allow an hour for this workshop if you have a small group, and two to three hours for a large group.

Break into work groups of three to five people each. Set up several flip charts with pens of differing colors at each work group.

Have each work group brainstorm and list all the things they have personally experienced on projects in the past and would like not to repeat on the current or next project. They write all those on one flip chart (or, more likely, several pages of that flip chart). Time box the activity so they don't go all afternoon!

On the other flip chart and with a different color pen, have them brainstorm and list all the things they have personally experienced on their own projects in the past (this is important, because otherwise they are likely to write down ideas they have heard about but not experienced), and would like to see repeated.

Spend some time combining and merging the common ideas in each list to make a single list of disliked/don't repeat and a separate list of liked/repeat items.

Giving each person a number, say seven, votes for each list, ask them to mark on each list the items they feel most important. They can stack all seven votes on one item or spread them around however they wish.

Count the votes for each item and sort by voting results.

At this point, you have a table of contents for project situations to "avoid" and ones to "keep," prioritized by personal significance to the people in the room.

During this workshop, you will not solve any of the problems mentioned. That is the work to do during the methodology shaping workshop. What you have is the information needed in that next workshop, which might take place on the same or a different day.

Methodology Shaping Workshop

The methodology shaping workshop is nothing more or less than a larger version of the periodic reflection workshop described next. In the periodic reflection workshop, the team already has a list of rules and conventions they are using, and reflect on which to keep or drop. That workshop should make relatively small changes to the set of conventions.

The methodology shaping workshop, on the other hand, starts with a group of people who have not done the exercise before and don't yet know what their operating conventions will be. Their output will therefore be a single large list of proposed ideas, rules, and conventions. The book *Agile Software Development* contains a sample thirty-six-point list that was the result of one such investigation.

The workshop starts with a review of the organization's fixed rules about software development. These are taken as given rules, unless someone on the team has an idea on how to shift any of them.

The people go through the list of "liked/keep" items that came from the project interviews and see how many of those they can easily arrange on the upcoming project. They table the difficult ones for separate study.

They go through the list of "disliked/avoid" items and brainstorm ways to avoid them on the upcoming project. The answers get written down on the list of ideas, rules, and conventions.

They locate the themes of the organization (as shown in the story at the start of this technique), and discuss how to handle, compensate for, or take advantage of those themes. They write their answers on the list of ideas, rules, and conventions.

They go through the difficult items saved up to now, discuss and brainstorm any ways to deal with them, given all the ideas they already have written down. They write down the ideas they want to try on the main list, and write down on a separate list the items they are worried about but don't have ideas for. (They look at this list later in the project, either to see if they have new ideas, or to discuss with the project sponsor and their managers, in case they run into exactly those problems.)

At this point, the list of ideas, rules, and conventions is probably quite long.

The people go through the list again, and mark the ones that are most important to pay attention to, and put into parentheses the ones that are interesting but possibly marginal. These latter ones are the ones that are nice to have but the first to go in case the team gets overloaded with following the list.

The team will update these conventions a month later during their first reflection workshop (I write the time "a month later" as a reminder that it should not go too long before review. The exact time chosen is up to the team to decide.)

Believe it or not, these are now the "starter methodology" details for the project!

Technique 2.   Reflection Workshop

The team should pause for an hour periodically—certainly after each delivery—to reflect on its working conventions. In the reflection workshop, the team members discuss what is working well, what needs improvement, and what they are going to do differently during the next period.

I like to do one of these halfway through the first iteration as a sanity check: "Working this way, are we on track to complete our assignment in this iteration, or do we need to compensate now, before it is too late?" Since my experience is that most teams schedule too much work to do in the first iteration, I pay less attention to bad estimates of how much can be done in the first iteration, and look for disastrously bad working conventions. Repairing bad working conventions is what I focus on in the first workshop.

People who hold reflection workshops on a regular basis tell me of a pattern that shows up: The group finds a lot to discuss in the first few workshops, and then, after a while, they find that there is little more to say from the previous time. In some cases, they lengthen the time between workshops, holding them only after each delivery. In other cases they use the time for a closer examination of their team values, personal working styles, and the like.

There are various formats for a workshop handling these themes. The one that follows is my favorite because it is both simple and brief (as are all of my favorite techniques). Norm Kerth (2001) wrote a book called *Project Retrospectives* that discusses many other exercises you could perform during a reflection workshop.

The Keep/Try Reflection Workshop

Very simply, capture the following three things on a flip chart and then post the flip chart prominently as an information radiator for the group to see as they work.

1. *What we should keep*. These are the conventions we don't want to lose in the next time period. The sorts of things that get mentioned often include sitting close together, noninterruptable focus hours, daily stand-up meetings, and automated regression tests.

2. *Where we are having ongoing problems*. It is not generally healthy to focus too much on problems, but people get stuck in the workshop if they can't mention a problem that is bothering them and subsequently see it get written on to the poster. Create a half-column or less on the flip chart to capture the problems that we are having trouble getting around. Topics that often get mentioned are too many interruptions, requirements changing too often, people changing code without notifying anyone else, unable to buy new tool suites.

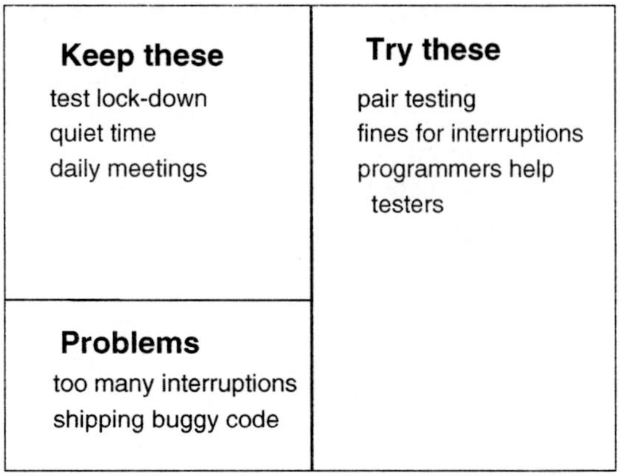

Keep these	Try these
test lock-down quiet time daily meetings	pair testing fines for interruptions programmers help testers
Problems too many interruptions shipping buggy code	

Figure 3-6 *Poster format for the reflection workshop.*

3. *What we want to try in the next time period.* In a sense, these are the most important of the three categories. These are what the team agrees to try for the next few weeks. Some of the suggestions I hear include: two hours of uninterrupted, for example, work from 10:00 A.M. to noon each day; use of coding standards; more unit or acceptance tests; occasional pair programming; daily stand-up meeting.

You might run your first reflection workshop in no more than fifteen minutes. This will constrain the time of the discussion so that people do not run too far afield, and focus the team on coming up with concrete suggestions for what to keep and what to change. This provides the team with a process miniature for the technique.

After the first one, you can decide how long to allocate for each workshop. One group chose to allocate two days in an off-site location every three months for the first year of their project. They used the first day for team building and reflection workshop, and spent the second day planning the next three-month delivery cycle. They eventually cut it down to just one day in their offices. I have used an hour in the cafeteria every couple of months, down to fifteen to thirty minutes every two weeks.

Figures 3-7 and 3-8 are photographs of reflection workshop results using the above technique. You will notice in the second one that we created an additional section just above the *Problems* to capture ideas that people had but didn't want to try right away. This section served to feed the discussion at the following workshop.

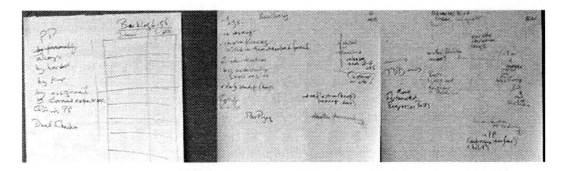

Figure 3-7   *Reflection workshop flip charts showing project history and ideas tried. (Courtesy of Jeff Patton and Tomax)*

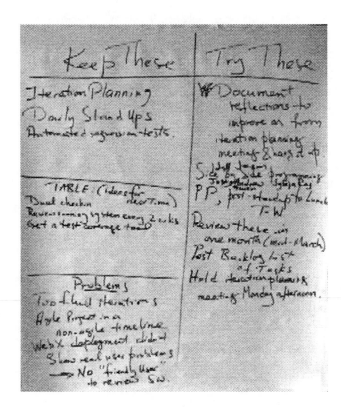

Figure 3-8   *Reflection workshop output. (Courtesy of Jeff Patton and Tomax)*

Technique 3.   Blitz Planning

The planning session is an opportunity for the executive sponsor, expert user, and developers to contribute together to build the project map and timeline. As always, there are several ways to work.

One technique is the "planning game" from XP. In the planning game, people place index cards on the table, one user story per card. The group pretends there are no dependencies between cards, and simply lines them up in the preferred sequence of development. The developers write on each card an estimate of how long it will take to produce the function; the sponsor or expert user puts them into development priority sequence, taking into account the development time and business value of each function. The cards are clustered into iterations, and those iterations are clustered into releases, usually not longer than a few months each. The planning game is described in detail in (Beck 2000).

The following describes the variation I like to use. I call it *Blitz Planning* to emphasize that it goes fast. However, I also like to refer to it on occasion as a *Project Planning "Jam Session"* to emphasize that everyone is supposed to play together and off each other in a collaborative way, as in a jazz jam session. If you lose the amicable collaboration, you can do the technique, but you lose many opportunities to creatively improve the project plan.

I find this technique works well for a planning horizon up to about three months. After that, the amount of detail is overwhelming. For time horizons longer than three months, I use the project map described among the work products.[5]

Here is a brief overview of the technique. I describe the steps in more detail below.

Gather into one room representatives of each stakeholder category, the executive sponsor, end users, and developers, in particular. Brainstorm onto index cards all the development tasks to be done. Collate and merge the tasks to avoid duplication. Sequence the cards according to priority and dependency order. At this point the developers put down the work time estimates. If a particular person is required for the task, add that person's name. If there is a dependency on an external group, write that somewhere else on the card.

Having the cards on the table, work through the plan looking for key milestones and optimizations. Identify the walking skeleton, the first delivery, and the first deliv-

---

[5]   This is an example of "two-tiered" project planning. The long-term plan is the coarse-grained project map, the short-term plan is the result of the blitz planning session. Two-tiered project plans are common in agile projects.

ery that produces a revenue stream. Look for excessive dependencies on any one person, and off-load that person. Look for early tasks that unnecessarily block early revenue stream, and tasks listed for later that for risk reduction reasons should be done early (e.g., load testing). Move those cards around to better places. Work with the sponsor to make sure the plan is delivering functionality in accordance with the project's true priorities.

The result is your project plan.

Figure 3-9 shows a sample of such a card, and Figure 3-10 shows a sample of how the cards look when laid out on the table.

Here are the steps in detail. Note that this technique is spelled out for Level 1 practitioners.[6] When you reach Level 2 with this technique, try some variations to handle situations where the requirements are not yet known, where the time horizon is longer than three months, using sticky notes instead of cards, and so on.

1. Gather the attendees.

   I subtitle this technique a project planning "jam session" because the technique allows the different project stakeholders to gather together and share ideas on how to make the optimal plan. Traditionally, the plan is made by the project manager or team lead without buy-in from the other stakeholders. That leads to two dysfunctions: First, the plan is of course wrong, since the poor person assigned to construct it can't possibly know all the tasks and times; second, when the errors in the project plan become evident, people find it easy to point accusing fingers at the person who made the plan. To counter these dysfunctions, make sure the executive sponsor, one or two key users, any business analysts, and the entire development team, including anyone involved in testing and deployment, are in the room. This group will name the talks more completely, the time estimates will be more reasonable, and, just as important, everyone will see all the trade-

| John |
| Migrate database |
| 2 wks |

Figure 3-9 *Sample blitz planning card.*

---

[6]   See "shu-ha-ri" (Fig. 1-2, p. 9).

offs made in constructing the plan. Everyone is jointly responsible for the result, and they all know it. As one person said, "We all made it, we all discussed the optimizations made."

2. Brainstorm the tasks.

   Everyone grabs cards and writes tasks on them as fast as they can. Usually the developers do most of the writing, but the executive sponsor and expert user often have a few tasks to contribute. List every task that will take half a day to several weeks, including interviewing users, programming specific functions, writing user help text, migrating databases, and installing the system (I often group tiny tasks together). The idea is to be complete. This step may last 5, 10, or 15 minutes.

3. Lay out the tasks.

   Everyone lays the cards out on the table in dependency order, the first ones at the head of the table, with successive tasks down the table. Tasks that can run in parallel are placed side by side across the table; tasks that run sequentially are placed above and below each other; duplicate task cards are removed. It usually requires a big table. I have used a large conference table and also several six-foot cafeteria tables placed end to end.

4. Review the tasks.

   Everyone walks up and down the table, looking for tasks that didn't get captured in the brainstorming. One person's card often triggers a thought from another person. Add cards as needed.

5. Estimate and tag the tasks.

   Whoever is going to do each task writes down their estimate for how long it will take (I write this on the lower left corner). If multiple people come up with different estimates, they have a brief discussion and put down their best second estimate. They also write down the names of any specific people required for any particular task (I write this on the top of the card). It often happens that the team lead's name is on a disproportionate number of cards. Seeing that person's name on so many cards should lead the team into a discussion of how to off-load that person or otherwise reduce the dependency. If a task is dependent on an external event or task, mark that on the card (I write this on the center of the right side of the card.)

6. Sort the tasks.

   In this step, the people work to identify more closely the presence or absence of dependencies, and to question the placement of cards on the table.

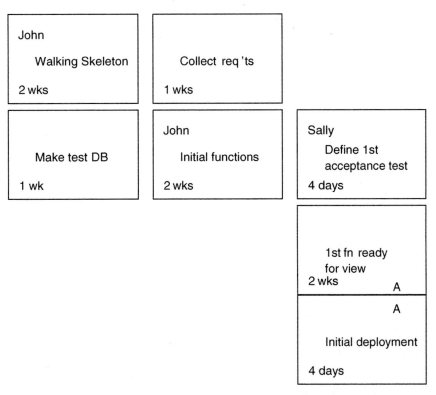

Figure 3-10 *Cards as they might be laid out on the table.*

Tasks that are placed sequentially often can be started in parallel. Identifying possible parallelism loosens the constraints on the plan. Also, it often turns out that there are parallel streams of activity, one for the expert user, one for the developers, or perhaps three separate streams for infrastructure, functionality, and user interface development. These parallel streams start to look like separate tracks of cards running down the table, occasionally coming together. Certain cards have a strictly sequential relationship, such that the second simply cannot be started before the first has finished (e.g., "Evaluate vendors" must fully precede "Set up contract with vendor"). Mark these pairs in some special way so that information doesn't get lost when the cards get moved around (I put the same capital letter, A, B, C, at an adjoining edge of the card, the bottom edge of the first card, and the corresponding point on the top edge of the second card). These strict dependencies are surprisingly rare; I rarely get beyond the letter E.

7. Mark the walking skeleton, the earliest release, and the earliest revenue.

Finding the first and smallest collection of functionality that can conceivably be of use to some users is critical. It is critical because that release represents the first time the users will see the system, their first idea of the look, feel, and shape of the system. Setting that point as early as possible gives the entire organization the most time to adapt to any new ideas or mismatches that show up from the initial release. On some occasions, this first release represents the earliest moment at which revenue can be gained; in this situation, the group should focus on getting all other cards out of its way.[7] All in all, three events of interest are located: the walking skeleton, the earliest usable release, and the point of earliest revenue. I mark these points by putting a bit of distance between the cards above and below those points. I have also used string, yardsticks, pencils—anything to demark those points. It requires cooperation between the expert user, executive sponsor, and lead designer to discover and optimally set these points, because some tasks will have to be moved up and others deferred. Whoever is moving the tasks around needs to be aware of the consequences of these moves, and that means each stakeholder group has to be present, alert, and cooperative.

A word is in order about the tasks that precede the initial release: Some of the early tasks are likely to be strictly technical, such as ordering software, setting up a contract, or loading a database. It is useful to have those tasks visible to the executive sponsor and expert user, because they need to explain the state of the project to other people. The technical task cards show what work needs to be done before business software will become visible.

Historically in our business, the user group gets told only, "The programming team says they have a bunch of technical work to do first." This often translates to months going by without deliveries or even visible progress. By making the tasks visible and public, the executive sponsor or expert user can report, "They have five technical things to do before we can see some software," "They still have two technical things to do before we can see some software," "They're on the last technical thing, and then they'll show us some running software."

This sort of visibility goes a long way to reducing the tensions between the groups.

---

[7] *Software by Numbers* (Denne 2003) is an excellent tutorial on this subject, using language of financial analysts. They plan in terms of "minimal marketable features."

8. Identify other releases.

   The group works out where other natural release points happen. Quite often, there is a particular cluster of function that really should be bundled together for the users to make good use of the system. At some point, the functions to be included simply become a long list, and at that point it may be more valuable to base the releases on regular time periods (monthly, bimonthly, or quarterly), rather than on collections of functionality. Neither Crystal Clear nor the Blitz Planning technique mandate what algorithm you use for choosing iteration lengths and release periods. Mark the key releases using a space between the cards, string, yardsticks, or whatever.

9. Optimize the plan to fit the project priorities.

   At this point, you have a plan. Typically the plan is not yet a *good* plan. It is my experience that when the numbers on the cards are added up, the team is in for "sticker shock" (this is the shock a car buyer experiences when stepping around to read the sticker posted on the car window announcing the price after all the car's options are added together). The entire group, and particularly the executive sponsor, expert user, and lead designer now have some creative problem solving to do to come up with an acceptable plan. What they shift depends on the priorities set for the project: time-to-market, cost, or feature set. This is where they really start "jamming." Typically, following the sticker shock, one of three things happen:

   ◆ The executive sponsor reconsiders the business need for the project (in one case, the executive team decided simply to buy a commercial package instead).

   ◆ The team removes tasks from the project.

   ◆ They shrug their shoulders and simply move forward.

   Pressuring the developers to change their estimates is not advisable. That not only makes a lie of the plan, but it convinces the developers that the executive sponsor is not being realistic, open, and honest.

   In the worst possible case, the executive sponsor has the right to say, "Okay, I see the tasks and the time estimates. However, I can't change the deadline, and I can't see anything else to remove, reorder or outsource. I'm going to multiply all estimates by 80 percent so that we can meet our target date. In the meantime, let's all keep our eyes open for new alternatives so we can reestablish these original estimates" (see the discussion on Crystal Clear and "Reallocation of Power," page 323)

   This is a drastic measure and should not be used lightly. The point of doing it is to make public both how the priorities affect the schedule, and the fact that the team's estimates are being overridden. Everyone has seen the cards and the original estimates. The team should track both plans, report against both in their status charts, and keep visibility of progress high.

Take it seriously if you have to resort to this measure even twice. That indicates there is another problem in the organization needing to be sorted out, having to do with the viability of the organization's business model, the trust between developers and sponsors, or the historic accuracy of the development team's estimates. Straightening those out will be crucial to the ongoing viability of the development team.

When optimizing the card layout on the table, the people look for three improvements in particular.

◆ They spot that a particular cluster of cards *almost* creates a coherent release having business value. By moving a card up higher, they can get that coherent business value much earlier. In one case, I heard the expert user say, "If we only had this card up here, we could start charging revenue with this release." You can guess that we immediately moved that card up, *and then moved down all cards not strictly needed to produce that release!*

◆ They spot a risk from having a card late in the project. This is typically done by someone with technical background playing the challenger.

I saw a card near the very end of the table labeled "Load Testing." Not thinking too much about it, I asked the lead designer, "How long will it take to perform?" He answered, "A few days." Still not worrying, I asked, "And suppose it fails, how long is it likely to take to revise the architecture?" He answered, "Oh, three or four weeks." At this point the expert user started looking alarmed. I asked, "Would it be possible to do it earlier?" "Sure," he answered.

We looked for the earliest moment at which he could do it without damaging the other critical business items on the table. I tentatively placed it just after the initial release. "Could you do it already here? (and then you'd have lots of time to revise the architecture if it fails)." I noticed the expert user vehemently nodding her head on the other side of the table and her large sigh of relief when he said, "Sure."

◆ They spot that one particular person has too many cards allocated to him or her. That person is going to be overloaded and will probably get into trouble. They brainstorm how to assign those tasks, or the bulk of some of them, to other people to reduce the risk to the project and the strain on that person.

10. Capture the output.

You have a plan, but it is only cards on a table. You need to preserve the information.

You can photograph the table, tape the cards together and mount them on the wall as an information radiator, or type them into another tool of your choice. I like to number the cards so that their placement on the table can be reconstructed. I number them 1, 2, 3, and so on down the table for the sequential relationships, 3a, 3b, 3c, and so on across any particular parallel set (and on occasion 3a1, 3a2, 3a3, and so on if there are nested subsequences).

*   *   *

There is one note I am obliged to put in here and that bears repeating several times in the book. A common interpretation of both XP's planning game and blitz planning is that the executive sponsor is at the mercy of the developers in constructing the project plan. In actuality, there is a three-way division of responsibilities: the executive sponsor's, the developers', and their joint responsibility.

The executive sponsor is responsible for choosing the priorities that drive which system features stay on the table, which are removed if scope is to be cut, and which functions should go into which release.

The developers are responsible for assessing the time needed to do their work. The executive sponsor needs to recognize that these are the people who have been hired to do the work; they are professionals and these are their best estimates.

They are jointly responsible for being creative in creating strategies to maximize their effectiveness. I usually find the initial layout of the cards on the table depressing and unsatisfactory for business reasons. The developers can't change the priorities and the executive sponsor can't change the estimates. What are they to do? They work together. The initial layout is usually inefficient. Working together, they come up with creative reorderings to get a better result. If the resulting plan is still unacceptable, the executive sponsor must decide what the top priority items are, what gets dropped, or perhaps whether the deadline or team be changed.

When they work together, they jointly see the constraints, jointly generate options, and jointly construct a plan that produces the best result for the resources expended. It is for this reason that I sometimes refer to this technique as a project planning *jam session*. (Done with good will, this technique also is a lot of fun—another characteristic of a good jam session.)

Technique 4.   Delphi Estimation Using Expertise Rankings

People always get around to asking, "But how should we estimate the length of time it will take to develop the software?" The true answer is, "Best guess." While technically correct, and practiced on every project, this answer is rarely comforting.

A group of us created an estimation technique one night, while trying to work out the bid on a $15 million fixed-price, fixed-scope project. I have since found the line of reasoning we took to have an interesting separation of questions. I am told that this corresponds to what is known as the "Delphi" technique (forecasting the future, but presumably without incense, vestal virgins, or answering in riddles).

This technique was first described in *Surviving Object-Oriented Projects* (Cockburn 1998). I present it here, in story form. The story relates to a larger Crystal Orange project, but you can still use it in adjusted form on a smaller project.

> Before beginning the project proper, but after spending two weeks gathering 140 rough use cases, we made our first project estimate. Our four best OO designers, the project manager, and a few other experienced, non-OO people made up the planning team. We split the session into four phases:
>
> ◆ estimating the size of the system to be built
> ◆ estimating work time according to the type of person we would need
> ◆ suggesting releases, by technical and business dependency
> ◆ balancing the releases into approximately similar sizes
>
> We held an open auction to arrive at a size estimate. We constructed a large table on the whiteboard. Each senior designer created row-labels for the factors he thought would determine the project effort. One wrote, "Technical frameworks, use cases, UI screens." Another added, "Business classes" and yet another added, "Database generation tool."
>
> Each person wrote in their column of the table his guess of how many of each factor was present. After everyone had had a turn, we ran a second round. The first person added a new column with his revised estimate based on what he had learned during the first round.
>
> We did three rounds this way. At the end, there were about twenty to twenty-five factors in all. Some people used multiplication factors from the estimate of business classes, some from use cases, some from UI screens. It turned out that the key drivers for the estimates were the number of:
>
> ◆ business classes
> ◆ screens

- frameworks
- technical classes (infrastructure, utility, etc.)

We discussed whether we had achieved convergence and what the differing factors were. In the end, we agreed on some numbers and understood where we differed.

In the second phase, we decided what type of person we would need for each section of code. Frameworks are hard, and there are only a select number of people who can write them reasonably, so we made that sensitive to the specific person we could hire. We decided that the business classes would be relatively easy to write, but would require business knowledge. Technical classes would be harder, but not require business knowledge. In the end we settled on:

- expert developers for the frameworks
- intermediate level developers for technical and UI classes
- relatively novice developers who knew the domain for those classes

We split the table of classes to be developed into those three categories, summed the classes per category, and decided on how many classes per month that level of developer could develop. We gave the framework developers 10 weeks per framework, the technical and UI developers 3 weeks per class, and the business class developers 2 weeks per class.

The sum of all those weeks gave us our first project time estimate. We hemmed and hawed over that for a long time, comparing it against other reasonability measures, such as the rate we could hire and train people. In the end, we kept the estimate.

Deciding the releases was straightforward. We already knew we wanted a release every three months. Nothing could be delivered until most of the infrastructure was done, so that went into release 1. (Note that it was later completely replaced, using the incremental rearchitecture strategy.) We created a *Project Map,* a dependency graph of the business functions, by technical and business dependence. From the size estimates, we circled areas of similar size. That gave us our release plan.

I tracked the project against our original estimate periodically during the project. Our progress tracked our original plan over the long run, but going slower at first and then faster at the end.

I present this technique here because I notice that most people who use a Delphi technique forget the crucial second phase, when the group assesses their ability to hire specific people with specific talents and skills. Without this information the result is not a plan, but a wish.

Technique 5.   Daily Stand-up Meetings

The daily stand-up meeting is a short meeting to trade notes on status, progress, and problems. The key word is short. The meeting is not used to *discuss* problems, but to *identify* problems. If you find you are discussing how to solve problems in your daily stand-up, raise your hand and ask that problem resolution be dealt with right after the stand-up meeting with only those people who have to be there.

The term "daily stand-up" comes from the Scrum methodology (Schwaber 2002). The idea is to get rid of long so-called status meetings where programmers ramble on for five or ten minutes about a piece of code they are working on or where management people ramble about various project initiatives. To keep people from rambling, the convention is that the meeting takes place standing up, so people can't fall asleep, type on their laptops, or doodle on paper. We want them sensitive to the passage of time.

The authors of Scrum suggest that each person simply answers three questions:

◆ What did I work on yesterday?

◆ What do I plan on working on today?

◆ What is getting in my way?

The daily stand-up meeting is amazingly effective for disseminating information; highlighting when someone is stuck; revealing when the item someone is working on is too low a priority, off-topic, or adding unrequested features; and generally keeping the group focused and on track. It is simple, and it has been added into projects using every imaginable methodology with good effect.

Technique 6.   Essential Interaction Design *(Jeff Patton)*

Most authors on agile development don't say much about the external design of the system,[8] giving the impression we think it is unimportant. Speaking at least for myself, I don't write about it because I have so little personal experience with this specialty, even though I recognize its importance.

For that reason, I include here four adaptations of usage-centered design (Constantine 1999) that Jeff Patton created for the agile context. Jeff highlights and simplifies the activities needed to define, design, and test the system's *personalities*[9] and its *interaction contexts*. These techniques are well suited to projects where people are collocated and have to get a lot accomplished in a limited time. (Just because you have easy access to expert users doesn't mean you get to waste their time!)

A software system presents *personalities* to its various end users through its help, information, and speed. It might be designed to be fast and efficient, for example, or warm, friendly, and informative. These are the personalities it presents to the outside world. Most systems present different personalities to different users, depending on those users' backgrounds and needs. Except most designers don't develop the personalities in any deliberate fashion. They simply throw together whatever they have on hand, and the personalities of the system are just whatever happens to come out.

There are probably one or two *focal* user groups that the sponsors really want to see satisfied with the new system. The team needs to find out who those are, what they need to accomplish using the software, what personality is best suited for each, and be sure they are properly served by the system. They need to detect, write down, and periodically recheck who those are.

Jeff illustrates with the example of a chain of retail stores. The cashier uses the system daily, gets familiar with it, and prioritizes for speed in registering sales. The store consultant, on the other hand, won't use the system very often, won't be fluent with its interface, but knowing all aspects of the store's operations, will want to do more functions than the cashier. The cashier wants a fast-and-efficient personality to work with; the store consultant wants an informative and helpful one.

When working through their tasks, the users will want to see information in clusters, which the interaction design community refers to as *interaction contexts*. Part of interaction design is detecting the clustering of information suited to each user's tasks,

---

[8]   Patton (2002) wrote an experience report about adding interaction design to agile development, and Cohn (2004) has a chapter on usage-centered design.

[9]   My term. It seems to me the interaction design community is missing this higher-level concept of their work.

and looking for commonality across those. The developers will convert those to user interface settings, often with a set of information matching an interaction context.

Essential interaction design produces

◆ Shared understanding among the sponsors, users and developers who were present in the room as to the roles and tasks to be addressed by the system and the relative priorities of each

◆ Paper-and-pen collages ("reminding markers" in cooperative-game language) showing roles, tasks, and interaction contexts, marked with notes so that the team can deliver them in business value order.

Jeff articulates four techniques, in all.

1. Essential Interaction Design (the Workshop)
2. Deriving the UI
3. Usability Inspection (during Design)
4. QA Testing the System Personalities

The first is essential interaction design itself, done either near the beginning of the project or the start of an iteration. After that, he presents short techniques for designing the screens themselves, for reviewing the UI with the users, and for testing internally that the finished software is appropriate for the user roles that will be using it.

Here are the techniques as Jeff describes them.

Essential Interaction Design (the Workshop)

The approach is based on the usage-centric design approach (Constantine 1999) except that this initial requirements elicitation and design process can be completed in a couple of hours to a couple of days. When an experienced facilitator is used, no advanced training of the business people is required. The techniques can be applied during initial requirements elicitation, when building incremental release plans, while defining the general form of the software, deriving user interface from use cases, acceptance testing, and even during end-user usability evaluation, if need be.

What follows is a step-by-step outline of the initial requirements elicitation and design process. The overall goal of the technique suite is to *hasten the discovery of requirements by bringing together people from each critical aspect of the project and allowing them to explain what they know to each other.*

Step 1. Get the right people into the room.

We're replacing weeks of interviewing and field research with conversation during this meeting, so it's critical the meeting involve members of each constituency the system will be serving, including those developing the system. Remember, if you're the facilitator, you aren't interested in what participants say to you, but rather what they say to each other.

In the workshop you will need selected key project stakeholders, selected key users, domain experts, and members of the development team, including test/QA people.

Eight to twelve people are good. It's sometimes hard to limit attendees to that number, but do it.

Set participants in a comfortable workspace with a big worktable and lots of wall space for hanging posters. Include markers, tape, 3″ × 5″ index cards, and lots of snacks to keep the less busy people occupied.

You're hosting a party.

Step 2. Capture and annotate user roles.

The term "actor" refers to any of job title, user role, or a mixture of both. We are after "roles," phrases that indicates what particular users' goals are. I always look for "thing doer" phrases to describe a role, or even, *"adjectived* thing doer," to make it more specific (only in English can a noun describing an adjective be used as a verb in the past tense!).

For example, we might find an "order taker" in the store situation, or a "special-order taker," or even better, a "hurried special-order taker." To handle customers who are angry because the special order is late, we find a "late-order researcher" or a "complaint handler." (People with such titles as sales associate and manager perform all the roles.) The extended role name makes it easier to keep the role clear enough so that anyone, with or without special domain knowledge, can understand what the role might be doing. It lets us know the person performing in this role is in a hurry and needs functionality and a user-interface that can support that.

Brainstorm user roles onto index cards—"card-storming," as Constantine and Lockwood (Constantine 1999) call it. After card-storming, refine your role list by removing duplicates and verifying the names are clear. Good names are important. We won't be relying on pages of documentation to describe each role, so the name is all you've got. Make sure it's expressive.

You are likely to name roles that you might consider stakeholders of the system, not necessarily users. Don't discard these. It's important to consider the goals of these people. It's important to ask how the software could support those goals. I often find that roles that might have been set aside as stakeholders actually need functionality in the system that supports proving to them that their interests were protected.

On the index card, write the role's primary goal or goals under the role name. What constitutes success for this user in using the system? What constitutes failure? We will keep checking that the requirements we capture really help user roles meet their goals.

Write only what constitutes success from the user role's perspective, not his boss's or some other stakeholder's. For example, a call center employee in a credit card service center, a "credit card application taker" might have a goal to take applications quickly enough and accurately enough to avoid a manager's attention. The manager, on the other hand, might want to improve speed and accuracy and reduce customer complaints. Other stakeholders may be concerned with up-selling credit insurance policies. The manager's and stakeholder's goals aren't necessarily those of the "credit card application taker." Make sure the appropriate goal finds its way onto the appropriate role card. If you want to capture the other stakeholders' needs, consider adding some roles, such as "efficiency watcher" and "up-selling watcher," and create role cards for them.

Write on each card a subjective estimate of that role's business value or importance, high, medium, or low. I mark H, M, or L on the lower left corner of the card.

Write on each card an estimate of how often the role will use the system. This can be high, medium, low, or hourly, daily, monthly, quarterly, yearly, or some other frequency you find suitable. I write these on the lower right hand corner of the card.

Figure 3-11   *The role modeling session. Be sure to listen for the conversations that occur during this process. (Courtesy of Jeff Patton)*

Step 3. Construct the user role model.
In this step you understand and mark the relationships, dependencies, and collaborations between roles. The result is the agile version of a *role model*.

Using a sheet of poster paper, the participants will cluster the user role cards on the table. The only important instruction to give is, "Try to cluster. Keep roles similar to each other close together, dissimilar roles farther apart." Once the model "feels" right, fix the cards to the poster paper with tape.

The roles probably got clustered together because they have similar goals or participate in the business process at similar times. Circle each cluster of roles. Label each with some indication of why those roles got clustered.

Draw a line from each cluster to other clusters where a relationship exists. I might, for example, draw a line from a cluster marked "order takers" to one marked "order fulfillers" and label it "sends orders to."

Make any other notes of interest on the model, possibly including a notable business rule, user role characteristic, or relationship across user roles.

Step 4. Identify the focal roles.
Participants now vote for the roles (not role clusters!) they consider being most critical to the success of the software (including also the roles where dire consequences

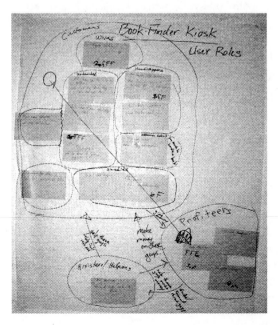

Figure 3-12 *A sample role-model. To those present during its creation, the marked-up sheet brings back a flood of conversation and information. (Courtesy of Jeff Patton)*

follow when they fail in their goals). I usually only allow folks with either domain expertise or strong and educated opinions to vote.

To get the focal roles, I may give five voters three votes each. Since there's usually candy (e.g., Hershey's kisses) on the table during our sessions, I like to use those as voting tokens. Have people place the tokens directly on the role cards they find most significant. Doing this with physical markers as opposed to just pen marks is helpful to people making choices. I often find people who've used up their votes will begin to lobby others to vote as they did, or vote for the role they didn't because they ran out of votes. These are interesting conversations. I often see perhaps 3 or 5 or so roles picked out as focal from 15 to 25 roles on the table.

After everyone is done, replace the physical tokens with marks such as an "F" for each vote. Write the F using a brightly colored ink. This makes it easy to find the focal roles in a busy role model. Roles with the most Fs are easy to spot. I remind folks to pay close attention to these.

You are likely to make interesting discoveries at this point, for example, that the most-voted on, or focal, roles may not be the ones with the highest business value or have the highest usage frequency. Discuss your results. Make any interesting notes directly on the model.

Step 5. Capture the tasks required to accomplish the goals.

Using the role model as reference, think of a person going to the system to perform a task to meet their goal in that particular role. Write that task name onto an index card. I like task names that start with a verb, such as "add items to order" or "choose customer from known customers." Just as with role names, the task names are important. The more clear and concise the tasks names, the less supporting documentation you'll need for them.

"Card-storm" the user tasks using this thinking activity, covering all roles. When there's likely to be a large number of tasks, I like to work on one cluster of roles at a time. Remove duplicates and clarify task names.

For each task card, note three things directly on the card:

◆ The goal of this task. What is a successful outcome for the task?
◆ Its frequency. You can use high, medium, or low, or time references such as hourly, daily, weekly, monthly, or yearly.
◆ Its business value. This is a subjective best guess, high, medium, or low.

Step 6. Build the task model.

In this step, you will identify relationships and dependencies that tasks have with each other, just as you did with the role model.

Figure 3-13 *Marking up the task model. Participants often invent notation meaningful to the domain and to themselves. (Courtesy of Jeff Patton)*

Arrange the task cards on a fresh sheet of poster paper. Without having to match the role clustering on the role model, cluster similar tasks and let dissimilar tasks fall far apart. When the model feels right, fix the cards in place with tape.

As with the role model, circle and label clusters of cards, then look for relationships between clusters. Draw and label relationship lines between the clusters.

See if you can spot a "timeline." Look for the task likely to be performed earliest. Start there and draw a line connecting each subsequent task until you arrive at the task likely to be performed last. I usually find the line runs from the upper left side of the model down to the lower right—but not always. The timeline helps to point out the overall workflow from task to task.

The task model should be a concise picture of the work the system needs to perform.

Step 7. Identify the focal tasks.

You need to understand and mark the tasks that are most critical to the success of the software. Just as with the role model, everyone gets three votes, or perhaps more if the task model has a large number of cards.

Have people vote for the tasks most critical to the software. What tasks deliver the most value? What tasks are done the most frequently? Alternatively, think of the tasks that if not done, or done incorrectly, can cause the most trouble. You can use the candy again if it has not all been eaten by now.

Write an "F" for each vote directly on the cards. As with the role model, use a brightly colored ink to write the Fs on the cards. Those are your *focal* tasks.

Look for interesting discoveries. Are there high-frequency tasks with high business value that weren't voted as focal? Why? Are there low-frequency, low-value tasks that were focal? Focal roles often perform focal tasks. Is this true of your models? Interesting details arise out of discussing these points.

Step 8. Extract interaction contexts.

An interaction context is a place in the software where a user might go to perform some of their tasks. It's the designer's job to find those places, organize them appropriately, and then put the right tools there so the task execution goes smoothly.

For example, if I were designing for a project called "my house," I might have some tasks called "put away groceries," "make dinner," and "listen to radio." I might decide those three tasks belong together in an interaction context I'll call "kitchen." In my kitchen I'll put tools I need to perform the tasks: a refrigerator, a stove, pots and pans, and a radio. You'll find interaction contexts in the software you use every day.

You'll find that the clusters in your task model are likely to be interaction contexts. The tasks clustered together because they were similar for some reason—often because they're performed at similar times by similar user roles.

Name each interaction context and write the name on a 3″ × 5″ card. Arrange these cards on yet another sheet of poster paper. Fix them with tape when the arrangement feels right. Draw lines between each interaction context card to indicate how a user might navigate from one context to another. This is a *navigation map*.

At this point you should start to be able to visualize the software. A well-named interaction context becomes a suitable module name and a good way to refer to the tasks performed there (just as when I say "kitchen" you can quickly imagine the kinds of tasks I might do there). You may find it useful to index sections of the project plan by interaction context. It's easier to explain that you are working on the "order processing" functions than it is to itemize all the tasks individually.

Step 9. Identify an incremental release plan.

You have in front of you a set of poster sheets that show you the roles that will use the system and the functions the system needs to provide them. What you still need to discover is the order in which to deliver them to the user community. You may be making multiple deliveries, in which case you want to deliver the functions in a *useful* order. If you are only going to make a single delivery, then you still want to develop and integrate the functions in the same order, for protection against the worst-case situation, that is, you run out of time before getting to everything.

My preferred order is "highest composite business value." I use that phrase because sometimes, to deliver a complete task thread, end-to-end, you actually have to develop and integrate one or more tasks that have lower individual value. If you don't include those tasks, then the users won't actually get full value from the most

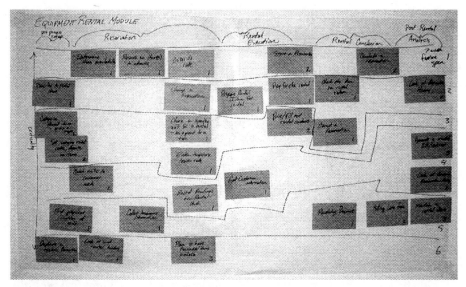

Figure 3-14   *A span plan, which lets you see both the work flow and possible releases at a glance. (Courtesy of Jeff Patton)*

valuable (focal) tasks. We want to deliver full business value, the composite value of the entire thread of tasks along a work flow.

The shortest, most useful path is what I call a "system span."[10] Develop this first, as an early victory to the users and what they will consider the walking skeleton of the system functionality. Subsequent releases will incrementally add features to that system span.

To build the incremental release plan, make a copy of the task cards. You can hand copy all the task cards. I find that keying them into a spreadsheet then printing them onto cards using a word processor works well. I do this during a break or at lunch that same day.

Place each task card on a (fresh) poster sheet according to its time and criticality.

◆ Time runs from left to right, referring to when a user role might perform that particular task.

◆ Business criticality runs top (most important) to bottom (least important). Criticality refers to how necessary the task is to perform (optional tasks will never be on the top row).

---

[10]   Borrowed from *Lean Software Development* (Poppendieck 2003).

You'll find the task cards start to arrange themselves in rows. The top row will contain critical tasks arranged in time order. Each subsequent row will contain other, less critical tasks, also in time order. Draw a line directly under the top row. This is the system span, the smallest set of features that can be released to perform an end-to-end business process flow.

Finally, it's the developers' turn. Have the developers present give rough development time estimates on each task card.[11] Course-grain estimates are fine at this point. I often restrict the estimates to 1 week at a minimum, 3 or 4 at a maximum. Draw lines left to right across the model where you'd like to group tasks for future releases. What you have here isn't the project schedule, but a way of identifying similarly sized clusters of function to develop in each iteration, that is, useful information for building the project map.

This concludes the session, exhausting but fun work that strengthens relationships between the users, sponsors, and developers.

Be sure to place the flip charts prominently in the development area as information radiators, constantly reminding the developers of the product features, the focal roles and focal tasks, and the conversations around how they came to be. This allows the developers to see the software through the eyes of those user roles rather than through the eyes of a project manager, developer, or tester.

Deriving the UI

When it comes time to develop the UI prototype, consider a technique described by Constantine, Windl, Noble, and Lockwood,[12] which I [Jeff] also practice and have slightly modified to suit my personal style.

Do the following for each user task, on poster sheets:

◆ Write in two columns a synopsis of the dialog between the user and the system. Put the *User Intentions* in the left column and the corresponding *System Responsibilities* in the right. This is what Constantine calls an "essential use-case" (Constantine 1999).

---

[11] Notes from Alistair: First, these should be seen as relative sizing estimates, not elapsed time estimates. It can be damaging to commit to a development schedule so quickly. I would recheck these numbers later using blitz planning, because you are likely to find additional tasks to be done that weren't noticed during the rush of this workshop.

[12] http://www.foruse.com/articles/canonical.htm.

- Place sticky notes next to the user intentions and system responsibilities that will be UI elements. Put those for input areas and user actions on the left side and those for information containers on the right side. For example, a user intention such as "user identifies self" suggests two input areas and one action (name, password, some sort of "GO" button). Write "username" and "password" on two sticky notes. Write "action" on a third, or just use one with a different size or color to indicate its presence. Stick all three next to the phrase "user identifies self." For a phrase such as "system displays open orders," you want a component showing a list of orders. Write "list of orders" on a sticky note and put it next to the phrase "system displays open orders." When you're done, the use case should be spotted with sticky notes.

- Transfer the sticky notes to another flip chart, representing screens the user will see, placing them in areas that seem appropriate for the user interface of the system. When you're comfortable with the placement, replace each sticky note with a simple line drawing of the component drawn approximately the size you'd expect the component to appear on the user interface. Do this with each component. You now have what is called a "wire-frame" drawing of the user interface.

Test the wire-frame user interface by referring back to the use case. One participant plays a user role performing the task, the other plays the role of the system. Make sure the user interface you've designed supports easy performance of the task.

Usability Inspection (during Design)

It is time to inspect your (running) design.

Project the running software onto a wall big enough for a group of participants to easily see it.

Choose a participant to perform the user role that will be using the part of the software being inspected. I prefer someone not familiar with the functionality. Give that person a task or list of tasks to perform that are chosen from the task model you drew at the start of the project or from the essential use cases.

The person performing the task explains out loud what he or she is doing. As the system displays information, you can explain what they're seeing. Everyone in the room notes defects or suggested changes on index cards.

After the tasks have been performed on the system, collect the cards. Eliminate duplicates, clarify issues, and prioritize the issues to be addressed by the development team. (Don't be depressed if you find dozens of issues on your first pass, that's normal. Just make sure you address the issues.)

Repeat this process as necessary until the user interactions move smoothly when executing the tasks.

QA Testing the System Personalities

Finally, you will need to confirm that the finished software is appropriate for the user role that will be using it. We often have a QA person pretend to be a user in the part of a role indicated by the role model.

For each role in the role model, assume the knowledge and goals of that role. Use the role description and any other information you can gather about the people who might step into that role. Method acting skills come in handy here.

Perform all the tasks assigned to that role using the running system, and write down, as though you were a person in that role, any problems you feel the person will have.

You may find you perform the same task many times. Each time, though, you'll be doing it from a different user role's perspective, and evaluating it differently.

*   *   *

Jeff summarizes:

> User-centric design leverages information about users' traits and goals throughout the development process and ultimately validates the system against that information. I've found this generally results in easier to use software that the actual end-users are happier with. I've found we generally have far less rework on finished features and we discover fewer unanticipated features late in development.

Technique 7.   Process Miniature

Any new process is unfamiliar and perplexing. The longer the process duration, the longer before new team members understand how the various parts of the process fit with each other. You can speed this understanding by shrinking the time taken by the process, using the *process miniature*. Here are three examples of its use:

> A large organization, using a methodology much larger than Clear, put each new employee through a one-week project. By the end of that project, the new employee had exercised every part of the process. He or she could then work on a real project knowing the connection between all the process activities and work products.

> "Extreme hour" was invented by Peter Merel to introduce people to XP in 60 minutes.[13] The group runs two half-hour iterations: 10 minutes for the planning game, 15 minutes to develop a solution and acceptance tests, 5 minutes for acceptance testing. The group runs through the process twice so they can experience reducing project scope partway through an iteration, pushing features from one iteration to the next iteration, and adding and shifting requirements within and across iterations. To make development time work in 15 minutes, the team designs something arbitrary, such as a mousetrap or a fishing device, and only draws their design on overhead transparencies.

> For a small, 50-person company with 16 programmers, I once ran a 90-minute process miniature that required programming, test creation, check-in/checkout, and integration across three architectural tiers. We used two 45-minute iterations and a very, very simple programming problem: an up-down counter run through a Web interface. It took us two tries to get through the problem in the 90 minutes. The first try we used as a practice session to understand what was being requested. The second try was done live in front of the entire company as a demo of the working method.

You may wish to introduce Crystal Clear by using a process miniature somewhere between ninety minutes and one day. This might be done before the initial methodology shaping workshop, or just after, so the team can "taste" their new methodology. The methodology shaping workshop itself can be sampled by running it in a very digested form lasting only half an hour, just so the team can learn how it works on a "safer" topic than their project.

Many techniques can be introduced using a process miniature to reduce the problem that people have with starting to use an unfamiliar process. You might run your first reflection workshop in just fifteen minutes as a process miniature. I run a process miniature for writing use cases in my use case course so that people can see the overall picture before we get into details.

---

[13]   http://c2.com/cgi/wiki?ExtremeHour.

Technique 8.   Side-by-Side Programming

"Programming in pairs" involves two people working on one programming assignment at a single workstation.[14] Some people find this to be too much togetherness. Side-by-side programming allows them to get some of the effects of pair programming without giving up their individual (programming or other) assignments.

In side-by-side programming, two people sit close enough to see each others' screens easily, but work on their own assignments. This is an amplification of osmotic communication for the programming context.

In Figure 3-15, Justin and Andrew have set the workstations so that the monitors are just two feet apart. The idea is that Justin should only have to turn his head or lean over a bit to see Andrew's screen. Then, they can work on their own respective assignments, but each can ask the other at any moment to look at a piece of code, run a test, or similar.

Studies have shown that design- and code-reviews are cost-effective ways to reduce defects in the software (McConnell 1998). People find it hard to find the energy and interest to either call a code-review meeting or attend one. Being right

Figure 3-15   *Side-by-side programming. (Courtesy of Jeff Patton, Justin Johnson, Andrew Lawrence, and Tomax)*

---

[14]   See *Pair Programming Illuminated* (Williams 2002).

next to each other, however, these two people can examine and comment on small amounts of code in short amounts of time, with little ceremony or disruption to their work. It provides the "peer code peering" described by Crystal in the first of the e-mails at the start of the book.

The developers who first told me of this method said it allowed them to work in parallel on their programming, so they were not both occupied by the same task. At the same time, they could review each other's code as called for by the complexity of the code. They were programming a client-server system at the time, one working on the client, the other on the server. One could say to the other, "I've got the stub compiled. Can you test it?" The other would run the system, and then return to his programming while the first person fixed whatever bug showed up in the test.

Another senior developer commented that he spent most of the day writing reports and managing conversations, rather than programming. Having him sit just two feet away from another programmer meant that he could be useful as a coach and a second pair of eyes without having to give up his nonprogramming work.

Jim Coplien has speculated that full-time pair programming is not the optimal amount of time for people to spend together.[15] Side-by-side programming allows people to mix and match the time they spend on the same task and on separate tasks.

As with many of the ideas in Crystal Clear, you may find side-by-side programming to be a useful stepping-stone to doing Extreme Programming, or as a fall-back in case people do not take to the full XP practice.

---

[15] Personal communication.

Technique 9.   Burn Charts

Burn charts have become a favorite way to give visibility into a project's progress. They are extremely simple and astonishingly powerful. They reveal the strategy being used, show the progress made against predictions, and open the door to discussions about how best to proceed, including the difficult discussions about whether to cut scope or extend the schedule. They have a natural mapping to the earned value charts used in military/government projects. They should use part of your standard bag of tricks for project planning and reporting.

It turns out that packing a house has striking similarities to software development as far as planning and tracking go. I use the following exercise to illustrate the use of burn charts:

> Imagine you have 30 days to pack up a house you are living in (with a couple of kids, just to make it more painful). Assume there are 14 rooms (or room equivalents) on 3 floors. Chart your plan so that you always know what is done, what is left, and how well you are doing.

Most people plan to pack the house as shown in Figure 3-16. They plan to first throw out all the junk, then pack the noncritical items, and pack the essential living items in the last few days. This is, of course, the technique I used the first two times I was in this situation, and I can speak with firsthand pain in saying that it is terrible.

The big flaw in it is the absence of clear intermediate milestones.

It is practically impossible to tell whether one is 60 percent or 70 percent done (speaking to both software and room packing). For most of the project, one sees neither the true size of the task at hand, nor the (slower than expected) rate of progress. Missing both of those, it is impossible to tell when one will get done. In both cases, an ugly surprise awaits at the end when a myriad of little unexpected items suddenly become visible (think about when you loaded all the boxes into a moving truck and walked back into the house, only to discover all sorts of things that suddenly "appeared" when everything else was taken out). The classical result on software projects is that programmers keep reporting that things are 80 percent complete, or "We'll be done when we're done."

The repair is to find "interesting" and clear intermediate milestones.

In packing, those milestones are rooms completely packed and empty, containing "not even a sock" (and possibly with police tape across the doorway to keep people from dumping stuff back into them!). The thinking is that if there is so much as a sock left, then there is possibly something else besides the sock, and the reporting is flawed. We will see an application of this "sock" idea in just a few pages.

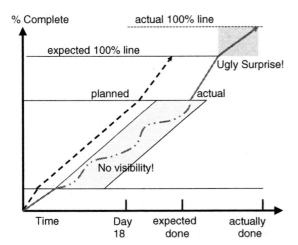

Figure 3-16 *Scheduling with no definitive milestones.*

In software, those milestones are the delivery of running, tested code, as described in the section on frequent delivery.

This new strategy has implications that make life a little awkward (again, both for software and house packing). In house packing, people have to move out of their rooms, and eventually the kitchen becomes unusable. In software, tests have to be rerun, and designs and documentation must be altered on each delivery. These are not free—cost and discomfort both come with the strategy.

The payback for the cost and the discomfort is improved visibility, improved tracking, and less likelihood of an unexpected project overrun. In most cases, this benefit is well worth the cost.

Let's look at this strategy on a software project.

◆ Make a list of all the items to be delivered. You might work from the project map, blitz planning, or XP's planning game. Associate with each delivery item a *relative cost*. Try to associate with each item also a relative *business benefit*, so that you can discuss with the executive sponsor the value being delivered to the business over time (Figure 3-17 shows a fragment of such a list). The reason for using relative estimates instead of absolute ones is that if you are, for example, 10 percent over on your first set of items, all the remaining items will scale accordingly. The burn charts will show this automatically.

◆ Sort and sequence the work items by development dependency, cost, and value, and cluster them into a sequence, as shown in Figure 3-18 (you may recognize the similarity of what we are doing here and what happens in a blitz planning session).

	Feature	Feature Description	Value	Est. Ideal Days	Est. Elapsed Days
1	User Interface	Allow the configuration to populate		**8**	
1.1	Configuration generates order line item comments	order line item comments with detailed configuration information along with configuration comments. Stop change of line item notes other than from within the appropriate configurator.	M	2	5
1.2	Configurator UI Rework: Verbose wizard style	Rework user-interface to match the prototye discussed in collaborative review session. Fast, simple data entry. No unnecessary frills.	H	6	15
1.3	Configuration generates customer specific pricing	Configuration is passed current order customer for use in determining customer specific pricing.	H	5	12.5
1.4	Allow adding a config-uration and continue	Currently a configured blind may be added to an order. To add a subse-quent similar blind you'd need to go back into configurator and reenter all the information. This feature would allow the user to accept a finished configuration and immediately allow adding an additional configuration using the data from the previous configuration.	L	2	5
2	Special Order PO Generation			**5**	
2.1	PO generated correctly for configuration	Currently POs are generated for regular order line items. Change to allow configuration components to generate one or more purchase orders at a cost furnished by the component.	H	5	12.5
2.2	Create/confirm vendor items exist for skus	Confirm that a vendor item exists for each sku used for base window treat-ments and options. Where no vendor item exists for an assigned vendor, dynamically create the vendor item.	H	1.5	3.75
2.3	PO generation is automatic	Currently Pos can be generated after a special order is saved and a deposit is made. Allow automatic PO generation immediately after deposit is tendered, or immediately if no deposit is required.	L	4	10
3	Advanced Order			**9**	
3.1	Advanced Order form shows more details	Alter Advanced Order form to show an "overflow" for each line item where additional information such as comments, Po number, PO order date etc., can be shown.	M	4	10

Figure 3-17   *Extract of feature list with estimates of size and business value. (Courtesy of Jeff Patton)*

Module	Feature Name	Value	Raw Dev. Time (ideal days)	Estimated Elapsed Days	Release #
1.1	Configuration generates order line item comments	M	2	5	1
1.2	Configrator UI rework: Verbose wizard style	H	6	15	1
2.1	PO generated correctly for configuration	H	5	12.5	1
2.2	Create/confirm vendor items exist for skus	H	1.5	3.75	1
3.1	Advanced Order form shows more details	M	4	10	1
3.2	Order fulfilled at PO cost	H	2	5	1
3.3	Repeat orders works with blind configurations	M	3	7.5	1
3.4	Configuration comments are viewable, not editable	L	1	2.5	1
4.1	Base hierarchy change	H	1.5	3.75	1
4.2	Style can locate price charts based on color selection	H	2	5	1
4.3	Assign specific color group colors to price charts	H	2	5	1
4.4	Separate messages from options	H	2	5	1
4.5	Separate questions from options	H	2	5	1
1.3	Configuration generates customer specific pricing	H	5	12.5	2
1.4	Allow adding a configuration and continue	L	2	5	2
2.3	PO generation is automatic	L	4	10	2
3.5	Order shows sq. footage & running length	L	2	5	2
3.6	Vendor orderable items show additional detail	L	2	5	2
3.7	Printed window treatments show disclaimers	M	6	15	2
3.8	Allow order line item copying	H	2	5	2
4.1	Associate style with Retail.net DCL	L	1	2.5	2
4.11	Grid validation	L	1	2.5	2
4.6	Assign customer specific selling discounts	H	3	7.5	2
4.7	Customer lookup	H	1	2.5	2
4.8	Customer account type lookup	M	1	2.5	2
4.9	Options may have required questions	L	3	7.5	2

Figure 3-18   *The Iceberg List with Product Backlog. (Courtesy of Jeff Patton)*

◆ Estimate how much can be accomplished in each iteration or delivery period. Draw a line under the last item that fits in each. Number the releases.

I have come to call this the *Iceberg List*. The "above water" part lists all the items that can be delivered in the current delivery cycle. The "below water" part lists every item that will be delivered in later delivery cycles. The name reflects that when you add a new item to the above water part, it pushes everything else down, and something that was above water falls below water (will not be delivered in the current delivery cycle). The iceberg list is particularly useful on projects where the requirements change frequently. In Scrum terminology, the below water part is referred to the *Product Backlog* and the above water part is the *Sprint Backlog.*[16]

The primary difference between this list and the standard systems engineering work-breakdown structure is that *you get no credits for any item that does not result in running, tested code.* Okay, you also get credit for *final deliverables* such as training materials and delivery documentation.

◆ At this point you can make a burn-up chart (Figure 3-19). Mark either relative work units or percent complete on the vertical axis, and calendar time on the horizontal. Draw a line from the origin to the completion point, either by estimating the rate at which work can be accomplished, or as often happens, the "drop dead" delivery deadline. That shows the "planned" progress.

After each iteration, mark how much relative work got completed. You will find that with just two marks on the chart you can see how far slower you are moving than you expected! Yes, that may be bad news, but at least it is *bad news detected early*, as opposed to *bad news detected too late to do anything about it!*

The burn-up chart resembles the classical earned-value chart (Lett 1998, Fleming 1988). The essential difference is that people traditionally include on the earned-value chart *tasks completed*, whether or not they resulted in code getting integrated. On agile projects, credit is only given when code is integrated and tested (the "no leftover sock" rule). The agile strategy yields more reliable information about the project's actual state than the general one.

The burn-up chart has many nice features.

◆ It shows both the status and rate of progress ("velocity") in a way that is both clear and easy to discuss.

---

[16]   More about Scrum's backlogs is online at http://wiki.scrums.org/index.cgi.

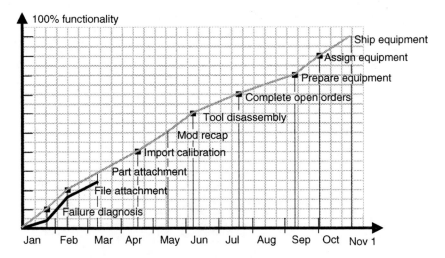

Figure 3-19   *The burn-up chart quickly shows progress and earned value. The long thin line shows the planned functionality and schedule; the short thick line shows progress to date.*

◆ If you plot business value on the vertical axis instead of development effort, you get a chart that properly shows how much value you have delivered over time. Plotting both on the same chart may help remind the team about where the real business value lies in their work. If you sequence the iceberg list to float the greatest business value items to the top, and track business value delivered, then no matter when the project gets terminated, it will be clear to everyone that they got the most business value in the time spent.

◆ Finally, the burn-up chart is a key part of a good one-page project status report (examples of status reports are shown in the Chapter 5). Such one-page status sheets simplify the work of executives looking at reports from many projects.

Even though the burn-up chart is very nice, there is a nasty surprise if you are not careful in choosing the units you use for the vertical axis.

In house packing, the obvious unit of estimation and tracking is the packing box. In programming, the obvious unit is the line of code (LOC). These are convenient and give wonderful detail.

The problem is that you won't know the actual number of boxes or lines of code needed until the very end (shades of "We'll be done when we're done"). The graph tracks *rate* wonderfully, but *progress* poorly. Not only will you not discover bad news

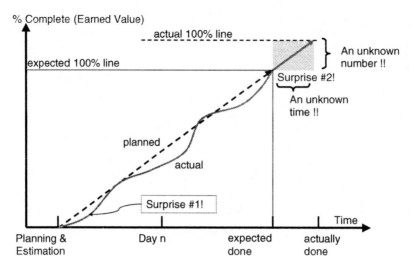

Figure 3-20   *A burn-up chart when the wrong units are measured.*

early, but also you will not know how many boxes or LOC you need until the last item is packed or programmed. That is too late.

The repair is to choose a unit of measure that can't possibly expand. In house packing, the replacement measure is easy: use rooms instead of boxes (it would be quite a surprise to discover a new room after you have packed all the rest). The answer is not generally obvious on a software project. You may be lucky and have a relatively stable number of use cases, or a fixed number of modules to replace, but there is no generally applicable answer.

I met two teams that had found an answer for themselves. They were doing system replacement projects where the subsystems communicated in a workflow pattern. Their nonexpanding unit was the workflow component. These teams were able to color each subsystem yellow as they started work on it, and then green as it was completed. They were able to use "components replaced" as their nonexpanding unit (see the sample status sheet in Chapter 5).

In the more usual situation, project scope does in fact change over time. Phil Goodwin and Russ Rufer introduced[17] the idea of marking the raising and lowering of the ceiling, or 100 percent mark, as the project progresses. This charting allows the team to show the original plan and actual accomplishments even in the face of scope

---

[17]   Private communication

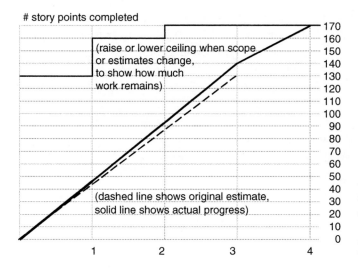

story points completed

(raise or lower ceiling when scope
or estimates change,
to show how much
work remains)

(dashed line shows original estimate,
solid line shows actual progress)

170
160
150
140
130
120
110
100
90
80
70
60
50
40
30
20
10
0

1   2   3   4

Figure 3-21   *A burn-up chart showing predicted and actual accomplishments, and changing 100 percent line, using the Goodwin-Rufer style.*

changes. Figure 3-21 shows the Goodwin-Rufer style burn-up chart in a situation where the team actually performed better than their estimates but had to deliver increasing scope. (The project actually used the standard Scrum burn-down chart shown in Figure 3-24. I think you will agree that their conversations with the sponsors would have been easier had they used either Figure 3-21 or 3-26.)

If you are lucky enough to have a good nonexpanding unit of measure, then you can use the *burn-down* chart, which some people find emotionally more powerful.

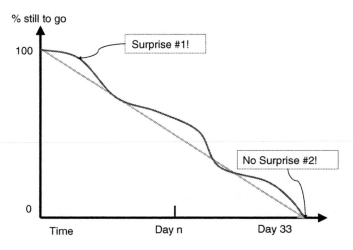

% still to go

100

Surprise #1!

No Surprise #2!

0

Time   Day n   Day 33

Figure 3-22   *The burn-down chart.*

The burn-down chart is emotionally powerful because there is a special feeling about hitting the number zero that helps people get excited about completing their work and pressing forward. I can speak firsthand in saying that as soon as we shifted our house packing chart to using rooms as the unit of measure and put the rooms on a burn-down chart, our confidence that we would actually meet our schedule increased dramatically. I have seen the same apply to a software project team.

It is easy to say, "We can't use the burn-down chart, because nothing is fixed on a software project." Oddly, the first people to say this were those working on the system replacement project just mentioned. After a bit of examination, we discovered that they had the house-packing problem in front of them. They were able to convert immediately to the burn-down chart, using replaced subsystems as their nonexpanding unit of measure.

*   *   *

There are three wrinkles left to discuss.

The first is the little white lie I just told in the last paragraph about nonexpanding unit of work. The team discovered after a short while that their executive sponsor kept adding demands for new functionality in both the old system and the replacement. In other words, although they were promised that the scope would be fixed (since the time and budget was), that wasn't really true. As if that were not bad enough, he was actually opposed to the project itself, and was obliged to support it only because of pressure from the user community (see how powerful user community support can be!).

This put the team in a damned-if-you-do-and-damned-if-you-don't position. They couldn't report that a subsystem was complete (not even a sock left in it) if he was going to keep throwing more socks back into the room, and they couldn't stop him from throwing more socks in.

Their eventual strategy has some bearing on burn charts, but also some bearing on the positive role of intermediate managers. The intermediate manager decided that they would take their project mission as originally stated to replace the existing system. They would deliver that successfully, and track all increased scope as growing "post-replacement" activity.

They charted this as shown in Figure 3-23. With this strategy and chart, they were able to keep their focus on the critical issue of replacing the existing system, show they were tracking the new functions being added, and keep the executive sponsor from derailing their project.

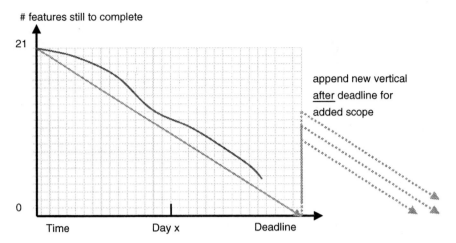

Figure 3-23 *The burn-down chart for a hard-deadline project with scope increase added at the end.*

Mike Cohn reports a similar situation in his (2004) book *User Stories*, although in friendly circumstances. The team was given 130 story points (a relative unit of size for XP user stories) to deliver in three iterations. After each iteration, the sponsors added new stories, and the team revised the relative sizes of the remaining stories. Both increased the estimate of the amount of work remaining. Mike and I discussed how they should chart the team's progress against changing scope, assuming they like the emotional power of the burn-down chart.

Figure 3-24 shows what the team showed the sponsors at their meetings (Cohn 2004). Mike and I felt that this chart conceals very important information. Figure 3-25 shows how I thought to modify the chart to illustrate the actual accomplishments against the changing scope, and Figure 3-26 shows how Mike proposed to modify the chart to show the changing situation. You may notice that Figure 3-26 is the downward version of the Goodwin-Rufer burn-up chart.

We offer these examples of charts to show different ways in which you can show predicted and actual accomplishments with simplicity and expressive power. There are probably more variations to discover, but these should get you started.

The second wrinkle to be discussed is the size of the selected unit of measure. This is very relevant at the start of a project because the team will almost always move more slowly at the beginning than expected, and just *how* much more slowly is a valuable piece of information.

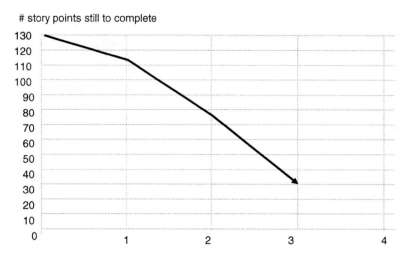

Figure 3-24   *Scrum-style burn-down chart as shown to the project sponsors (after Cohn 2004).*

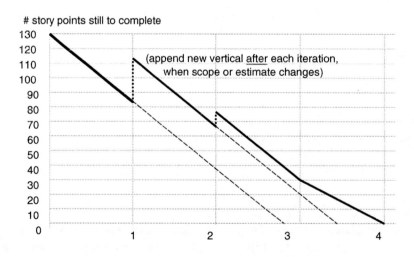

Figure 3-25   *Burn-down chart for the same project showing scope increase after each iteration.*

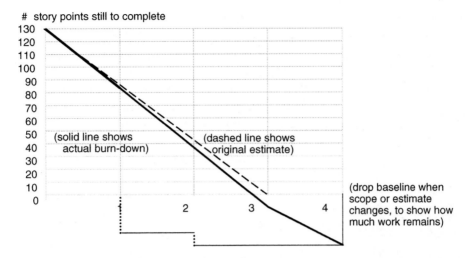

Figure 3-26 *Burn-down chart for the same project using the "down" version of the Goodwin-Rufer chart.*

Let us return to the house packing example to see this clearly. The graphs in Figure 3-27 show that the coarser the unit of measure, the longer the blackout period during which no information is available. Having already rejected "boxes

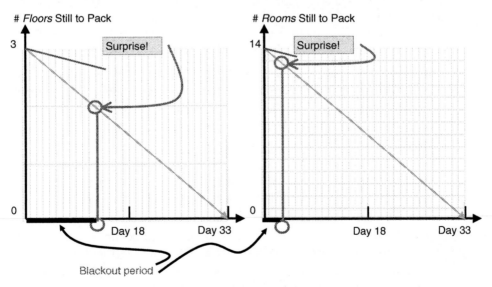

Figure 3-27 *Burn-down charts for two different base units. The smaller the unit, the shorter the initial blackout period.*

packed" as a good unit of measure, we can choose "rooms packed" or "floors packed" as nonexpanding units.

Figure 3-27 shows burn-down charts for both of those choices. In both cases, the people fall behind at the same rate. However, with floors as units, they don't discover how bad the news is until a third of the way through the project, which is a relatively long time. Using rooms as units, they discover how bad the news is after only a few days. The moral of the story is to choose the smaller nonexpandable unit of measure.

*   *   *

The final item to discuss is handling items that change priorities. This gets us back to the iceberg list, which has shown great utility on projects in which the priorities change frequently and violently.

> A large project was delivering value to a customer on a regular basis. The customer would change work assignments and priorities so often and so late that no project plan was meaningful. The customer was, however, happy with the software being delivered, so they kept requesting more work done.
>
> In desperation, the project manager just put all requested features into a single prioritized list with estimated sizes. He announced that whatever was above the "water line," as calculated from the size estimates and team's velocity, would get delivered in the next release, and everything else would be delivered "later." The customer could insert, remove, modify, or reprioritize features at any time, even affecting the current release. Without resorting to argument, all parties could calculate what would reach delivery during this cycle and what was pushed back.

The name *iceberg list* comes from the rising and sinking effect the list shows: adding high-priority items to the top of the list causes some above-water items to sink below the water line; removing above-water items may cause a new item rise above the water line. Just as with an iceberg, the above-water portion is only a fraction of the total size.

The iceberg list is useful in hostile environments, where the sponsors change the requirements and priorities on a daily basis and without warning. In such an environment, post the current iceberg list in a highly visible place, and make sure the contents of the next releases are *derived* rather than argued.

Figure 3-28 shows how this works, starting from the example in Figure 3-18. The size estimates have changed, and "automated PO generation" got moved above the water line. As a result, "separate messages/questions from options" fell below the water line and got deferred to a later release.

Module	Feature Name	Value	Raw Dev. Time (ideal days)	Revised Ideal Days Estimate	Release #
1.1	Configuration generates order line item comments	M	2	2.6	1
1.2	Configrator UI rework: Verbose wizard style	H	6	7.8	1
2.1	PO generated correctly for configuration	H	5	6.5	1
2.2	Create/confirm vendor items exist for skus	H	1.5	2	1
2.3	**PO generation is automatic**	**H**	**4**	5.2	**2**
3.1	Advanced Order form shows more details	M	4	5.2	1
3.2	Order fulfilled at PO cost	H	2	2.6	1
3.3	Repeat orders works with blind configurations	M	3	3.9	1
3.4	Configuration comments are viewable, not editable	L	1	1.3	1
4.1	Base hierarchy change	H	1.5	2	1
4.2	Style can locate price charts based on color selection	H	2	2.6	1
4.3	Assign specific color group colors to price charts	H	2	2.6	1
4.4	Separate messages from options	H	2	2.6	1
4.5	Separate questions from options	H	2	2.6	1
1.3	Configuration generates customer specific pricing	H	5	6.5	2
1.4	Allow adding a configuration and continue	L	2	2.6	2
3.5	Order shows sq. footage & running length	L	2	2.6	2
3.6	Vendor orderable items show additional detail	L	2	2.6	2
3.7	Printed window treatments show disclaimers	M	6	7.8	2
3.8	Allow order line item copying	H	2	2.6	2
4.1	Associate style with Retail.net DCL	L	1	1.3	2
4.11	Grid validation	L	1	1.3	2
4.6	Assign customer specific selling discounts	H	3	3.9	2
4.7	Customer lookup	H	1	1.3	2
4.8	Customer account type lookup	M	1	1.3	2
4.9	Options may have required questions	L	3	3.9	2

Figure 3-28   *The iceberg list from Figure 3-18 revised on the second iteration.*

REFLECTION ABOUT THE STRATEGIES AND TECHNIQUES

Crystal Clear states explicitly that no strategy or technique is mandatory. Why do I describe these particular ones and not others?

Both shaping the methodology and reflective improvement are required elements of Crystal Clear, even though no specific technique is mandated for them. Most people have never seen these things, and need to see a sample to get started.

The particular *Reflection Workshop* technique I describe is short and efficient and lets people both voice their thoughts and then get back to work. If you are doing any sort of monthly retrospective that allows free discussion, then you should be able to try different styles of workshops in successive months and generate your own personal style within a few months.

I describe *Blitz Planning* as an alternative to XP's "planning game." The two differ in three ways:

- The planning game cards list *user stories*, and the blitz planning cards list *tasks*.
- The planning game has the people assume there are no dependencies between stories, while blitz planning has people analyze the dependencies between tasks;
- The planning game assumes fixed-length iterations, while blitz planning does not assume anything about iteration length.

There are times when these differences are of interest. Blitz planning lets the team

- See the shape of the work ahead of them (producing the project map)
- Work out where the walking skeleton should show up and what it might consist of
- Work out the smallest set of tasks before revenue can start flowing
- Report to the sponsors the number of internal tasks that need to be performed before useful functionality becomes visible

These differences are of particular importance at the start of the project. Later in the project, the team may be able to simply list the features to be developed and their relative development costs.

The *Process Miniature* lets people build a short internal movie of how a new process works. Since moving to Crystal Clear is likely to involve quite a lot of change in working habits, it helps reduce tension and uncertainty.

The *Exploratory 360°* gives people a chance to catch certain kinds of fatal mistakes, mistakes that quite possibly everyone (incorrectly) assumes someone else has already checked. Since the exploratory 360° does not take very long, it has a high payback value for the time taken. It also aligns the team on the project's mission and approach.

Early Victory, *Walking Skeleton*, and *Incremental Rearchitecture* fit together. Even quite experienced developers disagree about how much architecture to develop early in the project. These three strategies describe a way to take advantage of incremental development to establish safety and value in the early stages of the project, and still deal with the mistakes and learning that form a natural part of architectural development.

Information Radiators are useful at every point in the project. Most agile teams make great use of them, but most teams outside the agile community do not take nearly enough advantage of these devices. It should be a pronounced strategy to use all of the available wall space for capturing information of use to the project team and their visitors (there is a danger of overloading the wall's visual space, but I have only encountered one team who had reached that point). Once you start using information radiators you may find you want to rearrange the office to make more walls available.

The daily stand-up meeting was introduced in the Scrum methodology. I have heard of people adding this single technique to every sort of project and methodology to good effect, and so I am happy to spread its use.

I include *Essential Interaction Design* because there is so little literature on how to work user-interface design and interaction design into an agile project. This adaptation of usage-centered design fits into both XP and Crystal Clear projects. Jeff Patton started an agile-usability discussion group, where you can pursue the topic.[18]

Burn Charts are extremely useful in the planning stages of the project, because they show the workload so clearly and people can respond with comments about the plan's feasibility. They are also well suited as status reports for the same reason: immediate clarity.

Crystal Clear lets a team use the techniques that work best for its members. I rather expect that simply as the normal course of professional activity, Crystal Clear practitioners will learn each of the techniques and strategies listed in this chapter, and uncover many more as they go.

---

[18]   http://groups.yahoo.com/group/agile-usability

Chapter 4

Explored (The Process)

Crystal Clear uses nested cyclic processes of various lengths: the development episode, the iteration, the delivery period, and the full project. What people do at any moment depends on where they are in each of the cycles. This chapter linearizes the cycles to the extent possible and points out some of their interactions.

Most of the development processes described from 1970 through 2000 were described as sequences of steps, even when the process recommended iterations and increments. This always caused confusion among readers. The text appeared to dictate a "waterfall" process, while the authors kept asserting it was not.

These linear-looking process descriptions suffer from two problems. The first is that they really describe the dependency graph between work products, the *workflow*. A dependency graph should be read in back-to-front order: The team cannot deliver the system until it is integrated and runs. They cannot integrate and test the code until it is written and running. They can't design and write the code until they learn what the requirements are (and so on). The workflow graph does not mandate a waterfall process; it simply reflects dependencies.

When a process is described by a workflow dependency graph, people mentally treat the dependency graph picture as encouragement to complete each mentioned work product before starting on the next work product in the graph. This is rarely a good strategy in software development. When looking at a workflow dependency graph, the relevant questions to ask are these:

◆ *How many* requirements, *at what level of completion,* are needed before design can usefully get started? (The answers are "relatively few" and "relatively low," respectively.)

111

◆ *How much of the system* must be designed and programmed before useful integration and testing can be done? (The answer is "relatively little.")

◆ *How much of the system, at what level of correctness,* is needed before being useful to the users or suitable for user review? (The answers are "relatively little" and "relatively low," respectively.)

The low levels of each actually needed comes as a surprise to many people.

Concurrent development is the name given when work proceeds in parallel on dependent work products. In concurrent development, many or all activities are in play at the same time. People trade notes continually to keep abreast of the changing state of each part. Concurrent development is not new, either to software development or project management in general.[1] It is done by almost every project team I visit, although few have noticed they do it.

Concurrent development is described at length in *Agile Software Development,* in the *Gold Rush* strategy in *Surviving Object-Oriented Projects*, and is generally presupposed in most of my writings. Therefore, I won't try to describe concurrent development here, nor the dependency graph in Crystal Clear (that should be quite obvious). Removing these two topics allows me to describe other interesting aspects of the process.

The second problem plaguing linear descriptions of process is that the processes they are trying to describe are cyclic, using multiple cycles of differing lengths.[2]

I notice seven cycles in play on most projects:

◆ The project (a unit of funding, which could be any duration)

◆ The delivery cycle (a unit of delivery, one week to three months)

◆ The iteration (a unit of estimation, development and celebration, one week to three months)

◆ The work week

◆ The integration period (a unit of development, integration and system testing, 30 minutes to three days)

◆ The work day

◆ The development *episode* (developing and checking in a section of code, taking a few minutes to a few hours)

---

[1]   *Simultaneous Development* (Laufer 1996) contains an excellent description of overlapped phases in civil engineering projects.

[2]   I am indebted to Don Wells's description of XP as nested cycles. See http://www.extremeprogramming.org/map/loops.html.

Crystal Clear requires multiple deliveries per project, but not multiple iterations per delivery. I will repeat this point several times, but I wish to draw your attention to it right away.

Teams using short iteration periods inside a long delivery cycle sometimes add a "supercycle" of perhaps four or six iterations, to provide an intermediate rhythm. They use this supercycle to reflect on their process, to celebrate, to unwind. I will not elaborate much on the supercycle in this chapter. Teams can derive what elements of the iteration and delivery cycles to move to the supercycle.

Each cycle has its own sequencing, its own rhythm. In any given day, different activities will be in play from the various cycles. The activities change from hour to hour, day to day and week to week. This makes a complete linear description of the process virtually impossible.

Figures 4-1 to 4-6 show several ways of unrolling these cycles. These simple sketches have to omit some of the interactions between cycles, a few of which I'll point out shortly. Notice that episodes, days, and integration periods can nest inside an iteration in various ways (Figures 4-2 and 4-3 show two possible ways); there are other valid combinations even more difficult to draw.

Figure 4-4 shows the expansion of each cycle separately, listing specific activities that occur specifically for that cycle type. Figure 4-5 shows these activities in a plausible time sequence (vertically down the page), placing each activity in a column for its cycle type.

Finally, in Figure 4-6, I have unrolled all the cycles and shaded the cycles in different ways so the activity can be connected to its cycle. The capital and small letters stand for project Chartering, iteration planning, daily standup, development, checkin, integration, Reflection workshop, Delivery, and project Wrap-up. Of course, I had to choose one particular relationship between the daily cycle and the integration cycle for this particular unrolling.

People interested in detail will notice that there is a line drawn through the R at the end of the last iteration of a delivery cycle. That indicates that team does not "reflect, deliver, reflect again," but rather, more naturally waits until after the actual delivery, then reflects just once.

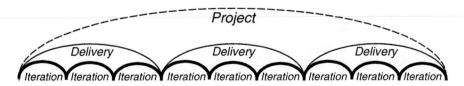

Figure 4-1   *Iteration and delivery cycles within a project.*

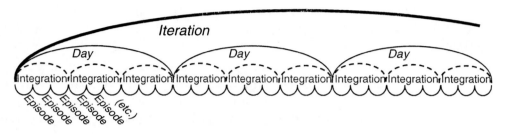

Figure 4-2   *An iteration cycle, integrating multiple times per day.*

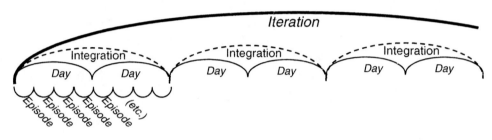

Figure 4-3   *An iteration cycle with multiple days per integration.*

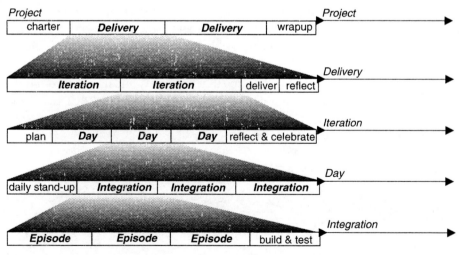

Figure 4-4   *The cycles expanded to show specific activities.*

Project	Iteration	Day	Integration	Episode
Charter				
	Plan			
		Daily standup		
				Design & Check-in
				Design & Check-in
			Build and test	
				Design & Check-in
				Design & Check-in
			Build and test	
		Daily standup		
				Design & Check-in
				Design & Check-in
			Build and test	
				Design & Check-in
				Design & Check-in
			Build and test	
	Deliver			
	Reflect and celebrate			
	Plan			
	(etc.)			
Wrapup				

Figure 4-5   *The activities in a plausible vertical sequence.*

Another detail is that the planning session in the first iteration of a delivery cycle is likely to have two parts: adjusting the coarse-grained project plan and creating a fine-grained iteration plan.[3]

These are the sorts of minor process adjustments that most teams make naturally, but make cyclic process so hard to describe explicitly.

The following sections expand on all but the weekly cycle.

---

[3]   Thanks, Jeff Patton, for making this explicit to me.

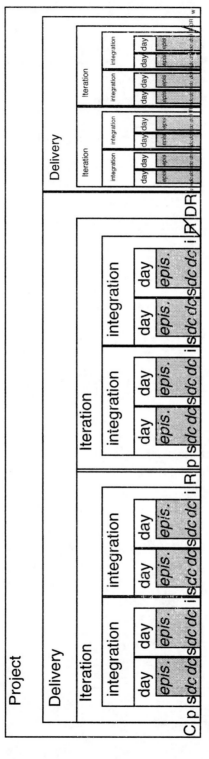

Figure 4-6 *The cycles unrolled all the way to show daily activities.*

THE PROJECT CYCLE

A project as a cycle? Although each project is funded as a once-and-for-all activity, it is typically followed by another project, in a cycle that repeats. It is useful for the organization and the development teams to get used to that cycle.

A project cycle in Crystal Clear has three parts:

◆ A *chartering* activity
◆ A series of *two or more* delivery cycles
◆ A completion ritual: the project wrap-up

Chartering

The *chartering* activity takes a few days to a few weeks. It consists of four steps:

1. Build the core of the team.
2. Perform the *Exploratory 360°* (which may result in canceling the project).
3. Shape and fine-tune the methodology conventions.
4. Build the initial project plan.

Note that having only one delivery cycle is a violation of Crystal Clear (for some definition of the word "delivery"). A project large enough to need a methodology description will benefit from multiple delivery cycles. I have seen projects that the sponsor thought were small enough not to need multiple deliveries that did quite poorly for the simple lack of feedback that comes at the end of a delivery. In the rare other cases, the projects were so small as to be a case of "just do it and go home." If it is not a matter of "just do it and go home," please arrange for at least two delivery cycles. Check the book sections on frequent delivery and delivery cycle to learn what constitutes an adequate delivery.

Chartering: Build the Team

A project of the type that will use Crystal Clear often starts with an executive sponsor and a lead designer, and eventually a key user.

Normally, two to five other people are added to the project, with a various mix of skills, experience, and ability. The more novices on the team, the harder it is for the lead designer to both train and develop software. Therefore, if there are more than four people involved, the team should include at least one other experienced and competent developer to back up and offload the lead. There should be an experienced and competent person for every two or three junior or novice people.

The Executive Sponsor

The executive sponsor is the person who ultimately cares that the project gets done. This person provides the money—or at least arranges for it to show up—and provides essential direction to the group. She highlights the priorities the group needs to be aware of, and gets the project not only monetary support, but also logistical and emotional support. Often, the executive sponsor is also the domain expert.

During the project, the executive sponsor needs to remind the development team of its true goal and keep it appraised of any changes in business direction that affects the project's direction. In return, the team needs to keep the executive sponsor appraised of the project's progress (burn charts are excellent for this).

A hazard lies in wait for the project with a highly technical executive sponsor: oversteering. It often happens, particularly for small projects, that the project's executive sponsor was once a superb technical designer. This sort of person can't resist spelling out for the design team just how they *might* implement the system, *not that they have to*, of course. In some cases, this person is correct, but still gets in the way of the team. The former top designer who is sponsoring a project will have to accept that the team may not create quite as superb a design as she could, and live with that.

One of the ways to keep the former top designer from interfering too much in the design is to use properly written use cases for the system specifications (see *Writing Effective Use Cases* (Cockburn 2001b)). Properly written use cases accurately specify the desired system behavior without specifying the design.

I have to mention that sometimes the executive sponsor does, in fact, know what is possible with the technology, or what is required, even if that appears difficult. In these cases, the best situation is for the sponsor and design team to develop a form of discussion that permits the sponsor to express what she knows without running over the team. After all, one of the primary contributions of the executive sponsor is team motivation.

The Lead Designer

The person given the assignment of lead designer has a complicated job description, which is not normally spelled out in advance. This person is often the best designer on the team, a person who could, in principle, design the entire system. This person is also supposed to train the younger members of the team, talk with the executive sponsor and end users, build a project plan, and manage the development of the project while also designing the most difficult part of the system. It is an impossible job description, except that it is carried out successfully by many (overworked) people around the world.

The best thing the executive sponsor can do for the lead designer is to provide a second expert developer. This second expert developer should be the one who handles the most difficult design tasks, because this second expert developer is not so likely to get caught up in meetings about users, plans, status, interfaces, and so on.

A key hazard surrounding the lead designer is that this person can get burned out before the project is over. In one case, I met a lead designer who was already working sixty hours a week at the start of the project. His own project plan had him teaching Java to the new programmers, as well as doing the most difficult design tasks, as well as . . . well, you get the idea. Although common, this situation is unhealthy. By the time the project passes its halfway mark this person is likely to be working ninety hours a week and sleeping under the desk for a few hours each night. Sometime after that, a calamity of some sort is likely to hit the project, and still more time is needed from this person.

It was for just this reason that Jens Coldewey devised the project management risk reduction strategy I refer to as *spare leader capacity*.[4] That strategy roughly says, "Ensure the technical lead has some spare capacity to assist in emergencies." We know that emergency situations do arise on most projects; if the technical lead has no spare capacity, she can't work through the emergency. Starting off a project at sixty hours a week does not leave the technical leader with much spare capacity, and at ninety hours a week, that spare capacity is all gone.

> In the case of the lead designer I just mentioned, we worked together to identify every task that someone else could possibly do, even if he was best suited for the task himself. By taking these loads off him (he would still have to set up or monitor them), we were able to reduce his work load to about 45–50 hours a week at the start of the project, so that he might be able to keep within about 60 hours during the high-load period of the project.

The Expert User

The system will be better suited to what the users need if the developers have access to an expert on system usage. The value the system brings to the organization is very sensitive to the information the developers get about the usage context. That means it is important that the team has easy access to proper usage experts.

How much of that user's time does the team need?

It would be nice to have the expert user available to the team the whole time, of course. That is rarely practical. Some methodologies suggest or require the user expert be present 50 percent of the time. That would also be wonderful, of course, but is usually also impractical.

---

[4]   XP uses the terms "energized work" (formerly "sustainable pace"). While that is sound, I find Jens's strategy to be usefully more specific.

My experience is that if the team can phone the expert user periodically during the week to ask questions, and gets a few hours (even as little as two hours) of dedicated time each week, they can work through their questions, get good requirements information, show demos, and get usage and design feedback of a quite adequate sort.

It may be that the expert user shows up each Tuesday afternoon for a ninety-minute meeting, and can be phoned half a dozen times each week. This is usually enough to put the project into the safety zone. If the user cannot even commit to one hour a week, then the project is not in the safety zone, but actually is in some danger with respect to appropriateness of requirements and adequacy of user feedback.

The Rest of the Team

Crystal Clear only names the above three roles specifically. There will be other people on the project. How they divide up the rest of the project roles is up to them. In particular, someone, or several people, will have to capture the requirements in use case or user story form. Also, someone will have to act as coordinator. Perhaps the lead designer can off-load this onto someone else who has good communications skill.

Chartering: Perform the Exploratory 360°

At an early point in the project, the team—including the executive sponsor—does a once-around check of the key issues. This is the *Exploratory 360°* described earlier, or an equivalent, such as RUP's "inception" phase (Kruchten 1999). In this check, they make sure the project won't founder on

- The business value
- The requirements
- The domain model
- The technology to be used
- The project plan
- The team makeup
- The methodology or conventions to be used

Each of these is reviewed in a coarse-grained fashion, to detect whether the intended team and projected methodology, using the intended technology around the projected domain model, can deliver the intended business value with the projected set of requirements according to the draft project plan. The exploratory 360° results in a set of adjustments to the project setup, or in the most drastic case, a decision by the executive sponsor to cancel the project (better now than later!).

Chartering: Shape the Methodology

Shaping the methodology can often be done in two days, and should not take longer than a week for a Crystal Clear team. It may be done using the *methodology shaping* technique, the RUP's development cases (Kruchten 1999) or similar.

Recall that a methodology is nothing more than the conventions the team agrees to adopt. Since the set of conventions will be revisited twice per iteration or delivery cycle, it would, in principle be possible to start from any methodology and simply tune it over time to suit the team. There is probably not enough time on a typical Crystal Clear project to follow that strategy. It will be fastest to start with the team's best thoughtful list, so that the subsequent tunings won't have to be so drastic.

As explained at length in *Agile Software Development,* there is a fairly high cost in using an overly heavy methodology: quite possibly that the team will fail to produce software for the first release at all. For this reason, start with a lighter initial set of conventions than you might suspect correct. With fewer rules, the team usually is more likely to deliver working software, and from reconsidering the conventions in the light of experience, they can add the missing conventions in the next reflection workshop.

Chartering: Build the Initial Project Plan

There are various ways within the tolerance limits of Crystal Clear of constructing a base project plan.

- My own favorite is to use the blitz planning technique described earlier.
- The most rigorous and careful method I know is DSDM's (Stapleton 2003). It involves a set of checks of the project objectives with the executive sponsor, followed by the construction of a release plan and a series of time-boxes, each one to three months long.
- Scrum's planning method fixes the time-boxes at one month long (Schwaber 2002).
- In XP's planning game (Beck 1999, 2000), the team, including its "customer," writes a set of story cards for the functional requirements and sorts those cards

into three-week time-boxes[5] (iterations). The team discusses with the executive sponsor the appropriate frequency of release to real users, and then groups the iterations into release periods, often about three months long.

Each of these techniques is within the methodology tolerances of Crystal Clear. Each provides an initial project plan, and is fast enough that it can be used on a regular basis to track changes in the project's situation and make an updated project plan. Choose one that fits you.

Reflection on Chartering

For the average project, the team is being assembled during the chartering period. The people doing the chartering have to deal with a number of variables. The people may or may not know each other, or may show up at some point in the middle of the project, needing time to learn to communicate with each other.

If the project emerges from exploratory 360° with a positive result, the team has a sense of where the project is headed, what problem it is tackling, the technology to be used, the project plan, and its business value. This creates an early alignment of goals and actions that strengthens the team.

The methodology shaping and initial project plan should take a couple of days. If the results have to be communicated to a wider audience, it may take a few more days to write up.

All of the chartering should take a few days to a week to complete, unless the project involves a new technology that is difficult to evaluate.

How important is the order of the steps I outlined earlier? I wrote them in the order that makes sense to me, but I can't see that the order is critical. Choose the order that makes sense to you.

The outcomes of the chartering activity are

♦ A *go* or *no-go* vote on the project
♦ A group of people with a draft charter and an idea of what they are doing

---

[5]   In practice, most XP teams seem to vary it anywhere from one to three weeks.

THE DELIVERY CYCLE

The delivery cycle has three or four parts:

◆ A recalibration of the release plan

◆ A series of one or more iterations, each resulting in integrated, tested code

◆ Delivery to real users

◆ A completion ritual, including reflection on both the product being created and the conventions being used

Recalibrating the Release Plan

On the first delivery cycle, it should, of course, not be necessary to recalibrate the plan just created. After the first delivery, however, the team members will find themselves with new and valuable information to feed into the project plan. They will have learned both how fast they really work and how mistaken their initial size estimates were. Furthermore, they and their users will have learned more about what is really needed in the system.

They have a choice: they can stick with the original set of requirements and merely update the plan, or they can revisit both the requirements and the plan. Crystal Clear does not mandate either strategy—that decision is up to the project sponsor. They would, however, be remiss in their professional duty if they didn't update their work estimates and reexamine possible strategies going forward.

I am obliged to repeat here the note from the blitz planning technique. There is an interpretation of agile development that the executive sponsor is at the mercy of the developers in constructing the project plan. This interpretation is faulty. What is true is that there is a careful allocation of responsibilities in the planning activity. The executive sponsor controls the project priorities, the development team controls the estimate of how long each task will take, and they *jointly* share responsibility for coming up with a plan to deliver the best results fitting the executive sponsor's priorities with the time and people available. If the executive sponsor still feels that the project is taking too long, she has exactly three options:

◆ Replace the team.

◆ Adjust the project's scope or time boundaries.

◆ Come up with a more creative strategy to get the work done with the time and people available.

My experience is that a combination of the last two works well to deliver maximum business value for resources expended.

Iterations

Iteration cycles are described in the next section.

Delivery to Real Users

As described in Frequent Delivery, delivery in Crystal Clear means "to a real user." In differing circumstances, that might mean full deployment with training classes, or it many be to only one person, a friendly user willing to give the budding system a walk through, either out of curiosity or just as a courtesy to the team.

The cost of deployment in the former case is quite expensive, and so "delivery" probably cannot be done every month or even two, but may have to be done quarterly. The second case is inexpensive. My experience is that you can usually find a friendly user if you try; the value obtained from this person is very high.

Many of my colleagues, used to deploying over the Web or to friendly, internal users not needing training materials, assail me regularly for suggesting that a team can go for three months before deployment. There are three reasons that I accept delivery in Crystal Clear to be as long as, but not longer than, three months:

◆ People seem to be able to retain their work focus and detailed memory for about three months, but not noticeably longer. In all my project interviews, I found a few teams able to make quarterly delivery cycles work reliably, but only one at four months, and none longer than that.

◆ The cost of delivering a system ready for full-scale use, complete with user training, is much higher than delivering the same system to just one or a few friendly users. The time and money cost of testing the system, writing the manuals, and creating the training is sufficient that it is often impractical to do it more than quarterly.

◆ Quarterly delivery of value to the business is quite often sufficient for the executives (the contrasting view, of course, is that their business might itself become more agile if delivery could be done monthly).

Completion Ritual: Reflect on the Delivery

Pressure is typically quite intense toward the end of the delivery period.

Unwinding is part of a general human need for rhythm. I was surprised to hear three XP masters talk about burnout after a year or two of successful XP practice. They said that their work was operating at a constant pressure, day after day, week after week, month after month. It was not that the pressure was high, but that it was unrelenting. The same was reported by a pair of programmers using Crystal Clear with two-week iterations. After a while, the monotony of work life was getting to them. In other words, people need a chance to unwind and "shake it out," so they can ramp up again for the next period of intensity.

Therefore, after delivering the software, unwind. Use the reflection workshop as part of "shaking it out." Instead of holding a reflection workshop at the end of the last iteration before delivery, save it up until just after the delivery, then reflect.

Include a celebration after a delivery. I have heard of people holding a party, going for a walk in the mountains, going sailing as a group, going home early, or allocating some days for people to work on a new technology, something other than the system under development.

One manager arranged for a two-day off-site meeting after each of the first few (quarterly) deliveries. They spent the first day on team building, socializing, and reflecting. They spent the second day planning the next delivery cycle. With the exception of "team building and socializing" (which alert readers will recognize as essential activities in agile development), the same time was spent on project activities as they would have been in the office. The difference was that both the place and the pace were different, so that the team returned to their offices in a refreshed state. After several deliveries, they decided they didn't need two days any longer, and held the combined activity on-site within a single day. However, they still got the completion ritual and change of pace they needed.

After a delivery, the team has two additional issues to reflect on:

◆ How did the deployment go? What different actions should be taken early in the delivery cycle to reduce the pain of deployment and training?

◆ What do the users think of the system? What are its strong points and weak points? Most importantly, can the team learn anything about what is *really needed* by the users, compared with what was originally requested?

Reflecting on the delivery process is the same as for any other reflection workshop. The group asks: What do we like and want to keep the same? What would we like to do differently? The only difference is that the changes affect either work habits throughout the delivery cycle or activities that should take place early on, perhaps in the first iteration.

To evaluate the system, the team may sit and watch the users, they may videotape some users using it, they may hold customer focus groups, or they may even hire an outside firm to evaluate the system in use. The point to be made is that it is the *product*, not the process, that they review here.

THE ITERATION CYCLE

Iteration lengths and formats vary with different teams. I shall describe two possible iteration cycles: a one-week iteration and a two-month iteration. Yours is likely to fall in between these two.

An iteration has three parts:

◆ Iteration planning
◆ Daily and integration cycle activities
◆ Completion ritual (reflection workshop and celebration)

Within the iteration period, the team will find itself adding to its requirements set, trying out user interface designs, extending the system's infrastructure, adding functionality, showing the system to the user(s), adding tests, and adding to the automation capabilities of their working environment.

The One-Week Iteration

In the case of a one-week iteration, the planning is likely to occur on Monday morning and the reflection and celebration late on Friday afternoon.

The planning session on Monday morning is used to set the team's priorities for the week. Since a week is not a long time, the team must divide their work into fairly small pieces in order to guarantee that they can develop, test, and integrate the pieces by Friday afternoon. The good news is that since a week is a short time, they probably do not need to spend much time estimating and analyzing dependencies. I would hope that the planning session for the week would not take more than about an hour on Monday morning.

Each morning, noon, or late afternoon, the team is likely to have its daily *check-in*[6] or *stand-up* meeting. Many teams report that meeting for five to ten minutes every day increases the rate of flow of information within the team and improves the team members' awareness of both political and technical situations that may become relevant to them. The essence is to keep the meeting short (ten minutes) and to let each team member know what is happening to the other team members.

During the week, aside from the above meetings, the team simply operates in its normal development activities. Their development episodes consist of nothing more

---

[6] Jim McCarthy has written a complete protocol for people to register their moods and intentions during the project (McCarthy 2002). The *check-in* protocol is the one used to announce readiness to work.

than picking up a work assignment, developing it and checking it in to the configuration management system, plus performing an integration build and system test, if that is the convention in use on the team. They will discuss and possibly show their work to their executive sponsor and expert user according to the rhythms they have set up.

The hazard for teams that use short (one- and two-week) iterations is that they forget to ever bring in real users. If this is your situation, consider adding a supercycle that includes user viewings, or at least create an explicit *User Viewing* schedule (see Chapter 5).

Completion Ritual for the One-Week Iteration

For an iteration only a week long, the iteration's closing ceremony is more about providing emotional closure than anything else.

The burn-out syndrome described in the delivery cycle is most likely to show up when the iteration cycle is very short. As Ron Jeffries wrote:

> Another thing that I like is the varying rhythm of an iteration. It starts with a plan, it builds up over a couple of weeks, then spins down. (If there's a frenzy at the end, we're not doing it right yet.) The iteration-free mode, it seems to me, would be just a relentless march, march, march. We did that on C3 for a while and it drove us mad, do you hear me, mad.—Ron Jeffries, 9/24/03, xp-egroup

With longer iterations, the final integration and the longer reflection workshop and long succeeding planning session provide a form of decompression. That is less the case with weekly iterations, and so a series of computer games, ping-pong games, a light discussion on any professional topic, a bike ride, or a visit to the pub could be in order.

With a one-week-long iteration, do not expect too much from the post-iteration workshops. After a few weeks, the team is unlikely to be able to think of much to change, and they are likely to become very short. Once this happens, consider holding the full reflection workshop once each month or two, and block out an entire hour for it, so that people can reflect over what has happened over a longer period of time and notice repeating patterns that need altering. (Note that this creates the supercycle mentioned at the start of this chapter.)

Some teams capture suggestions during their daily stand-up meetings. This is excellent, but it shouldn't replace the end-of-cycle reflection workshop. During the daily stand-up a suggestion for improvement allows the team to respond immediately. The end-of-cycle workshop gives people a special time to reflect on what they find positive and negative about their working habits. It is for this reason that a monthly or postdelivery reflection workshop may be an hour to half a day long.

The Two-Month Iteration

The planning for a two-month iteration may take half a day or a full day, depending on the technique used and the practice the team has had doing it. It is common to plan the next iteration immediately following the post-iteration reflection workshop. For those without an effective planning technique, I recommend starting with either the blitz planning technique in this book or XPs planning game (Beck 2002; Cohn 2004).

During the iteration, the same daily activities occur as for the one week iteration: daily check-in or stand-up, development episodes, integration-build-and-test, visits with the user and the sponsor, and so on.

When the iteration is two months long, it is useful to hold a mid-iteration reflection workshop. This is shorter and simpler than the end-of-iteration workshop. The primary purpose of this reflection session is to discover whether anyone has detected anything that will completely derail this iteration's success. If not, then perhaps the people have found something they want to improve, or else the meeting is just very short. If they have discovered a major danger, then obviously they must work out what to do about it. The purpose of these workshops is to catch mistakes while there is still time to correct them.

Completion Ritual for the Two-Month Iteration

The team might use an hour to half a day for the reflection workshop if they hold it every four to six weeks. They should take the time to review every aspect of their work, from their relation with their sponsor and users, to their communication patterns, hostility and amicability, the way they gather requirements, their coding conventions, the training they get or don't get, new techniques they might want to try out, and so on.

After the first iteration or delivery cycle, very often teams tighten their standards, get more training, streamline their work flow, increase testing, find a "friendly user," and set up configuration management conventions. At the end of subsequent cycles, their changes tend to be much smaller, unless they are experimenting with a radically new process.

Most people get caught up in their work and do not have the time or inclination to reflect on their work habits. The point of this periodic reflection workshop is to catch mistakes in time to repair them within the project and to give people a chance to notice ineffective patterns.

In Japan, they call these sessions *Kaizen* workshops.[7] See an example output from a (nonsoftware) *Kaizen* workshop in Chapter 5.

---

[7]   Strictly speaking, *Kaizen* is more frequent and typically has a specific form and output. However, even in Japan I have not found many groups doing *Kaizen* on their software process. Whether using my reflection workshop or the standard *Kaizen* form, the idea is to examine and improve the working conventions frequently.

THE INTEGRATION CYCLE

An integration cycle can run from half an hour to multiple days, depending on the team's practices. Some teams have a stand-alone machine run a build-and-test script continuously. Others integrate every few design episodes, staying in close touch with each others' activities. Still others integrate once a day or three times a week. Although shorter is generally better, Crystal Clear does not legislate the length of time to use.

For more on integration, review the property, *Technical Environment with Automated Tests, Configuration Management and Frequent Integration.*

THE WEEK AND THE DAY

Of the various cycles, only the daily and weekly cycles are calendar rhythms.

Many group activities occur on a weekly basis. These may include such things as a Monday morning all-hands or department meeting, team leaders' report meeting, a regular bring-your-own-lunch ("brown bag") technical discussion seminar, or a Friday afternoon wine-and-cheese party or beer bust (depending on your culture!).

A work day also has its own rhythm. It is likely to start with a daily stand-up meeting, and then consist of one or more design episodes, with a lunch break thrown in at some point.

Some teams integrate their code multiple times a day, in which case the integration cycle doesn't interact much with the daily and weekly cycles. Other teams do a nightly, twice-weekly, or weekly build.

THE DEVELOPMENT EPISODE

Ward Cunningham coined the term *episode* to describe the basic unit of programmer work in agile development.[8] During an episode, a person picks up some small design assignment, programs it to completion (ideally with unit tests), and checks it in to the configuration management system. This might take between fifteen minutes and several days, depending on the programmer and the project conventions. Keeping the episode less than one day in length generally works best.

(*Important note*: To me, as to the many people in the world who work in the Crystal style, *designing* and *programming* are such closely linked activities that they are not worth prying apart. Thus, there is only the role "designer-programmer" in Crystal Clear and Crystal Orange, not the two roles, designer and programmer.

Consequently, I write "to program" meaning "to design and program" or "to design" meaning "to design and program." I write "programmer" meaning "designer-programmer." Thus, in the last paragraph, the phrase "picks up a small design assignment, programs it to completion," means picking up a small assignment that requires designing and programming, then designing, programming, debugging and testing it, to completion.

I need to clarify this because many readers naturally think of designing and programming as actions of two separate job categories carried out by separate people. That would be a serious misinterpretation of Crystal Clear.)

---

[8]   http://c2.com/ppr/episodes.html

REFLECTION ABOUT THE PROCESS

Due to the history of our literature, most practitioners are used to seeing a linear version of their process. The mental shift to accommodate a cyclic process is hard. It is not that the *practice* of a cyclic process is hard—you probably already work in cycles on your current project. However, I find that even the most experienced project managers and methodologists can't *explain* cyclic processes, and particularly their boundary interactions (such as the absence of replanning at the start of the first delivery cycle and the absence of the reflection workshop at the end of the last iteration in a delivery cycle). To be honest, I've been trying to explain them for over ten years and only now feel I have a proper handle on the matter.

The difficulty is that some activities occur on daily and weekly rhythms that repeat without creating any particular sense of "forward motion." These *operations* types of activities include daily and weekly status meetings, checking in code, running unit tests, going for lunch, convening around the coffee or soda machine. Operations activities contrast with activities that show "forward progress," such as design reviews, getting requirements sign-off, moving into test or alpha release phases. People tend to catalog the progress activities in the process and neglect the operations activities.

The nested-cycle view allows the discussion of both progress and operations activities. Both are important to the life of the team member, both are part of the "process."

Two cycles need a little more clarification: the iteration and the delivery.

In the recent literature of our field, "iteration" is used without much distinction. It could refer to strictly internal iterations, as I describe it in this book, or for iteration-with-delivery. Many people forget about fulfilling the delivery portion of their iterative process. See the discussion under *"We colocated and ran two-week iterations—why did we fail?"* in Chapter 6.

In Crystal Clear, you are allowed to have just one iteration per delivery cycle, but if you do this, you *must* have some intermediate viewings by real users. If you have multiple iterations per delivery, some of those *must* include viewings by real users. If you don't do this, you are building an effective software-producing team that makes the wrong software very efficiently.

Chapter 5

Examined (The Work Products)

This chapter describes team roles and the work products, showing examples of each work product. These particular work products are neither completely required nor completely optional. They are the ones I can vouch for, both one at a time and taken all together. Equivalent substitution is allowed, as is a fair amount of tailoring and variation.

Although this is where the argument is most likely to occur, it is where the argument is least likely to affect the project's outcome.

Just as describing a methodology through its process introduces problems of interpretation, so does describing it with its work products. In a small methodology such as Clear, the number and formality of intermediate work products is reduced quite significantly. The team lives from their personal communication, notes on the whiteboards or posters around the room, and demos or deliveries to the user base.

Nonetheless, a description of the work products is necessary. People just starting with Crystal Clear need to see what counts as an "acceptable" set of work products. Executives and sponsors need to see what they are entitled to ask for. Teachers need a set of work products to have students practice on. Teams that are doing too little in the way of planning and documentation need to see what is worth preparing in even a light agile methodology. People working to understand a methodology will want to examine the work products as part of the overall methodology package.

In this section, I describe roles and the work products. These work products should be seen as the default set for a typical Crystal Clear project because they have demonstrated their value to many projects. It is, of course, up to the project team to add, subtract, or modify the list based on their situation.

Each item serves a communication purpose in the economic-cooperative game. Sometimes the economically appropriate artifact is *low-precision* (not very detailed) and *large-scale* (summarizing a large topic), examples being the project's mission statement and the release plan. At other times, a *medium-precision* artifact is needed, such as the actor-goal list, which outlines functional requirements at a glance. Sometimes, *high-precision* (detailed) descriptions are needed, the final code, user manual, and test cases being examples.

There are almost two dozen work products, depending on how you count them. People coming from a traditional project background may be shocked by how few there are; dyed-in-the-wool agile developers are shocked by how many there are (they are shocked because unless they are doing XP, they just haven't counted how many similar work products get produced on their current projects). The work products here are light and distributed across the roles, so that the team should not find them burdensome in practice. As an exercise, I suggest counting the total number of work products generated on your current project. My experience is that the number is seldom less than sixty. Compare them to the ones listed here.

The question arises over work products more than over any other aspect of a methodology: "Do we have to do *all* of these?" The answer is difficult to give, as it lies somewhere between the answer I was able to give for Properties ("For Crystal Clear, absolutely the first three, and as much of the next four as possible.") and the one I was able to give for Techniques ("Completely at the discretion of the team; here are an interesting and useful starter set to consider.").

If you skip too many of these work products, you lose alignment and visibility. Your direction and support can suffer accordingly. On the other hand, it would be just silly for me to insist you do all of them as given—the specific work products needed by teams varies according to changing techniques, technologies, communication habits, and even fashions.

I have been asked to name the "core" work products, as I was able to name the "core" properties, but this is not possible. If I was going to choose one work product to drop, it would be the project map (however useful it might be). If I was going to choose another, it would be the viewing schedule (that could be done verbally and on the fly). If I had to drop another couple, I might suggest merging the coarse-grained and fine-grained iteration plan and status and dropping the fine-grained iteration plan. It could happen that another person would drop them in another order, or I might drop them in a different order on a different project.

Misalignment within the team and miscommunication with the outside world grow with each omission. The risks accumulate, slowly at first, until the project is not in the safety zone, and it is never clear when it moved from being safe to being unsafe.

It is very easy to overburden a project with work that is useful individually, but which, when taken all together, slows the group to the point of losing more safety than it adds. This set of work products consists of items I can defend individually and all together. Even if your team does every single one of them, it should not be over-burdensome. You may still be able to find a way to substitute for or omit some of them. Discuss it in your methodology-shaping workshop, and discuss it again in your monthly or quarterly reflection workshops. That's what those are for.

In the pages that follow, I describe each work product, indicating which role is ultimately responsible for it. I include several examples of each work product to show variations in style and format different teams have adopted. Where possible, I show informal and formal renderings, graphical and textual. Seeing this range, you can choose a form that works for you and the external groups you need to keep informed.

THE ROLES AND THEIR WORK PRODUCTS

The sponsor is responsible for producing just one item:

the Mission Statement with Trade-off Priorities.

The team as a group is responsible for producing two things:

the Team Structure and Conventions, and
the Reflection Workshop Results.

The coordinator, with the help of the team, is responsible for producing

the Project Map,
the Release Plan,
the Project Status,
the Risk List,
the Iteration Plan and Status, and
the Viewing Schedule.

The business expert and expert user together are responsible for producing

the Actor-Goal List,
the Use Cases and Requirements File, and
the User Role Model.

The lead designer is responsible for producing the

the Architecture Description.

The designer-programmers (including the lead designer) are responsible for

the Screen Drafts,
the Common Domain Model,
the Design Sketches and Notes,
the Source Code,

the Migration Code,
the Tests, and
the Packaged System.

The tester (whoever is occupying that role at the moment) is responsible for producing

the Bug Reports at that time.

The writer is responsible for producing

the User Help Text.

ROLES: SPONSOR, EXPERT USER, LEAD DESIGNER, DESIGNER-PROGRAMMER, BUSINESS EXPERT, COORDINATOR, TESTER, WRITER

There are eight named roles for Crystal Clear, four of which probably have to be distinct people. The other four can be additional roles assigned to people on the project. The first four people are

◆ Executive sponsor
◆ Expert user
◆ Lead designer
◆ Designer-programmer

Executive Sponsor

This is the person who is either allocating or defending the allocation of the money for the project. The executive sponsor is supposed to keep the long-term view in mind, balancing the short-term priorities with those of subsequent releases and subsequent teams evolving or maintaining the system. This is the person who will create outside visibility for the project and provide the team with crucial business-level decisions. If there is a question of balancing the money being spent for the value being delivered, it is up to the executive sponsor to make the decision of when and whether to continue or stop, and if continuing, how to trim the remaining system functions to recover the business value. Part of the methodology involves giving the executive sponsor good information to make those decisions.

Sometimes it is the user community who is actually paying for, or sponsoring, the project, and they, as a department, work through an executive, who directs the development team. It is easy in this situation for the executive sponsor role to get awkwardly split, where the executive does not have the same long-term interests, priorities, or vision as the user community. There is nothing that a methodology like Crystal Clear can do to remove the potential conflict here. You, as a combined group of people, have to recognize the hazards of this situation and work extra hard on communication to keep priorities and goals aligned and visibility and amicability high.

Expert User

This is the person who is supposed to be familiar with the operational procedures and the system in use (if there already is one), knowing which are frequently—and infrequently—used modes of operation, what short-cuts are needed, and what information needs to be visible together on the screen at the same time. This is a different knowledge base than the business expert is expected to have. The person holding the role of business expert is expected to know the business rules needed within the system, what business policies are stable versus which are likely to change. The business expert is not expected to have intimate familiarity with the minute-to-minute activities of the user population, whereas the expert user is.

Lead Designer

This is the lead technical person, the person supposed to have experience with software development, able to do the major system design, tell when the project team is on-track or off-track, and if off-track, how to get back onto track. In terms of levels of competency, the lead designer is expected to be a level-3 designer.[1]

There are arguments about whether agile development requires top-notch programmers to succeed. I have never had the luxury of only using top programmers, nor were the teams I interviewed made up of them. They were made up of the usual mix of people one finds in a company. It is most important though that at least one person on the team was competent and experienced, that is, level 3.

The ratio of level-3 people to level-1 people is a factor that I consider significant enough that I offer it to researchers to examine as a primary correlation factor to project success. My experience is (and I suspect the research will show) that this applies to both small and large projects, both low- and high-ceremony projects. High-ceremony projects need much more boilerplate work done, and so can live with a higher mix of less talented people to the talented ones. Barry Boehm and Rich Turner (2003) capture this difference on their radial diagram (*Balancing Agility and Discipline,* p. 56), where one of the axes is the ratio of level-3 to level-1 people.

Since there are only three to eight people on a Crystal Clear project, at least one of them has to be competent and experienced, that is, level 3. Usually, there are a couple of trainees or junior people on the project. For the purpose of project safety, then, I designate the lead designer role separately from the other roles.

The lead designer is likely to have major influence in the methodology-shaping workshop. Very often, the lead designer is the only experienced designer on the team. If the entire team is experienced, then of course the methodology-shaping workshop can work in a peer-to-peer fashion.

---

[1]   Remember from Chapter 1, level 1 skill is the "following procedures" stage of learning, level 2 is "breaking away from specific procedures," and level 3 is "fluency" or mixing and inventing on the fly.

I use the word "designer" for this role to shorten the role name from the overly long "lead designer-programmer." The lead designer is expected to both design and program, just as are the other designer-programmers.

Usually, but not always, the lead designer is the most experienced person on the team and also handles the most difficult programming assignment. Although this is common, it actually presents a risk for the project. The lead designer tends to get overloaded, having the role as coordinator as well as architect, mentor, and most experienced programmer. Anything that can be done to offload the lead designer is likely to improve the risk profile of the project. The obvious choice is to have someone else play part or all of the coordinator role.

Designer-Programmer

I merge the words "designer" and "programmer" in the designer-programmer role to highlight that each person both designs and programs. Designing without programming is full of flaws due to lack of feedback (in projects of all sizes). It very particularly has no place on a project of the Crystal Clear type. Programming by its very nature involves designing. Neither designer nor programmer stands alone as a role name, hence designer-programmer.

The Other Roles

The coordinator is probably a partial occupation for someone on the team; projects of only four to eight people seldom have a dedicated project manager. There may be a person managing several projects, and playing the coordinator role for each of them. Alternatively, the executive sponsor or lead designer may get this role, or even other people may take turns holding this position.

The person occupying the coordinator role must, at the minimum, take notes at the project planning and status sessions, as well as comb the information for posting and presenting. The coordinator is responsible for giving the project sponsors visibility into the structure and status of the project. With luck, the coordinator also is someone with a good human touch, who can facilitate discussions and reduce strife.

The Business Expert is the expert on how the business runs, what strategies or policies are fixed, what is likely to vary soon, often, or seldom. This person will answer all the varied questions the developers will have about the heart of the system. It is different information than the expert user typically provides, although in some cases it may happen that the expert user is also the business expert. In various situations, I have seen the executive sponsor, the lead designer, or the expert user act as the business expert. Sometimes an external person is brought in for that expertise.

Tester and writer are likely to be rotating or temporary assignments. I give these separate role names, but in many Crystal Clear projects there are only the four to eight people, all programmers, sitting in the room. In this case they obviously have to take turns occupying these roles. Some teams may get use of a writer for periods of time, or have a dedicated tester working and even sitting with them.

A NOTE ABOUT THE PROJECT SAMPLES

In the following, I draw from a set of projects, some but not all of which were Crystal Clear projects.

The PRTS project was the project to build a system to track all purchase requests issued by employees of the Central Bank of Norway, whether they were fulfilled from the internal warehouse or external vendors. This project, for its short life, consisted of four people who worked on it exactly one day each week. It met the Osmotic Communication requirement because nobody worked on it at all for four days, and then we worked together on the fifth day each week.

I was the coordinator for this project. We proceeded from mission statement, through blitz planning and through the exploratory 360°. During the exploratory 360°, the proposed project failed both the technology spike and the business evaluation tests. The programmers wanted to keep going on it, but the executive sponsor decided to purchase a package for the system in order to free up the programmers for work more important to the business. Not only was this the correct business decision,[2] but the programmers found their next project much more exciting, since it involved both critical business value and new technology.

Consequently there are work products for PRTS up through that point.

The NICS-NBO project. Due to a bank failure in the early 1990s, all Norwegian banks have to keep a "checking account" with the Central Bank, and all bank-to-bank transactions must be funneled through these checking accounts. The bank union, representatives from key banks, and the manager of the banking division of the Central Bank comprised the steering committee for a series of projects. The NBO project here was the third in the series. I was coordinator for this project.

At the beginning it was staffed with the same three programmers who had done the first two projects. It looked like an easy candidate for Crystal Clear, even though the technology was mainframe with COBOL, assembler, CICS, and LU6.2. Over time, we lost the lead designer (paternity leave), as well as half of the second senior person (Y2K projects), and were left only with the junior developer and a new hire. The staff then grew in number and lost osmotic communication. At this point, the project was out of Crystal Clear range. The work product sample I am using here is the coarse-grained project-plan and the single-sheet combination of status and risk list that we used to report to the steering committee each month.

---

[2]   Niel Nickolaisen (2004) has written a simple business evaluation procedure to decide which projects to develop in-house and which to outsource, see http://agiledevelopmentconference.com/files/nickolaisen.ppt.

The BSA project. This was a project performed as part of a senior year course at Weber State University. The small team met once a week outside class and communicated by phone and e-mail otherwise. They used database technology for the project, so the domain model consists of a database schema. I would like to thank Dr. Christopher Jones and this team, Eric Schultz, Keith Deppe, Tony Hess, and Bethany Stimpson for this project.

Project Winifred. Project Winifred is the fifty-person, $15 million, eighteen-month fixed-price, fixed-time project I described at length in *Surviving Object-Oriented Projects,* and for which we constructed the original Crystal Orange. I use the project map and coarse-grained delivery plan from that project, because it seems interesting to me that our eighteen-month project had a coarse-grained plan consisting of about eight bubbles (backed by about 240 two-paragraph use cases).

The CamCal Camera Calibration prototype. This was a trial run of Crystal Clear in Thales, an ISO 9001 certified organization. This project involved four people for four months and fit the Crystal Clear guidelines. They were kind enough to let me include their experience report and auditor recommendations in this book (see Chapter 8).

Additional projects are represented in the work product samples. These, however, are sample descriptions of the sorts of projects used.

SPONSOR: MISSION STATEMENT WITH TRADE-OFF PRIORITIES

The mission statement is a brief description, typically a paragraph to a page, of what is to be built, its purpose in a larger context, and the project's priorities in sequence, from the most critical to those that can be sacrificed.

It is produced by the sponsor, before the project starts or during project chartering. It is reviewed by the business expert and lead designer, and referenced by everyone on the team. Any major change in the mission statement triggers a team meeting, so that everyone on the team understands the new mission.

A good mission statement retains its clarity and relevance over time, keeping the work efforts focused on the most important features of the system.

Because people can generally only protect one and possibly two project priorities, it has no more than two top priority items. The priorities might be chosen from hitting a particular delivery date, cost, ease of use, ease of learning, speed in use, correctness, performance, ease of maintenance, design flexibility, legal liability protection (you may

---

CamCal Camera Calibration Mission Statement

The mission of the camera calibration project is to:

◆ Develop a maintainable, simple to use, portable, and extendable software tool that will enable intelligent video surveillance system installers and repairers to rapidly, accurately, and efficiently calibrate their system cameras with respect to a predefined three-dimensional scene model.

◆ Establish a basis for developing a future tool set that can manage all aspects of intelligent video surveillance system installation and repairers activities. Such a tool set will include the camera calibration tool and will add scene model creation capabilities. It will be able to grow with the technology growth of the video surveillance market.

◆ Develop and trial the use of new software development methodologies and processes, with a view to improving the software development process used for small- to medium-size software projects.

The development priorities are:

Sacrifice others for this:	Complete by end of January
	Ensure accuracy and quality
Retain if possible:	Usability, potential to grow into a more extensive tool
Sacrifice these first:	Execution speed, portability, additional interfaces, internal format storage.

Figure 5-1.   *CamCal mission statement. (Courtesy of Stephen Sykes at Thales)*

The "BSA Progress Tracker" is designed for scoutmasters to track the progress of scouts through their advancement in the Boy Scouts of America program toward Eagle Scout.

Development Priorities
> **Overarching:** Delivery Date, Functionality
> **Foreground Constraints:** Ease of Use, Formal Correctness
> **Sacrificial Lamb:** Performance

Figure 5-2. *BSA mission statement.*

come up with other choices for your project). The mission statement makes clear to the team what can be sacrificed if necessary to preserve the top priorities. I note here that it is unlikely to succeed at both quick delivery and correctness as the top two priorities. Those are two that need to be traded against each other.

I provide three examples here, from the Camera Calibration project, the Boy Scouts tracking program, and the PRTS project, respectively. See also *Agile Project Management* (Highsmith 2004) for examples.

The "Purchase Request Tracking System" has two goals. The first and most essential is to provide a basic system for the official buyers of the company to track what they have ordered from vendors against what has been delivered. The second is to simplify the lives of people who wish to order things, who must sign purchase requests, and who are to track the purchases against budgets.

Project Priorities:

	Sacrifice Others for This	Try to Keep	Sacrifice These for Others
Simple to use	X		
Low cost to develop	X		
Defect freedom		X	
Deliver soon		X	
Ease of learning			X
Performance			X
Design flexibility			X

Figure 5-3. *PRTS mission statement.*

TEAM: TEAM STRUCTURE AND CONVENTIONS

Team structure is an allocation of people to roles. Team conventions are a collection of rules, practices, and conventions the team agrees to adopt.

Team conventions shift constantly. This is appropriate, because the situation in which the team finds itself is constantly changing. The team should not only be conscious about these changes, but should deliberately search for the optimal set of conventions for their project.

The published part of Crystal Clear contains a large number of agreements and conventions for the team to adopt. Being written for many projects, it cannot be complete. The team needs to settle additional conventions, at least the following:

◆ Allocation of people to roles

◆ Programming conventions such as naming, formatting, commenting

◆ Code ownership conventions

◆ Design and code-reviewing conventions, whether code reviews or pair programming or none

◆ Iteration length and forms of reporting status, frequency of user viewing

◆ Configuration management conventions

Depending on the experience of the team, the conventions may be built through an open methodology-shaping workshop, or drafted initially by the lead designer and allowed to evolve by suggestion and consensus of the entire team in reflection workshops ("consensus" means each person is willing to accept and defend it, even if it is not that person's personal preference). Some conventions require consensus of the sponsor as well.

The conventions should be consciously reviewed at the post-iteration reflection workshop, or at least every three months. Reread the Iteration Cycle in Chapter 4 to review this. At any time, of course, someone on the team may discover that something is really not working, and may request a change to the way the team is working.

Team conventions are often spoken rather than written. Some may get written on the information radiators. Coding conventions are often shown via sample code.

I categorize a methodology as "successful" if

1. The software gets delivered.
2. The team is content to work the same way again.

This may seem to be a very low threshold for success, but recent project reports show it to be surprisingly difficult.

If your methodology fails on either count, change it using the methodology-shaping workshop technique.

The team structure in Crystal Clear should be quite straightforward to establish. Four roles are crucial: executive sponsor, lead designer, designer-programmers, and expert user. The other roles, business expert, coordinator, testers, and writers can be combined roles, assigned either to additional people or shared by people having other roles. Quite often, the executive sponsor, lead designer, or expert user is the business expert.

Figure 5-4 is an example of role assignment.

A simple example of a convention adopted by a testing department team follows. They were trying to move from manual to automated testing, but ran into the problem that they spent most of their time fighting fires (using manual tests), and had trouble getting themselves to sit down and write automated tests. They therefore established for themselves the convention: "No manual testing before 3 P.M."

This simple rule gave them the focus (both priority and time) they needed to get over the initial hurdles and build a starter set of automated regression tests.

Figure 5-5 is an excerpt of some team conventions we created for a fifty-person company (fifty people puts it in the Crystal Orange category). There were several dozen conventions, which we divided into five categories: Regular Heartbeat with

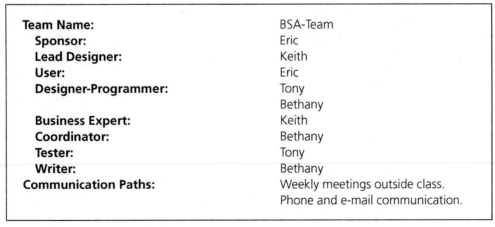

Team Name:	BSA-Team
Sponsor:	Eric
Lead Designer:	Keith
User:	Eric
Designer-Programmer:	Tony
	Bethany
Business Expert:	Keith
Coordinator:	Bethany
Tester:	Tony
Writer:	Bethany
Communication Paths:	Weekly meetings outside class.
	Phone and e-mail communication.

Figure 5-4. *BSA role assignments.*

Maximum Progress, Minimum Distractions

The purpose of this category is to ensure that people are working on what is of greatest value to the company and they have the time to focus and make progress on that work.

1. The top corporate key initiatives are prioritized and visibly posted for each two-week production cycle.
2. They are allocated to individual people so that each person knows his or her top two or three personal priority items for the cycle.
3. Work is broken into what can be completed and tested in the two-week cycles and is further broken down into things that can be accomplished in one to three workdays.
4. *Each person who is working on more than one initiative is guaranteed at least two consecutive days to work on any one initiative without being pulled to another assignment.*
5. The developers post on the whiteboards outside their office the current status of the work they plan to complete during a given week.
6. Every morning, the developers meet with the business owner of the current work initiative and conduct a short meeting to determine the current state of the work and the top work priorities and to discuss any questions.
7. *The business owner is not permitted to ask for status again the rest of the day.*
8. The period 10:00 A.M.–12:00 P.M. each day is declared "focus time," in which no meetings take place, and everyone in the company is encouraged to turn off the phone.

Figure 5-5. *Project conventions. (Courtesy of eBucks.com)*

Learning, Basic Process, Maximum Progress, Minimum Distractions, Maximally Defect Free, and A Community Aligned in Conversation. I list the entire set of conventions in *Agile Software Development*. For space reasons, I include in Figure 5-5 only the third section as illustrative.

TEAM: REFLECTION WORKSHOP RESULTS

The reflection workshop results is an information radiator that shows what the team has concluded after its reflection workshop. It is often a flip chart containing "Things we should keep," "Things to try," and "Ongoing problems" (see Reflection Workshop in Chapter 3). The chart is hung in a highly visible place so the team can notice what conventions and practices are the themes of the iteration.

The output is produced by the entire team during or at the conclusion of the reflection workshop. Feedback from teams indicates that it is not a good idea to give one person the job of "cleaning up" the flip chart used in the workshop: For the first part, that person usually changes the words on the chart, so it is no longer the words that received the team's approval. For the second part, the "cleaned up" version simply looks different than the people recall, and so they don't identify with it as well. Generally speaking, it doesn't much matter if the chart is a bit messy as long as it is readable. If you are going to clean it up, do it as part of the workshop.

A good reflection workshop results chart is big, visibly placed, and shows the team what they should pay special attention to in the coming weeks. Thus, it is better to use the phrase "Try This" (which states concretely what everyone should try) as opposed to "Needs Improvement" (which reminds everyone of what is bad without suggesting a remedy). Figures 5-6 and 5-7 are examples.

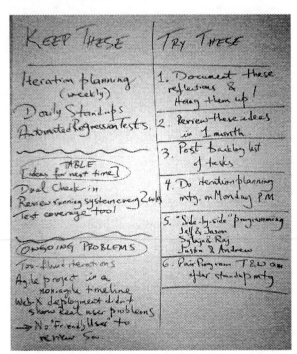

Figure 5-6. *Reflection workshop output. (Courtesy of Tomax)*

Figure 5-7.   *Kaizen output chart from Japan. (Courtesy of Satoshi Basaki, Schlumberger)*

COORDINATOR: PROJECT MAP, RELEASE PLAN, PROJECT STATUS, ITERATION PLAN AND STATUS, VIEWING SCHEDULE, RISK LIST

The sponsor, the development team, and the users all need to be able to plan their activities around when the system functions are supposed to become visible and available. The team needs to know the order in which to create them and the target dates, and the users need to know when they must allocate time to evaluate them or start using them.

Crystal Clear projects operate with two distinct time horizons: long term and short term. The long-term horizon typically refers to anything over three months, although it can be used for anything longer than a single iteration. Planning and tracking for the long-term horizon is coarse grained. This allows the team to provide the executives with the resource and expense estimates needed for overall enterprise planning, while taking into account that the team won't know what the actual costs will be until they get further along.

The short-term horizon typically refers to a single iteration. Fine-grained planning and tracking is used for the short-term horizon. This is so everyone can see the team's progress and detect problems quickly. The short-term plan and status are usually captured on information radiators in the team room.

The following work products are produced at different times and maintained in different ways:

◆ Project map
◆ Risk list
◆ Viewing and release schedule (the coarse-grained plan)
◆ Project status (coarse-grained)
◆ Iteration plan (the fine-grained plan)
◆ Iteration status (fine-grained)

As mentioned earlier, there may be a dedicated person acting as coordinator on the project, but more often it is the sponsor or lead designer who takes that role. Some groups find it helpful to have someone else take on the coordinator's role to reduce the load on the typically overburdened lead designer.

COORDINATOR: PROJECT MAP

The project map is a dependency diagram identifying the major work to be done and which ones depend on others (see the blitz planning technique). Its purpose is to show the structure of the problem and the sequence of attack. It contains no dates. That is partly because it is often drawn up before the team members and their capabilities are known, but more generally, to permit different staffing and timing strategies to be considered. It is intended to be viewed at one time, either on a conference room table or on a wall, using index cards as task markers. This limits the number of items that get put onto the map.

The project map is produced by the business expert, lead designer, and the sponsor in the coordinator role. It is approved by the sponsor, referenced by everyone on the project, and updated by the coordinator. It is produced very early in the project, before the release coarse-grained project plan. It is likely that the project map morphs into the project plan as the dates are added, and changes are made directly into the project plan as the project shape changes.

A good project map answers at a glance: "In what order are we delivering what? What do we build next? What are the dependencies between our releases?"

Some project teams discard the project map as soon as the release plan is produced, others find it useful to retain.

Figure 5-8 is an example.

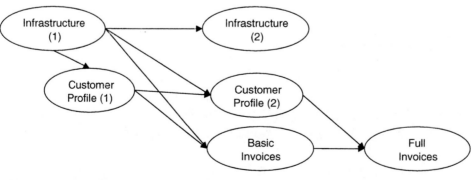

Figure 5-8.   *Sample project map.*

COORDINATOR: RELEASE PLAN

The Release Plan is an association of dates with major milestones, which are usually iteration ends and deliveries. The project map may become the release plan as dates are added. The release plan may itself directly become the Project Status (the NICS-NBO release plan, below, evolved into that project's project status).

Coming up with dates requires everyone's input. Usually, the first release plan is produced by the coordinator and lead designer. The business expert and sponsor check the priorities of the plan. The plan is rebuilt at the start of every delivery cycle, possibly even at each iteration (recall, there are multiple deliveries per project, and one or more iterations per delivery cycle). Once the team is familiar with the project assignment, the entire team can contribute to updating the project plan.

Figures 5-9 to 5-12 are examples from real projects, in graphical and text form. Comment on the formats used: Many team leaders getting started with Crystal Clear and other agile development approaches feel obliged to put their plan onto a Gantt chart. Gantt charts quickly become out of date, are tedious to update, and are hard to read. Project leads and sponsors who have moved from Gantt charts to dependency diagrams and lists report that the latter are easier to read and maintain.

Figure 5-13 is adapted from a reengineering project to replace a workflow system. Each name is the name of a workflow station. They didn't use a burn-down chart for their project plan. I include it as an example of how one might do so.

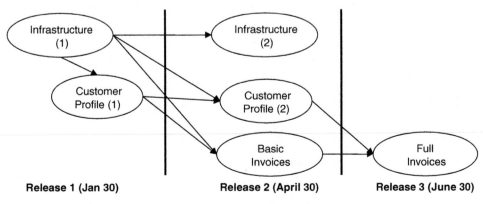

Figure 5-9. *Sample release plan derived from the project map.*

Release 1, Jan. 30: Single function. Buyer can enter a request that was completed and signed on paper, and generate POs that can be printed. Receiver can mark delivery against PO and request. Supports split and partial deliveries.

Release 2, April 30: First reports (searches, collects, and prints selected reports), and first security functions. Allows requestor to create request, collects approval from approver, notifies buyer.

Release 3, June 30: Full function, with full database functions.

Actor	Goal	Release
Requestor	*Initiate a request*	1
	Change a request	1
Buyer	*Complete request for ordering*	1
	Initiate PO with vendor	1
Receiver	*Register delivery*	1
Any	*Check on requests*	1
Authorizer	*Change authorizations*	2
Approver	*Complete request for submission*	2
Buyer	*Change vendor contacts*	3
Authorizer	*Validate approver's signature*	3
Requestor	*Cancel a request*	4
	Mark request delivered	4
	Refuse delivered goods	4
Buyer	*Alert of nondelivery*	4

Figure 5-10.   *Release plan from PRTS project.*

	Milestone	Planned
I 1	A single, simple transaction makes a round trip between the computers.	Feb 1
I 2	Simple purchase transaction successfully posted from GUI through database.	Mar 31
I 3	Reports of active requests and work flow through buyer.	Jun 30
I 4	All work flow sampled. All reports run.	Sep 1
I 5	All functionality works	Sep 30
I 6	User acceptance	Oct 10
I 7	Deployment	Oct 20

Figure 5-11.   *Release plan using Norges Bank's milestone charts.*

Module	Feature Name	Value	Release #
1.1	Configuration generates order line item comments	M	1
1.2	Configurator UI Rework: Verbose wizard style	H	1
2.1	PO generated correctly for configuration	H	1
2.2	Create/Confirm vendor items exist for SKUs	H	1
3.1	Advanced order form shows more details	M	1
3.2	Order fulfilled at PO cost	H	1
3.3	Repeat orders work with blind configurations	M	1
3.4	Configuration comments are viewable, not editable	L	1
4.1	Base hierarchy change	H	1
4.2	Style can locate price charts based on color selection	H	1
4.3	Assign specific color group colors to price charts	H	1
1.3	Configuration generates customer specific pricing	H	2
1.4	Allow adding a configuration and continue	L	2
2.3	PO generation is automatic	L	2
3.5	Order shows sq. footage & running length	L	2
3.6	Vendor orderable items show additional detail	L	2
3.7	Printed window treatments show disclaimers	M	2
3.8	Allow order line item copying	H	2
4.1	Associate style with Retail.net DCL	L	2
4.11	Grid validation	L	2
4.6	Assign customer specific selling discounts	H	2

Figure 5-12.   *Release plan using "iceberg list." (Courtesy of Jeff Patton and Tomax)*

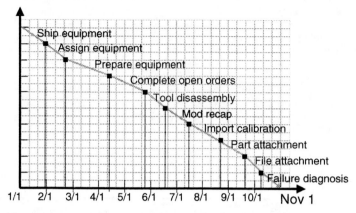

Figure 5-13. Release plan using a burn-down chart.

COORDINATOR: PROJECT STATUS

The Project Status is a listing of the state of the project with respect to the release plan. It is often just that with the status marked. The status information might include the currently predicted due date, or the originally scheduled completion date, foreseen completion date, and foreseen risks. On one project, we were asked to also compare original and projected cost figures on this chart. The project status should generally take less than half a page; you can use the other half of the page for the risk list, making a complete project report on a single sheet of paper.

The project status is maintained by the coordinator, in conversation with the development team. It is used by the sponsor and the manager of the user community to plan their separate efforts. It is updated every few weeks or every month.

A good project status is brief, easy to read, and shows the information the readers need in order to assess the cost, date, and risk trajectory of the project.

Figures 5-14 to 5-17 show some examples. Comments on the strategy and formats used: People are increasingly using simple tables to report status. The second

	Milestone	Planned	Delivered	Notes
l 1	A single, simple transaction makes a round trip between the computers.	Feb 1	Feb 3	Complete
l 2	Simple purchase transaction successfully posted from GUI through database.	Mar 31		Underway. Uncertainty over the DCOM components, still in learning curve. Experiments underway.
l 3	Reports of active requests & work-flow through Buyer.	Jun 30		Started. Initial design work.
l 4	All work flow sampled. All reports run.	Sep 1		not started
l 5	All functionality works	Sep 30		not started
l 6	User acceptance	Oct 10		not started
l 7	Deployment	Oct 30		not started

Figure 5-14.   *The project plan of Figure 5-11 became a status chart.*

example shows one of the differences in agile development techniques: something of business significance gets delivered approximately every week, with a full cycle every month. By completing a full conversion in the first month, the team has a chance to learn about what is involved and where they are running into problems, and still have plenty of time to learn how to do better in subsequent cycles.

Figure 5-15 is a status sheet for a project involving conversion of 200 applications and their databases. In preparing this example for publication, I just numbered the systems, where the company had system names. The dates in parentheses are the predicted completion dates; the bold dates without parentheses are the actual completion dates.

Figure 5-17 is a chart showing changing status over a two-month period. White means not started, medium-gray (green in the original) means completed.

System	New Tables Operating	Migration Code Works	Old Tables Converted	Old Tables Removed
1	(Feb 1) **Feb 3**	(Feb 7) **Feb 10**	(Feb 14) **Feb 18**	(Mar 1) **Mar 1**
2	(Mar 1) **Mar 1**	(Mar 7)	(Mar 14)	(Apr 1)
3	(Apr 1)	(Apr 7)	(Apr 14)	(May 1)
4	(May 1)	(May 7)	(May 14)	(June 1)
5	(June 1)	(June 7)	(June 14)	(July 1)
(etc.)				

Figure 5-15. Status chart for a proposed project to convert 200 databases.

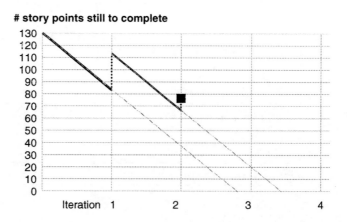

 # story points still to complete

Figure 5-16. Status chart using a burn-down chart.

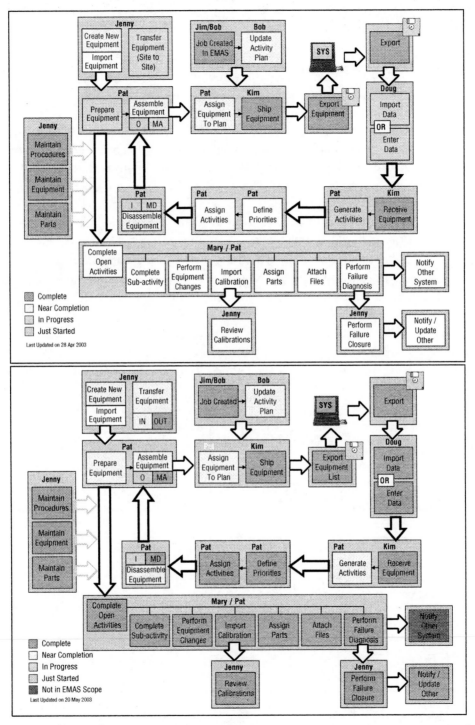

Figure 5-17. *Chart showing status changes over a two-month period. (Courtesy of Marty Lacy and Omar Alam, Schlumberger)*

COORDINATOR: RISK LIST

The risk list consists of the top risks facing the project, how significant and likely each is, the damage it can cause, and what prevention or response is possible. I like to track whether they have grown or shrunk recently.

The risk list is produced and maintained by the coordinator in conversation with the team, updated weekly or monthly. It is used in discussions with the sponsor.

Creating the risk list is trivial. The hard part is deciding what to do in case the risk materializes. As with the mission statement, the brevity of the work product belies the thought put into constructing it. There is a very satisfying feeling from watching a risk materialize and realizing that one has a response ready for it.

The risk list can live on an information radiator or in a spreadsheet.

Figure 5-18 is styled after the NICS-NBO project. This plus the project status resulted in a one-page project summary sheet examined at every steering committee meeting.

Priority	Risk	Possible Result	Likelihood	Response	Change	Milestones Affected
1	Very high performance demands in a new, untested technology	Unexpected failures in system operation	Quite high	Test performance early	As before	2–5
2	User community changes their idea of require-ments late on	Delays in delivery	Medium	Show users as soon as possible	As before	5
3	Need to test on factory floor as well as in development	Misunder-standings, delays in delivery	Low	Clear test routines	Less	2–6
4	Year 2000 compatibility	Bad data in system causes faulty operation	Medium	Special Y2K test	Less	6
5	Data conversion problems	Delay in delivery	Medium	Create conver-sion strategy	As before	6–7

Figure 5-18.   *Risk list using format from Norges Bank project.*

COORDINATOR: ITERATION PLAN → ITERATION STATUS

The fine-grained iteration plan lists what is being developed in this iteration. Each item may be something that could take from a day to two weeks to develop, depending on how long the iteration is. The iteration plan may show dependencies between work items (if, for example, it was produced by blitz planning), it may treat all work items as being independent (if, for example, it was produced by XP's planning game or is simply a list of product features), or it could be a marking of selected sentences in the use cases.

The iteration plan is produced by the coordinator working with the development team. It is kept up to date by the coordinator in the same way, usually becoming the iteration status directly.

A good iteration plan lists all the work items the team has to complete so that they can be checked off when completed, so that the sponsor and the developers can see all significant work items. The granularity varies with the iteration length and the team's knowledge of their assignment.

Figure 5-19 is an iteration plan, courtesy of Thoughtworks Corporation. In this case, one XP user story is written on each flip chart. Tasks for each story are written on sticky notes and attached to the flip chart (the tasks below the flip charts have been taken out of scope for the iteration).

The iteration status lists the state of the iteration with respect to the plan. It is often written on an information radiator. It is usually just the iteration plan items with their current work state, usually marked either started or done, with nothing in between. I have seen some require a third mark, integrated, for when the item passes integration testing. Although the tasks are often so short that it is not really useful to

Figure 5-19.   *Iteration plan becomes iteration status. (Courtesy of Thoughtworks)*

mark percent complete, the first example below does show one creative way to do this.

The iteration status is created by the coordinator, in conversation with the development team. Updating is in principle done by each developer, but typically that requires directed effort by the coordinator. The status chart serves to broadcast to all the rate of movement through the iteration's work list.

A good iteration status is easy for all to see and shows at a glance what has been done versus what needs doing.

Figure 5-20 is an iteration status for the user stories on the flip charts discussed earlier. Each was copied to a sticky note, started at the bottom left of the graph, and moved to the right as it progressed, up as its quality improved. Viewers could tell the state of each user story by how far to the right and how high each story's sticky was. This picture was taken toward the end of a one-month iteration.

Figure 5-21 is an iteration plan marked up for iteration status. The two boxes on the left indicate "started" and "done" (there is, of course, no interesting in-between state). The numbers on the right are relative size estimates.

In this chart, the red index cards are the task cards from the planning session. They copied the text onto the whiteboard to track iteration status. Here we see the team using one-week iterations, with fifteen work days available between them. They are estimating they can get 9.5 relative units of work completed this week.

Increasingly often we see people move the sticky notes across columns to show changing status. The columns are titled Not Started, Started, and Done.

The picture shown in Figure 5-22 was taken at their thrice-weekly status meeting. Géry is moving an item's marker from started to done.

Figure 5-20. *Iteration status on information radiator. (Courtesy of Thoughtworks)*

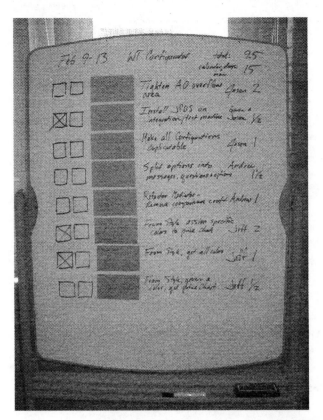

Figure 5-21. *Iteration plan/status on rolling whiteboard. (Courtesy of Jeff Patton and Tomax)*

Figure 5-22. *Iteration plan and status using sticky notes. (Courtesy of Géry Derbier)*

165

COORDINATOR: VIEWING SCHEDULE

The viewing schedule is a listing of when, during the iteration or delivery cycle, the expert user or other users should plan to come and see the new growth of the system. This work product is needed when the users' time is not so easy to get, they have to travel far, or there are too many of them. It is not needed if the expert user visits the project every day or every week.

The viewing schedule is produced by the coordinator, in cooperation with the development team at the start of an iteration. The development team uses it as a reminder of when to target completion of their work (minor milestones). It is a living document, the coordinator changing it as necessary to balance two opposing forces: giving viewers and testers as much advance notice as possible and giving the developers the most time to react to the changes in their design. It may live on an information radiator or in e-mail.

As noted in the section Reflection on the Process, and also discussed in "We co-located and ran two-week iterations—why did we fail?" in Chapter 6, the viewing schedule is more important to the outcome of the project than its modest size would indicate.

Figure 5-23 is from the Boy Scouts tracking system.

Release 1: March 1, 2002. Input system to allow scoutmaster to enter personal information about scouts and personnel including name, address, phone, e-mail, rank (where applicable), etc.

> **Viewing 1:** February 15, 2002
> > Screen shots or screen mock-up sketches
> **Viewing 2:** February 22, 2002
> > Completed databases and GUI screens
> **Viewing 3:** March 1, 2002
> > Completion of Release 1

Figure 5-23.   *Sample viewing schedule.*

BUSINESS EXPERT AND EXPERT USER: ACTOR-GOAL LIST

The actor-goal list is a two-column table or use case diagram. In two-column form, the left column names the person, organization, or computer system that will drive the system, calling upon its service promises. The right column names that service promise, which is the actor's goal with respect to the system, what he wants to accomplish using the system. The goal, a short verb phrase, becomes the name of the use case describing the details of the function.

The actor-goal list is created primarily by the business expert and expert user, and is reviewed for completeness and prioritization by the sponsor. It gets referenced by everyone. It gets created either within or immediately after the project chartering activity, and updated as needed over the course of the project.

A good actor-goal list captures every primary actor (one that will drive the system) that the system must recognize (must show specific behavior for), and for every primary actor, every major goal of that actor with respect to the system. Goals are stated at "user task" level, that is, complete transactions of value to the actor. (Goal levels are described in detail in *Writing Effective Use Cases*). A well-constructed actor-goal list contains entries that the sponsor and business expert feel are at a reasonable and interesting level of activity (not too detailed, not too high level), and they can review to declare that it is complete, omits a goal, or has unnecessary goals.

The project team may decide to start work on the project even when the actor-goal is known to be incomplete.

The actor-goal list is an index into the total functionality needed from the system. It serves both as a low-precision requirements statement and also as scaffolding for the project status. It is used to help construct both the coarse-grained project plan (see the final example) and the fine-grained iteration plan. Some people use it directly in reporting project plan and status.

When used for reporting the project status, the use case names (goals) are useful for the first few releases. Later in the life of a system, the functions being requested tend to get so small as to not be worth writing use cases for. They tend to be features such as "hyphenation," "export to RSS format," and the like. Once that moment is reached, the team often changes to tracking the fine-grained progress by features rather than use cases. Why don't we just start with features, then? The first reason is that there are usually too many features. The team needs a shorter list to work with, to see at a glance what they will get. The second reason is that at the start of the project, the users need to see what the system will do for them in their work context. That is difficult to get from feature lists, but is exactly what use cases provide.

I include the actor-goal list as a separate work product from the requirements file (which follows) because it gets created earlier than the rest of the requirements file, and often it is maintained separately. Figure 5-24 is an example.

Actor	Goal
Requestor	*Buy something*
	Initiate a request
	Change a request
	Cancel a request
	Mark request delivered
	Refuse delivered goods
Authorizer	*Change authorizations*
Buyer	*Change vendor contacts*
Approver	*Complete request for submission*
Buyer	*Complete request for ordering*
	Initiate PO with vendor
	Alert of nondelivery
Authorizer	*Validate approver's signature*
Receiver	*Register delivery*
Any	*Check on requests*

Figure 5-24. *Sample actor-goal list.*

BUSINESS EXPERT: REQUIREMENTS FILE

In a conversation about requirements back in 2000, Kent Beck made one of his provocative pronouncements, that "there are no such things as requirements, there are only wishes." As has happened so often, I have found his pronouncement to be right on the mark. Try rereading this and the related sections with the thought in mind that when someone says, "The requirement(s)," they are really expressing something closer to a wish, which is probably adjustable under suitable circumstances.

Particularly with incremental delivery with product and process feedback, there are plenty of opportunities for the sponsor and user community to learn that they didn't really require what they originally asked for, but perhaps something else would be more cost effective or more useful, or simply adequate in the circumstances.

Crystal Clear is already difficult enough to adopt without me breaking standard convention yet again, and calling this section "The Wishes File." Therefore, I stay with Requirements. However, plant the seed that they are closer to wishes, and see if that improves the communication between the sponsors, users and developers about just what should be produced.

Crystal Clear requirements are not intended to be so complete and comprehensive as to be clear specifications for an external contract programmer not familiar with the domain (writing requirements specifications that explicit would be a waste of money in the Crystal Clear context). The requirements file is intended to hold in place requirements information that might otherwise be forgotten, as records of decisions that the team needs to remember, giving a context to those decisions.

A good requirements file for a Crystal Clear project communicates to the people on the project with their particular knowledge base and communications channels. The more they know and the more they can learn by talking to someone close by, the briefer the requirements can be.

The requirements file is a collection of information, indicating:

♦ What is to be built
♦ Who is intended to use it
♦ How it provides value
♦ What major constraints affect the design

The requirements file may be a written document, or it may simply be files scattered across the disk that, taken together, comprise the requirements. In many organizations the concept of requirements as a document is both foreign and unnecessary. What is important is that there is a place where these things are recorded.

There are many sensible formats that can be used for the requirements file, and many timing strategies on when to fill in the details.

◆ In some cases, such as for a fixed-price, fixed-scope bid, the requirements need to be locked down early in the project.

◆ In other cases, such as for shrink-wrapped products, in-house development, or time-and-materials contracts, the requirements may evolve over time or be created in a just-in-time fashion.

Crystal Clear does not legislate any format or timing strategy. Typically, though, requirements do evolve over the course of the project, and the team needs to both update and adjust to the changes at the start of each iteration. The team needs to discuss periodically in their reflection workshops just how and how often the requirements should be updated.

Quality in a requirements document is relative to the team. One test for clarity and completeness is if a company executive or other business expert from the same company sits down with the business expert who wrote the requirements, they can be satisfied that no areas are forgotten, and, within each area, they understand what is written. Comprehensiveness means that all issues have been thought through (this is, of course, harder to test for).

In general, a full sample requirements file is too long to insert here. One is available online at http://alistair.cockburn.us/crystal/articles/srd/systemrequirements document.html. It outlines typical sections in a complete requirements file, such as:

◆ The mission statement

◆ The actor-goal list, followed by use cases with annotations, particularly performance requirements

◆ Particular business rules for the use cases that may be needed; references to other sources of business rules, legal requirements, etc.

◆ Data descriptions, formats, and validation rules

◆ Technology requirements

◆ I/O protocols and formats for external communications

◆ A glossary of business terms (often recommended)

It is unlikely that a Crystal Clear type of project will need all of these written down, given that they have close communication with the users and the sponsor. As an example, Kay Johansen contributes the following complete requirements example with the introductory note:

Alistair,

I dug around and came up with two examples of "requirements" from a project I was on around 1999. It would probably count as a Crystal Clear project: two programmers in a room (one of the programmers is also a user expert) a couple of other user experts in a nearby office, plus access to the "paying customers." Some automated tests. Release about every 2 months to customers.

We drew up the requirements jointly with the user experts for the two new features that mostly defined the 2.61 update of the product. The product was a small business accounting/inventory/service contract system. The requirements got sent to the customers requesting these features, for their review. Customers were satisfied, and the programmers worked from this document.

Contracts

User Story
- Create a service contract with a prepaid balance that is debited based on services rendered to the customer.
- The contract maintains an unearned balance, minimum balance, and amount to be billed.
- The contract should include discounted percentages for labor and parts for the services rendered under contract.
- As service calls are cleared, the labor and material costs (less discounts) are deducted from the unearned balance of the contract.
- The customer is billed the billing amount when the contract unearned balance is less than the minimum balance.

Code Changes

Contracts
- Add a Bill by Services Rendered check box to indicate that the contract balance is debited based on services rendered.
- Add a Minimum Balance to the contract so that the contract can be billed when the current balance falls below the minimum balance.
- Add a Renewal Billing Amount to allow the billing system to renew the contract and replenish the contract balance.
- Add a Labor Discount Rate for labor calculations.
- Add a Materials Discount Rate for parts and supplies calculations.
- Store this additional information in the database.

Contract Billing
- The contract billing system needs to check for contracts that are Our Contracts (Services Rendered) that have gone below their Minimum Balance. It will then create contract billings based on the Renewal Billing Amount.
- Billings that are negative will sum the absolute value of the negative amount with the Renewal Billing Amount to bring the account up to the positive minimum.

Figure 5-25. *Sample requirements. (Courtesy of Kay Johansen)*

Dispatch Console
- When a call is cleared for Our Contracts (Services Rendered), all labor and material costs will be discounted by the Labor Discount Rate and the Materials Discount Rate for the contract, respectively.
- The cleared call will debit the unearned balance of the contract, and the call will show a zero balance due. If the services exceed the current balance on the contract, the contract balance will go negative and will bill for the excess cost on the next renewal.
- The cleared call will debit the unearned balance in the GL Account and credit the revenue account. It will use the same accounts specified for the accrual unearned balance and revenue transfers.

Block Time Billing

User Story
- Create a Sales Order for 10 hours of training at $100/hr (overhead of $50/hr) and 5 sets of documentation at $50/ea (cost of $25/ea). Bill this as fulfilled.
- Invoice immediately for 3 sets of documentation and 5 training hours.
- The customer pays $650 for this invoice.
- Fulfill 1 set of documentation and 4 training hours.
- Examine the status of the sales order—view amounts ordered, fulfilled, and billed in both dollar amount and item quantities.
- Fulfill the remaining 4 sets of documentation and 6 training hours.
- Invoice for the 2 sets of documentation and 5 training hours that have not yet been invoiced.
- Customer pays $600 for this invoice.
- The Sales Order is now complete.

Code Changes
- To create a Sales Order you would use the same method that exists now. Training Hours would need to be set up as a nonstocked ICItem. The Sales Code on the item will determine where the unearned revenue will go.
- You can open the Sales Order and view the current status of all line items sold. This information is available in both Dollar Amount and Quantity. The "Bill" command button will allow you to generate an invoice for this, or a portion of this, Sales Order. The invoicing action will debit the A/R account and credit Unearned Revenue.
- When the customer pays on the Invoice, the existing functionality will be used with appropriate adjustments to the Cash and A/R accounts.
- The Sales Order may be incrementally fulfilled by opening the Sales Order and using the "Fulfill Items" and "Fulfill Services" buttons. Fulfillment will make appropriate adjustments to the Unearned Revenue, Revenue, Cost of Goods Sold, Inventory, and Cost Applied accounts.

Figure 5-25. (Continued)

- A new report will be created which allows you to see the current status of the Sales Order, including all line items with amounts ordered, fulfilled, and billed. This information would be available in both Dollar Amounts and Quantities.
- If the total Sales Order has not yet been invoiced at the time of final fulfillment, an invoice can be generated at that time. The invoice process will debit the A/R account and credit the Unearned Revenue account.
- The customer can pay this final invoice using the existing functionality.

Figure 5-25. *(Continued)*

BUSINESS EXPERT AND EXPERT USER: USE CASES

A use case is a text collection of scenarios describing how an external actor achieves something of value using the system. It starts with a success scenario in which the external (primary) actor requests something of the system. That scenario describes the actions and interactions between the system and various other actors in satisfying the primary actor's request. After that, it describes how the system behaves when things go wrong, possibly failing to satisfy the primary actor's request. Use cases describe what the system should do; they don't capture UI design, performance requirements, interface definitions, or data definitions.

The use cases are created jointly by a designer-programmer, a business expert, and an expert user. Responsibility can move between those three roles. I write that the business expert is responsible for them, but in my experience, it doesn't matter which one of them is primary, as long as the others are proofreaders and knowledge providers. It does cause trouble if one of them is absent. Nonprogrammers tend to write loosely or ambiguously and not fully consider consequences and alternatives. Programmers are usually good at those, but tend to get too detailed, start describing their intended design, and get business rules wrong. Working and reviewing together, they can cover each other's mistakes.

A use case is often written in two phases, the success scenario in a first stage, the failures scenarios later, as the team needs delves deeper into the requirements, either to estimate the complexity of the job or to work on the design. At some point, the writers or the team may declare that the use cases are "complete" for the iteration, meaning that no more use cases will be considered for that iteration and that no more details or extensions will be added to them.

A good use case is easy to read, identifies the system's responsibilities, and considers the most interesting failure cases. The complete set of use cases covers all the goals the primary actors have with respect to the system, including covering every external event that triggers the system. A good Crystal Clear use case is different than a good use case on a larger, distributed, or life-critical project. Because the Crystal Clear team sits together or very close and can get clarification on the content easily, they can write in a briefer, more casual style.

Most people get too fancy about the use case format, making them very detailed rather than communicative. For Crystal Clear projects, I suggest starting with the two-paragraph form. This consists of a title, a description of success in the first paragraph, and a description of failures and recovery in the second. Once the team has practiced with the two-paragraph form, they can investigate other use case formats (see *Writing Effective Use Cases*). For example, even though I understand the two-paragraph form, I usually find it just as easy and more legible to write with numbered steps. I always write down the use case's goal level, the name of the system being designed, and the system's stakeholders and their interests in use case. This additional information communicates a lot to the readers without adding a lot of time to the writing. Try the two-paragraph form, first, though, before adding anything else.

Figure 5-26 is an example of a user-goal-level use case in two-paragraph form from the BSA system. Figure 5-27 is an example of a summary, two-paragraph use from the PRTS system. (Note: An underlined phrase represents a hyperlink to another use case.)

View a Scouts' Progress (user-goal level)

The scoutmaster searches for and selects an individual scout. The system shows the information about the rank the scout is currently working on.
If the scout is not in the system, the scoutmaster can Add a New Scout.

Figure 5-26.   *Sample two-paragraph use case at user goal level.*

Buy something (summary level)

The Requestor initiates a request and sends it to her Approver. The approver checks that there is money in the budget, check the price of the goods, completes the request for submission, and sends it to the Buyer. The buyer checks the contents of storage, finding best vendor for goods. The Authorizer validates the approver's signature. The buyer then completes the request for ordering and initiates a PO with the Vendor. The vendor delivers goods to Receiving and gets a receipt for delivery (out of scope of system under design). The Receiver registers delivery and sends goods to the Requestor, who marks request as delivered.

At any time prior to receiving goods, the requestor can change or cancel the request. Canceling it removes it from any active processing. (delete from system?) Reducing the price leaves it intact in process. Raising the price sends it back to approver.

Figure 5-27.   *Sample two-paragraph use case at summary level.*

EXPERT USER: USER ROLE MODEL

A role model is a two-dimensional map showing user roles and their relationships. It highlights the focal roles, the ones the system should satisfy the most (see Essential Interaction Design in Chapter 6). A user role is a name representing a high-level goal that the user of the system might step into; similar roles cluster closely together and dissimilar roles appear further apart. Relationship lines connect roles or clusters.

The role model is created jointly by a designer-programmer, a business expert, and an expert user. Although responsibility can move between those three roles, I attach it to the expert user to indicate the importance of this person in the process.

The role model is used

◆ To prioritize work when roles, business value, focal status, and frequency of use are issues that affect priority of feature development

◆ When writing use cases—the collaborations between roles furnish use cases with additional actors or dependencies

◆ To help make specific decisions about user-interface and interaction design

◆ In testing when the tester assumes the goals and attributes of a user role

A good role model names all the roles that will use the system, reveals quickly the focal roles and key relationships, and serves as a reminder to the team as to who their software will be serving.

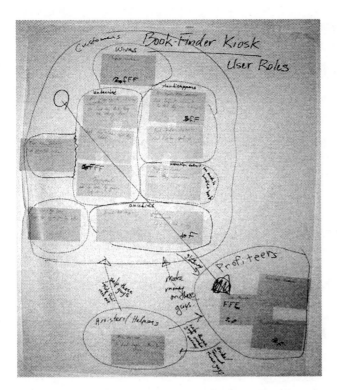

Figure 5-28. *Sample user-role model. (Courtesy of Jeff Patton)*

DESIGNER-PROGRAMMERS: SCREEN DRAFTS, SYSTEM ARCHITECTURE, SOURCE CODE, COMMON DOMAIN MODEL, DESIGN SKETCHES AND NOTES

The question always arises as to just what documentation is needed. In Crystal Clear the answer is:

> whatever the sponsor and the team decide.

There are four reasons for this answer:

◆ The system will always be changing, both in function and in design. The time, effort, and resources put into documenting the design subtract from those making progress toward delivering the system. The documentation will always be somewhat out of date and therefore incorrect.

◆ At the same time, the designers need to leave a trail behind, to jog their own memories some months down the line, and to lead other designers to understand what they have done.

◆ The above are in conflict, and the correct resolution of them depends on the game of software development being played on this particular project. Only the sponsors and the team can guess what trail is the optimal one to leave behind, balancing the need for progress and the need for clues. What is certain is that I can't, in this book, make that decision for all small teams everywhere.

◆ Finally, technologies change. The correct form of documentation changes somewhat with the technologies being used. Database systems, mainframe systems, scientific systems, object-oriented systems, and real-time systems all have different appropriate documentation formats. These things change often enough that, again, it is not for me in this book to legislate what is correct for the team; only the team knows.

Crystal Clear projects operate with two time horizons with respect to documentation: Getting the software written (the less time spent documenting the better), and handing the software over to a different group (the richer the documentation the better). One might think of the first set as greedy actions (meeting the first goal in the cooperative game), and the second as investment actions (setting up for the next game). The two are in conflict with each other, so the team inevitably plays a game of brinkmanship with the documentation.

Ideally, the team produces the archival documentation as late as possible, as fast and cheaply as possible. This is allowed in Crystal Clear.

However, "none" is not a valid answer. That would only be a valid answer if it is known that no one will maintain or extend the system later on. Such a project is unlikely to need even Crystal Clear for its rule set.

Thus, teams using the extreme programming rules within a Crystal Clear project must discuss with their sponsors what forms of documentation to leave behind. They can use either XP's planning game (Beck 2002) or the blitz planning technique to integrate this need for documentation into the ongoing project work. This is the only addition to XP needed to be a valid implementation of Crystal Clear.

In addition to discussing what to document, the team needs to discuss how to document it, and when. The when part is easy to understand although not so easy to choose—the later they leave it, the more up-to-date it will be and the less it will need to be changed. However, the later they leave it, the more likely they are not to do it at all. There is inevitably brinkmanship involved in making the optimal choice.

The team should be creative about how to document their designs. Typed-in, paper-based documentation is one of the most expensive, time-consuming, and least communicative forms available (never mind that it is traditionally the most frequently requested).

◆ Effective small teams supplement their typed-in documents with photographs of their whiteboards, flip charts, and other information radiators.
◆ There is no reason why a hand-drawn diagram can't be scanned in and stored online as an image, included in HTML or other documents.
◆ Paper napkins happen to be my favorite documentation medium. They can be posted on the wall, photographed, or scanned.
◆ The team can videotape one of their designers explaining and discussing a section of the system design with a designer from outside the team. This discussion should be held to ten to fifteen minutes per topic, as described in Agile Software Development.

Smart teams are likely to come up with their own alternate cheap and effective documentation forms.

The points to note are that

◆ Some documentation is needed.
◆ The team is in the best position to decide what, how, and when.
◆ The team, in conjunction with the sponsor, are in the best position to decide how much is appropriate for this particular project.

Finally, software development is not just a game of communication, but also a game of invention. Some work products facilitate the creation of new ideas and help the people make new moves in the game. Paper-based prototyping (Snyder 2003) is an example, as are CRC cards (Cunningham url crc, Cockburn 2001a) and the instance diagrams in UML (Fowler 2003).

Invention-enhancing work products are not archived, and as a consequence we tend to overlook their importance in a project. To help correct this imbalance, I call out screen drafts as a specific work product. These help the team work out the user interface design collaboratively with the users. They are specific, useful work products with short lifetimes.

In the following sections, I describe three work products that almost certainly need to be produced—system architecture, common domain model, and screen drafts—inside of the larger category, "design sketches and notes, as needed."

DESIGNER-PROGRAMMER: SCREEN DRAFTS

Screen drafts are low-cost renditions of the way screens will look, used to explore the ways that users might interact with the system, and invent better ways for them to get their goals accomplished. Very often they are just drawings on paper (Constantine 1999, Snyder 2003). The team may prefer screen-prototyping software.

Screen drafts are created primarily by whichever designer programmer is designing the user interface, in tandem with the expert user. They may hang on the wall during the iteration, or they may get converted to software prototypes or real code and discarded. I mention them here because, although they are transient work products, they are immensely useful and often overlooked on projects.

A good set of screen drafts is inexpensive to construct (hence made from paper and markers or from special storyboarding software) and easy for the expert user and other users to walk through with respect to the use cases and usage scenarios (see the technique for walk-throughs in Essential Interaction Design in Chapter 3).

Figures 5-29 and 5-30 are examples of screen drafts.

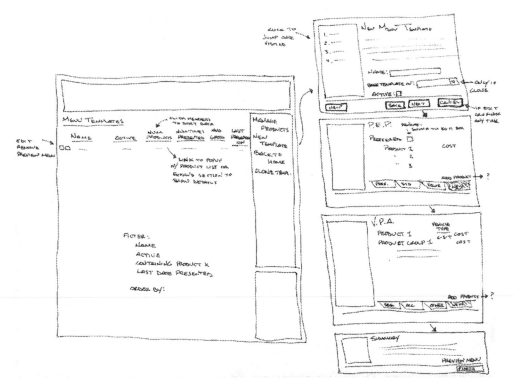

Figure 5-29.   *Sample screen draft. (Courtesy of Nate Jones)*

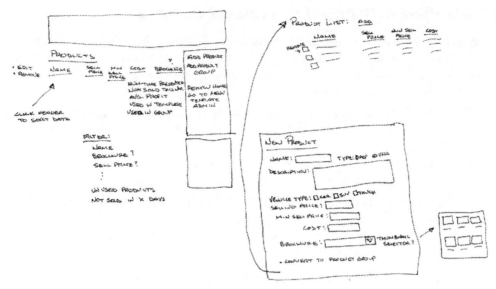

Figure 5-30. Another sample of screen drafts. (Courtesy of Nate Jones)

LEAD DESIGNER: SYSTEM ARCHITECTURE

The system architecture description is text and/or drawings showing the major components and interfaces of the system. There is a lot of controversy about just what constitutes an architecture, when it should be made and how it should be documented, all of which are out of scope of this book to decide. There does need to be some description of the system's main design to unify the team members' work and to educate follow-on system designers. On larger projects, two architectures may occur: the technical (infrastructure) architecture and the domain architecture. *Domain Driven Design* (Evans 2003) has examples of domain architectures.

The system architecture description is created by the lead designer, usually fairly early in the first iteration. The architecture will probably evolve, particularly if the *Walking Skeleton* and *Incremental Rearchitecture* strategies are used. This means that the architecture document will need to be updated during each iteration.

A good system architecture speaks in the language of the technology being used and the designer programmers. It may consist of a technical memo with descriptive text and drawings, or just text, or just drawings. It shows or describes the major interfaces and the interaction paths.

Figures 5-31 to 5-35 are samples of very different styles of architecture documentation.

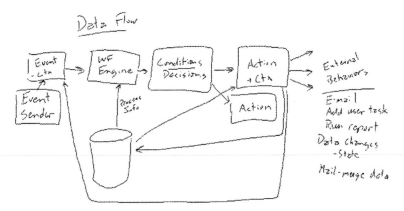

Figure 5-31.   *Design captured by a Mimio whiteboard device.*
(Courtesy of Darin Cummins, ADP's Dealer Services)

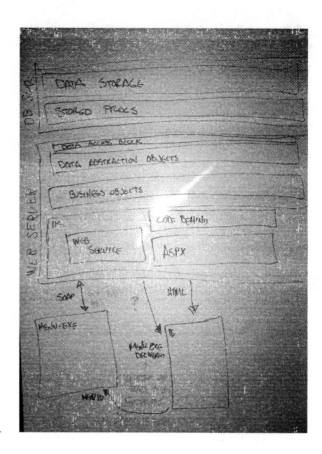

Figure 5-32. *Architecture kept on a whiteboard. (Courtesy of Nate Jones)*

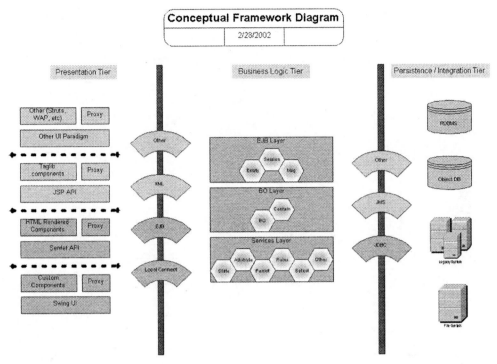

Figure 5-33. *Architecture drawn into a drawing tool. (Courtesy of Jonathan House)*

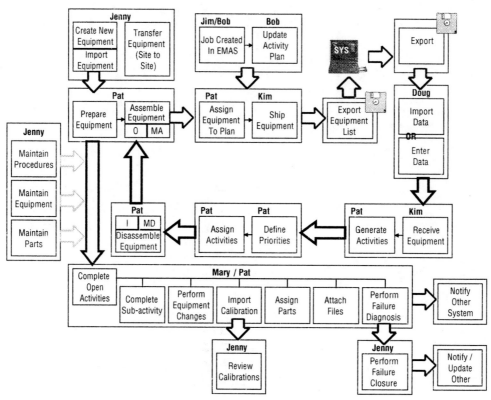

Figure 5-34. Workflow architecture. (Courtesy of Marty Lacy and Omar Alam, Schlumberger)

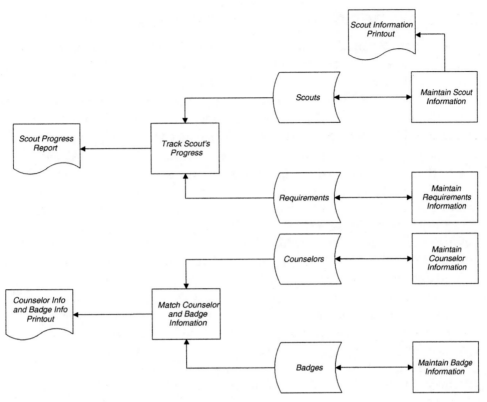

Figure 5-35.   *Architecture from a non-OO system.*

DESIGNER-PROGRAMMER: COMMON DOMAIN MODEL

The common domain model is typically a drawing, either a database schema or a class diagram, showing the principal entities or classes used in the system. Some teams still prefer straight text to describe their domain model.

The common domain model is created by the designer-programmers as they understand the domain and incorporate increasing amounts of it into their design. It is reviewed by the business expert, who may help to construct it in the first place.

There are several timing strategies for constructing the domain model. In some cases, there is an intense domain-modeling activity at the start of the project, which results in draft #1 of the common domain model. The model gets revisited and adjusted continuously throughout the project after that. This is the mode of work described in *Surviving Object-Oriented Projects* (p. 141). The other strategy is a just-in-time strategy, in which the model is built incrementally and minimally, with little or no looking ahead at future requirements. Crystal Clear does not legislate which of these strategies is preferred. That is up to the team to discuss and decide.

There is a reason I call this work product the "common" domain model, as opposed to the "analysis" model, the "design" model, or just the "domain" model. Having multiple models creates two hazards to the project. The first is double maintenance: You have to resynchronize each model as soon as either changes. Typically, that doesn't get done, so the models simply get out of sync. The other is that there is a tendency to think that the analysis model is magically "true" in some way, and the design model needs justification for each difference. In actuality, there are many "true" models of the domain. The final implementation should contain one that is both correct and a good design with respect to maintenance, performance and system resources. The initial analysis model may be correct, but is quite likely to be weak with respect to those design criteria. As a result, it is a better strategy to keep only one model of the domain, and evolve it so that it is both a valid domain model and a strong design. This topic is discussed at length in *Surviving Object-Oriented Projects* (Cockburn 1998). Eric Evans refers to the evolving common domain model with his pattern, Ubiquitous Language (Evans 2003).

We decided on Project Winifred that the set of classes to put into the common domain model should be the "public elements of persistent classes." I found this to be a useful guideline. The model that results is very much what an analyst would call an "analysis model," which means that it contains only items that should be in the business expert's (and probably the expert user's) vocabulary and sphere of caring. At the same time, it names classes and relationships that actually exist in the implementation—it is an "implementation model." Having an analysis model that is an extract from the implementation model keeps the team from maintaining two models and raises the likelihood that the entities and classes put into the implementation actually are meaningful business terms.

A good common domain model is both understandable to the business expert and current with the implementation.

Figures 5-36 to 5-38 are examples of domain models.

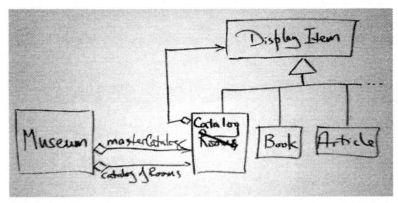

Figure 5-36.   *Common domain model on paper.*

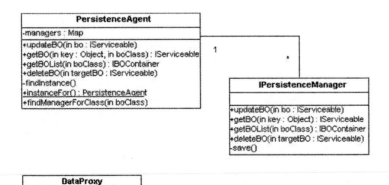

Figure 5-37.   *Common domain model in a CASE tool.*
(Courtesy of Jonathan House)

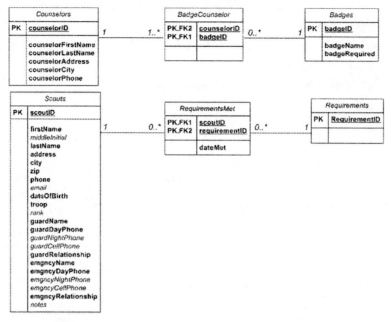

Figure 5-38. A non-OO domain model. (Courtesy of the BSA project)

DESIGNER-PROGRAMMER: SOURCE CODE AND DELIVERY PACKAGE

I have to include this page just so people don't think I forgot that the designer-programmers actually produce source code and delivery packages, besides all the various items used to plan, track, test, and describe them.

Crystal Clear does not regulate the language, naming, formatting, and commenting conventions you use. Those are for your team to decide.

I hope you already know what source code looks like. If you really want to look at some, turn to the JUnit test example.

DESIGNER-PROGRAMMER: DESIGN NOTES

Crystal Clear requires "design sketches and notes, as needed." This is an open-ended phrase, allowing teams to write technical memos, create UML diagrams, create WikiWiki webs[3] describing their design, take photographs of their whiteboards, or videotape mini-lectures about the design.

The design notes are produced by the designer-programmers continuously throughout the project.

In terms of the theory of software development (see Chapter 7), design notes serve one of two purposes and have different paybacks in the economic-cooperative game.

◆ They can serve to remind, as part of the greedy action set, aimed at the primary, near-term goal of delivering this system soon.

◆ They can be among the investment actions, aimed at the secondary goal of setting up for the next game.

Even within the greedy action set, *reminder markers* serve a valuable service in reminding people what they previously decided. Being only for the people who were present (including yourself a month or two later), they are naturally drawn on napkins, flip charts, and the like. These markers rarely need to be redrawn (and may even lose information when redrawn).

Informing markers are created as part of the investment activity to help those who come later to catch up to the group. They are longer and more laborious to produce. The economic payback is that the same information doesn't have to be repeated over and over again by the busy senior developers on the project.

It is useful to keep several things in mind when deciding what and how to produce these markers. First, it will never be possible to convey the entire theory of the design through these documents. Second, even the people who have been on the project from the beginning don't have a shared or complete understanding of what is in the code and what theory best describes it. That means the design notes can never be complete, consistent, and fully instructive. Therefore, don't think it is your goal to make them such. Your goal is to get them close enough so they can ask good questions, or develop their own theory far enough that they can get into the code and find out more on their own (and, hopefully, so that the theory they come up with is not too far distant from your own).

---

[3]   http://c2.com/cgi/wiki?WelcomeVisitors

Good design sketches and notes leave a trail for another designer-programmer to follow. The best ones describe not how the system currently looks, but why certain choices were made and others rejected.

Part of both reminding and informing is retaining and conveying the history of the choices that were made. Recently, a few people have reported that using a Yahoo eGroup type of chained-e-mail system, or a newsgroup-type system like Starteam with threaded notes is useful in this fashion. These systems allow people to follow the chain of discussion about various particular topics. I add the note that the chain of history is more informative in both reminding and informing than is the summing up at the end of the chain. This method is clearly suited to larger and distributed teams. When the team consists only of three to five people all located in one room, it may be less natural to have people go online to add these notes.

There is an ongoing cost to creating, changing, and maintaining these documents as the design itself evolves, and a competing cost to not creating them. Just how that tension is resolved is up to the team, including the sponsor, who must consider the balance between the short-term and the long-term health of the system. It is unlikely that the sponsor will be happy with no documentation at all for following teams, and so Crystal Clear requires some design notes to be produced.

Figures 5-39 to 5-42 are examples of design sketches and notes.

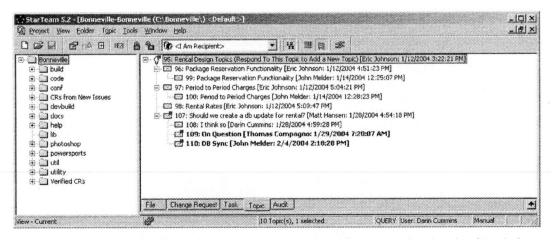

Figure 5-39. *Screen shot from the Starteam newsgroup-style system, showing the threaded discussion trail. (Courtesy of Darin Cummins, ADP's Dealer Services)*

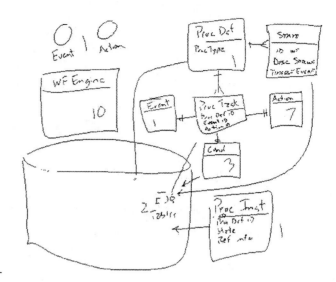

Figure 5-40. *A reminder design note captured with the Mimio device hooked to a whiteboard and a laptop. (Courtesy of Darin Cummins, ADP's Dealer Services, who says he periodically pulls up this and similar Mimio whiteboard captures for reexamination)*

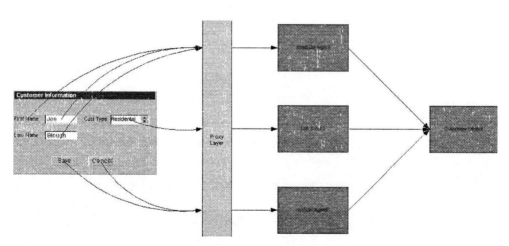

Figure 5-41. *An informing note about binding visual components. (Courtesy of Jonathan House)*

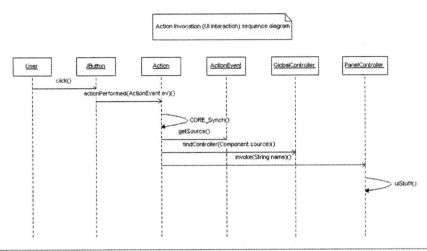

This is the second of two diagrams that illustrate how the Swing interface will handle action invocations to allow both for CORE server interaction and for traditional client UI controller work. Note that this is a suggested implementation that reflects the CORE reference implementation of a Swing interface. Other architectures can be used as well to solve the UI interaction challenges.

This sequence starts out with a click of a button by a user. From there the JButton generates an ActionEvent which is passed to our Action. The action first performs any CORE synchronization (if needed) and then will pass that event on (roughly following the delegate pattern). It does this by referencing a GlobalController (think Singleton). This GlobalController would then find the appropriate Controller instance for this action. Our current thinking is that this would be done by getting the ActionEvent source (the JButton in this case) and using it as a key to look up the appropriate controller for that UI component. If no controller is found for that specific UI component we would climb the Swing component hierarchy until we found a UI component that there was a Controller for (the details of how UI components match up with specific controllers is not solidified yet).

Note: The self-message on the Action ("core synch") represents the interaction that takes place to synchronize the client side object with the server instance of that BO. This process is shown in detail in the Action Invocation (CORE interaction) sequence diagram.

Figure 5-42. *Sequence diagram annotated with a textual description, part of a series of domain model fragments intermixed with sequence diagram and explanatory text, each section illuminating just one aspect of the design. (Courtesy of Jonathan House)*

DESIGNER-PROGRAMMER: TESTS

A test is preferably executable code that tests an aspect of the system. Nonexecutable tests involve a person following a written document that describes what the person must do to test the system. There are times when these are also necessary.

Tests are produced continuously during each iteration. Although there may be an external test group, I wish to highlight that it is not acceptable for the designer-programmers just to write code and hand it over to a test group to repair. Creating and running tests is an intrinsic part of the designer-programmer job description.

These days, with the availability of the JUnit unit test harness and its variants, cppUnit, VBUnit, StUnit, and so on, there is little excuse for not writing automated unit tests. GUI-driving acceptance tests are harder to automate. Good designers find ways to automate at least data-manipulation tests, if not mouse, button, and keystroke tests. The test harness httpUnit and its relatives help automate testing of Web interfaces. The frameworks FIT and FITnesse[4] help business people, not just programmers, write data-driven acceptance tests. There is a fairly strong literature on automated testing, including books on test-driven design (Beck 2003, Astels 2003, Hunt 2004).

A good unit test not only tests what it is supposed to, but also has a name that shows what "concern" is being tested (the test name reads as "test that something is true"). Attending to readability in naming the concern means that the collection of test case names illustrates a set of concerns that went into designing the system. That list serves as a portion of the design documentation for the next programmer.

Good acceptance tests are readable to the domain expert, as well as testing the normal and boundary cases of the system. This readability serves to inform the next domain expert along.

Figures 5-43 and 5-44 are examples of JUnit tests, courtesy of Andy Pols and Jeff Patton. Note the use of concern-based test names in both. In Figure 5-44, I include the names of five test cases so you can see how the list of names serves as informing markers of design concerns. (In Figure 5-43, the assertEquals message will tell the test report reader what went wrong; in Figure 5-44, the assertEquals message is telling the programmer what concern is being tested here. Both styles work.)

---

[4]   http://fitnesse.org

```
public void testInitialFormDefaultsToUseTheAntBuilder() throws Exception {
  // execute
  String result = myAction.doDefault();

  // verify
  assertEquals("Should be in input mode, once the form has been initialised",
                              Action.INPUT, result);
  assertEquals("Should have ant as the default builder on the input form",
                              "Ant", myAction.getBuilder());
}

public void testPreventsAddingDuplicateProjects() {
  // setup
  String duplicateProjectName = BeetleJuiceStub.DUPLICATE_PROJECT_NAME;

  // execute
  try {
    myAction.setName(duplicateProjectName);
    fail("Should have thrown an exception");
  } catch (IllegalArgumentException iae) {
    // verify
    assertEquals("Should have returned the correct form error message",
                        "This Project already exists.", iae.getMessage());
  }
}
```

Figure 5-43. *Test cases with "concern-based" naming. (Courtesy of Andy Pols)*

```
public class DatabaseModelTest extends FrameworkLocalTestCase {
       public void testDataModelCanBeCreatedFromClientDirectives() {
       public void testDataModelCanBeCreatedFromDirectivesFoundInXMLFile(){
       public void testDataModelCorrectsExistingSchema() {
       public void testTableCanDropItself()
       public void testDataModelCanDropItselfFromDB(){

// Just the one test expanded here…
       public void testDataModelCanBeCreatedFromClientDirectives() {
              DatabaseModel dm = new DatabaseModel("test");
              assertEquals("databaseModel was created and name is correct",
                                      "test", dm.getName());

              Table tb = new Table("parent");
              assertEquals("table was created", "PARENT", tb.getName());

              assertEquals("database model has no tables",
                                        0, dm.getAllKnownTables().size());
              dm.addTable(tb);
              assertEquals("database model has a table",
                                        1, dm.getAllKnownTables().size());
              assertEquals("table knows its parent model",
                                        dm, tb.getDatabaseModel());

            Column col = new Column("parentId", java.sql.Types.VARCHAR, 20);
              assertEquals("table has no columns", 0, tb.getAllColumns().
                                        size());
              tb.addColumn(col);
                assertEquals("table has one column", 1, tb.getAllColumns().
                                        size());
              tb.addColumn(col);
              assertEquals("table still has one column after double add",
                                        1, tb.getAllColumns().size());
       }
```

Figure 5-44.   *Test cases with "concern-based" naming. (Courtesy of Jeff Patton)*

TESTER: BUG REPORT

A bug report is a note logging an error, saying what circumstances caused the error.

Automated test harnesses such as JUnit automatically produce such reports. Automated build-and-test systems such as Cruise Control[5] automatically produce and e-mail them to the designated test owner. Manually run acceptance tests require that the tester type up test reports during acceptance testing so the team can go back and change the requirements, design, and code as required.

Many Crystal Clear projects have no dedicated external test team. The users become the system testers. Even in these cases, they report bugs. A popular open source bug report system is Bugzilla, and there are other open-source ones being developed (e.g., http://projects.edgewall.com/trac provides Trac, which uses WikiWiki technology for bug reporting and tracking).

A good bug report provides enough information to make the test easy to re-create.

Figure 5-45 is an example of a manually typed bug report from the BSA project.

Test Incident Report	Scout 01
Test Case Identifier	AddNewScout
Incident Description	
Date:	14-Apr-03
Tester(s):	All
Actual System State:	Code has a counter for the scoutID, but the database had an autocounter and could not be manually inputed.
Actual Output:	When clicking of New Scout, an error message would pop up stating that scoutID field could not be changed.
Defects Detected:	The scoutID had an error and system crashed when trying to save a new scout.
Test Environment:	Regular Regression Testing
Attempts to Repeat:	Ran the test twice with same error and crash happening
Anticipated Impact	No scouts can be added into system, therefore making the system useless.
Resolution	Problem was found, and the autocounter in the database was taken out so the counter in the code could work correctly.

Figure 5-45. *Sample incident report. (Courtesy of the BSA project)*

---

[5] http://cruisecontrol.sourceforge.net

Date	Build	Module	Bug Description	Status	Orig	Bug #
12/30	21	Client	Home link produces a 404 error from the widget.html page. Linked to home.htm and should be linked to index.html.	Open	NJ	52
1/16	23	Client	The refresh rate entry box accepts non-numeric values. fresh every 0.r4a min. OK	Open	AC	70
1/22	23	Business Tier	Receive the following error when saving a purchase order. busObj.PO divide by 0.	Open	NJ	77
1/23	23	Web Service	.disco file not found.	Open	NJ	80
1/27	24	Data Tier	Unable to run procedure app_getapo. Invalid parameter list.	Closed	AC	85
1/27	24	Database	When searching for vendors the response times out after 30 seconds.	Closed	AC	86

Figure 5-46.   *Build report. (Courtesy of Nate Jones)*

WRITER: HELP TEXT, USER MANUAL, AND TRAINING MANUAL

I assume that you have seen help text, user manuals, and training manuals before in your life, so I won't belabor the point by describing what one is. I include these in the work products list for completeness. The team will have to decide not only who writes each, but also how much of it should get written for each iteration and delivery.

Paper user manuals are increasingly being replaced by online help text, so it may be that from a work product point of view, the two are equivalent. Remedying the general uselessness of most online help text ("To turn on hyphenation, click the box marked 'Turn on hyphenation'") is outside the scope of Crystal Clear.

I assign these work products to the writer role, because some teams may hire or contract an external person to write them. Others may assign them to team members.

For obvious reasons of size, I don't include an example here.

REFLECTION ABOUT THE WORK PRODUCTS

That is a set of work products that I feel I can defend as a group, is quite light and still safe, and that you should be able to adapt to your situation. Some developers break into a sweat when they see a listing of all the work products that get produced on a project, so I hope that didn't hurt too much.

I want to thank the people who contributed the work product samples. They have provided a wide range of different formats for your consideration. You have seen that some people use standard, formal documentation; some use whiteboards, flip charts, index cards, and sticky notes; and some use custom notations created with various sorts of tools. Each group found a way to convey the needed information with both clarity and economy.

It is worth revisiting two ideas.

♦ There is no single, required, core, or minimal set of work products in Crystal Clear, the way there is with the seven properties. Taking the intersection from all the successful projects I have visited yields too small a set to be generally safe, taking the union yields too large a set (unsafe due to its bulk). The set in this chapter should be close to what you need.

♦ The economic-cooperative game involves two goals: delivering this system and setting up for the next game. Crystal Clear is for small teams communicating closely, with both goals in mind.

Attending to the first goal means that the intermediate work products should be quick and cheap in order to produce, with a primary emphasis on reminding markers. They should attend to informing markers if new people will be added to the team within the project, because they may come out ahead even within a six-month time horizon by spending time creating a learning path for new teammates to follow, so they don't ask quite so many questions for their first weeks.

The second goal is setting up for the next game. There is again a dual emphasis: improving the abilities of the team members so they will be better on the next round and setting into place informing markers for the next wave of developers. Don't forget that the people on the team are themselves highly effective "informing markers" and "information radiators." Build a strategy for training the next wave of developers using the existing people (having the new people do pair programming in rotations with existing team members is one such strategy).

Finally, there are several stakeholders in the question of documentation. The current developers are interested in a light set of markers, primarily reminding ones.

The future developers are interested in informative (and not-so-boring) markers for catching up to the group. And the sponsors are interested in the long-term stability of the knowledge base.

None of these stakeholders is to be forgotten. I believe that with some inventiveness, you may come up with even more expressive, less expensive, and less painful ways to satisfy their combined interests.

Chapter 6

Misunderstood (Common Mistakes)

You think you are using Crystal Clear, yet your project is not working. What's wrong? Crystal Clear can fail, but let's first double-check that you really are doing Crystal Clear. This chapter presents sample project situations. Some of them fulfill the intention of Crystal Clear, others violate it. The purpose here is to provide you with a personal warning system that you are or are not in tune with the intention of Clear.

Misinterpreting Crystal Clear is inevitable, no matter how many words I write. One way to help reduce the misinterpretations is to discuss specific situations and questions that have arisen.

Here are some situations I have run into. The first series indicates clear violation of Crystal Clear; the following series discuss violations of intention and borderline situations.

"WE COLOCATED AND RAN TWO-WEEK ITERATIONS—WHY DID WE FAIL?"

The software development community currently overuses the word *iteration*[1] and underappreciates the *user*. The literature accentuates *iterations* instead of *deliveries to real users*. XP calls for an *on-site customer*, which, while laudable, is often so difficult to arrange that organizations simply throw up their hands and don't involve a real user at all.

Recall that Property #1 of Crystal Clear is *Frequent Delivery*, not *frequent iteration*, and Property #6 is *Easy Access to Expert Users*.

The issue was driven home to me the other day when I visited a group whose habits derived from XP. They knew about pair programming, test-driven design, automated regression tests, short iterations, and all the rest. They had evolved over the year, as is quite often the case, to something similar to Crystal Clear. We were doing a reflection workshop at the time of this story. Half of the people in the room were winding up a five-month project. They kept referring to a section of the system that was "just plain wrong," despite the fact that it worked and had a good set of supporting tests.

> We drew a timeline of their practices over the previous year. They had gathered their requirements from what was supposedly a well-informed set of stakeholders. After three months, they had deployed an early version of the system to the customer site using Web-X, and had held an online discussion of the system. All went well in this practice deployment.
>
> After the fourth month, a week before our little workshop, five future users of the system came to the development site and sat down with the developers to practice using the system. That's when they told the developers it was "wrong." You can imagine this shocked the development team no end. The Web-X deployment had somehow not caused the same detailed examination of the software as the visit.
>
> We discussed what they could have done differently and what they might do differently in the future. Much to our mutual surprise, the team discovered that they never really had had access to a "friendly user" who could take tentative deliveries and examine the growing system, and worse, they still couldn't see that they could get one in the near future.

---

[1]   In recent discussions with user groups around the world, we are finding the phrase "iterative development" itself is problematic, because iterative implies rework, which many sponsors find threatening right from the start. The alternative, "incremental development," is much more reassuring as it implies "adding onto." To keep from constantly fighting standard terms, I have adopted the industry-standard word *iteration* in this book to refer to an internal development period. I still refer to the overall strategy as *Incremental Development* with *Incremental Delivery,* to reduce stress in the sponsors' minds.

In other words, looking back at their timeline, they couldn't see how they could have avoided this major surprise.

The story has a happy ending, I'm glad to say. This was a productive group, they still had a month left, so they gutted the "wrong" piece and rewrote it to meet the needs of the users.

This team had listened to their sponsors and users, colocated, integrated frequently, and reflected after each of their iterations, and they hadn't seen this coming. They still had no way to fix it. That responsibility lies with the executive sponsor, who is the person who has to arrange for more visits by real users. Fortunately, this particular executive sponsor is aware of the importance of the issue and is actively engaged in improving it for future projects.

Iterations provide feedback to the team about their process, early wins for their morale, and a steering mechanism to see they stay on track. But they do not provide end-to-end feedback about the fitness of the software for business use. That requires involvement of real users.

If I had to choose between two-week iterations without access to real users, or giving up the short iterations and delivering only quarterly but having real users come into the development lab twice in the delivery period to review growing software, I would choose the latter. This is the reason for the work product *viewing schedule*, and the reason that I stress *delivery* cycle over *iteration* cycle.

"TWO DEVELOPERS ARE SEPARATED BY A HALLWAY AND A LOCKED DOOR."

"Oh, come on, Alistair, how much does it really matter? We can't get our people into the same hall space. It just happens that we have a combination lock on that hallway door."

It matters if you want the safety offered by Crystal Clear. Crystal Clear is predicated on people exchanging small pieces of information at a high frequency over the course of a day, without losing their ability to complete the task at hand. That speed of communication creates a safety net for the project.

Suppose a person can stand up, look over a low partition, ask and within a few seconds get the answer to: "Did you really mean that the users will never have to retype their password? We have three servers in use, each with their own password system." Her total time spent away from the task at hand is perhaps forty-five seconds. Her ability to continue with the task at hand is excellent.

Contrast that with the same person thinking, "I don't know if I want to stop this just yet to walk across the hall, punch in the combination. Maybe Pat isn't at her desk right now. I'll see her sometime today." The result is either no answer at all, or several minutes, involving a number of very different subtasks and a high chance of getting distracted, spent away from the task at hand at least. Her ability to continue with the task at hand is moderate at best.

When negotiating the hallway, steps, locks, a person has to deal with subtasks that intrude on her cognitive state of mind. This breaks her line of thinking for a period and makes getting back into the problem-solving state energy consuming. Dealing with these cognitive shifts slows information flow between individuals several orders of magnitude, blocking the exchanges that make a team productive and successful.

It is true that many projects have shipped software despite developers sitting across hallways. However, team leaders repeatedly tell me, "Give me three to five developers in one room, keep the distractions away, and I can get the software out. Don't spread us out." That means they visit each other, draw on each others' whiteboards, and look over each others' shoulders at their programs and tests.

"WE HAVE THIS BIG INFRASTRUCTURE TO DELIVER FIRST."

Sometimes it does take a long time to get the infrastructure set up to deliver just the first, smallest piece of functionality. That is why the allowable increment period is as large as three months. Any larger than that, and project leaders tell me they can't keep focused on the design at hand and that the possibility for error in the design is just too large. More and more, teams want to deliver new functionality in three- to six-week time frames, saying that they don't want to wait longer than that to get feedback. They implement a skinny version of the infrastructure first, and then evolve the infrastructure in parallel with the functionality (the *Walking Skeleton* and *Incremental Rearchitecture* strategies).

Crystal Clear is based on getting feedback from running code and active users. The feedback is not just on the code, but on the requirements and the development process, as well as on the ability of your team to deliver systems.

Rapid feedback on the code lets the team further reduce writing down requirements and designs in excruciating detail. If you lengthen the time before you have running, tested, examined code, you have to put more into writing just to keep the memory of it alive. Rapid feedback on the process allows the team to locate unexpected problems and set up corrective action. It also boosts morale and establishes the habit of delivering that is one of the critical success factors of working teams.

Short iterations and delivery cycles are beneficial for four reasons:

- To avoid having to write down so many design details
- To get real feedback on the design decisions
- To find and fix problems in the development process
- To establish a habit of delivering

"OUR FIRST DELIVERY IS A DEMO OF THE DATA TABLES."

No good. Each delivery cycle should produce running, tested code that is, at least in principle, of some use to some user.

Moving to agile development requires learning how to divide the development assignment into chunks that can be integrated end to end, exercising the full development process and as much of the architecture as is needed for the growing functionality.

It is a comforting trap to develop the user interface design, or the tables, or a small prototype, and call that "a cycle" (of some sort) after which a reflection workshop is held. I have heard of teams that called writing all the requirements "an iteration," and then reflected on their requirements-gathering process. This does not work for the dual reasons that they cannot know how well they gathered and documented the requirements until they see how it all meshed with the rest of their development process (i.e., after delivery).

"NO USER IS AVAILABLE, BUT WE HAVE A TEST ENGINEER JOINING US NEXT WEEK."

A test engineer is not a user. Neither is a manager or supervisor who "once worked in the field." Your expert user validates and breaks your UI designs. A test engineer can double-check your own tests to tell you if your code is broken, but cannot tell you whether the system is what the users want. In a published study of project managers, each of whom had experience with and without direct links to the users, the project managers overwhelmingly felt that the projects with direct user linkage were more successful than those without (Keil 1995). When they had users present, the users alerted them, early on, to mistakes they were making in the concept and layout of the software and allowed them to produce software better suited to the needs of the users, with fewer unneeded features.

A Crystal Clear project can get by with relatively informal intermediate work products because of the ability of the designers to simply ask a user at intervals no longer than a week apart. The best projects have a user available full time, and some can get a user to visit several mornings a week. At the very least, an hour each week should be scheduled for user interview or shared design time.

*　　　*　　　*

Those were the obvious violations. Here are a set of questions and situations that either violate the intention of Crystal Clear or question the boundary.

"ONE DEVELOPER REFUSES TO DISCUSS HIS DESIGN OR SHOW HIS CODE TO THE REST."

As expert developer Pete McBreen said, "The days of claiming that code is private are long gone." Willingness to discuss the design and find possible faults in her own design or code is important.

People being willing to discuss their code is part of the *Personal Safety* property. Programmers often disagree about what constitutes good design, and often are quite nasty about it. Providing people with the needed personal safety may require that a few people step forward and show their designs so that the team can learn how to discuss the design technically and not emotionally.

A project is unlikely to pull off a Crystal Clear process if they are afraid to trust their designs to their teammates. Ask yourself how you and they can manage a design discussion without insult, letting different people work at their own levels of competence, still sufficient to deliver a working system.

"THE USERS WANT ALL OF THE FUNCTION DELIVERED TO THEIR DESKS AT ONE TIME . . ."

"[W]e don't want to annoy them by having to install new versions so often."

It happens with certain sorts of systems that the users can't be disturbed with many deliveries of a changing system, especially changing user interface. However, you should be able to bring a user in to see and use the system to get feedback on your technical and usage design decisions. Once that portion of the system is designed, tested, viewed, and accepted, you can relax on those decisions and move on to the next.

Where it is not appropriate to actually install the software on the users' machines, set the constructed, tested functionality to the side (properly versioned, of course), and wait to add the next increment's functionality. In other words, you will develop exactly as though you had delivered the functions to the users, even though, in this case, you didn't. The key to the Crystal Clear process is that you get closure and feedback on your development and deployment process, as well as your software.

Crystal Clear can be used when you cannot keep delivering system updates to all the users. Modify the process by finding a "friendly user," and deploy the different versions to just that one person.

"WE HAVE SOME MILESTONES LESS THAN A USE CASE AND SOME BIGGER."

"Our milestones are like these: implement new communication commands, implement HTML tags, implement class Blob. Some of them are inside a use case, some of them span use cases. Will those do?"

Implementing class Blob is not an "interesting" milestone in the Crystal Clear vocabulary. Getting a communication command implemented and tested is. Implementing a pair of HTML tags implemented, tested, and integrated is.

There is no obvious violation here. Keep asking, "What counts as a usable piece of functionality?"

"WE WROTE DOWN A BASIC CONCEPT AND DESIGN OF THE SYSTEM. WE ALL SIT TOGETHER, SO THAT SHOULD BE GOOD ENOUGH."

This is a reference to "You have a project mission statement, you are using usage-based requirements, probably use cases, and you have a description of the system design using one of the many description techniques you can invent," questioning just how many requirements are needed, and how much design documentation is needed.

I find use cases useful at the start of projects (less critical as the system fills out), and so of course I recommend them. However, a number of teams like feature lists or requirements formats that are neither use cases nor feature lists. Some live almost entirely by verbal agreement. If you all sit together, then it may be enough that you have some combination of an actor-goal list and/or user stories or use case briefs or feature lists as your requirements "table of contents," and this is sufficient to hold your conversations in place. There is no violation of Crystal Clear here, as long as the sponsor and expert user are part of the agreement to work this way.

The same rule of thumb applies for design documentation.

Watch out, though, for one person becoming overly loaded as "the expert" on the requirements or domain or master design, and slowing down the team.

"WHO OWNS THE CODE?"

I used to have a rule in Crystal Clear requiring that "every function, class, and work product has a clear owner." During the revisions of this book, that rule dropped low enough in priority not to make the final cut. However, code ownership is still a hot and even dangerous topic on many projects.

On many projects, everyone is allowed to add code to any class, with the consequence that no one feels comfortable deleting someone else's code from the increasingly messy class. The result is something a lot like a refrigerator shared by several roommates: full of increasingly smelly things that *almost* everyone knows should be thrown out, but nobody actually throws out.

I have seen a group of three people sitting around the same workstation for days, working their way through every class, negotiating which lines of code to delete or move. This situation comes from absence of an ownership model and is expensive.

You have a clear ownership model for your work products if you know who it is that can change, update, and, most important, delete any part of it. The answer may be a single person, anyone in a given subteam, or even anyone on the team. You should never have to have the whole team sit around the screen and ask, "Who put this in here? What is it doing there? Can we delete it?" If you have to do this, you know you have a breakdown in the ownership model.

One person wrote me: "Good point. We just found ourselves all sitting around the screen last week, reviewing all the classes we have so far. It seems we had all been adding, and no one removing. It took a full day just to sort that out. Now we are organized with use case ownership and class ownership. Anyone can make a short-term change to a class when we hit panic mode, but that person notifies the class owner, who can double-check it."

People often think that XP has no ownership model. This is untrue. XP has a strong ownership model: *Any **two** people sitting together and agreeing on it can change any line of code in the system.* The ownership model is explicitly communal, with the safety check that two people have to agree to the change (and also that all the tests have to run!).

Most of the Crystal Clear projects I have visited adopt the policy, "change it, but let me know."

"CAN WE LET OUR TEST ENGINEER WRITE OUR TESTS? HOW DO WE REGRESSION TEST THE GUI?"

Regression unit tests are for the *developers* to write and use, not the test engineer. They are there so the developers can go home at night knowing that the changes they put in during the day did not unexpectedly wreck the system; they can make changes with greater rapidity, find mistakes faster, and sleep better at night.

Programmers traditionally dislike writing tests, and have a tendency to pass their code along to someone else called the tester to test as soon as the code "sort of runs." While this is not a strict violation of Crystal Clear, it is a violation of its intention and a bad idea, socially and professionally. Write your own tests.

This raises the question of testing again. Review Property 7, which discusses GUI-less system tests, GUI-driven system tests, and usability tests.

"WHAT IS THE OPTIMAL ITERATION LENGTH?"

I don't know that there is an "optimal" iteration length in general. I have heard adequate defense of everything from one week to one month. It is useful to bear in mind the different negative effects come from them being too long, too short, and all the same.

Too long. Most development organizations use iteration lengths of anywhere from three months to two years. This produces the rhythm so neatly described on the Scrum eGroup by Daniel Gackle (who was writing about even a monthly iteration!):

> "Meander, meander, meander, realize there isn't much time left, freak out, get intense, OK, we're done. Repeat monthly."

This "meander, meander, freak out, get intense" syndrome is one that incremental and iterative development is supposed to remove. The question remaining is, How long is too long for you?

Two good initial choices are two weeks and one month. Two-week iterations could be good, because this cycle length will illustrate to the programmers how much they need to change. It will teach them to estimate in small quantities and develop in micro-increments. It may, however, be too difficult initially. A cycle length of one month is less of a shock to the system and may allow the team to ease into the new approach. You may find, however, that one-month iterations are not efficient enough for your purposes.

You will, of course, be holding reflection workshops after each iteration, so you can question the iteration length within a few iterations. Some groups change from two weeks to a month, others from a month to two weeks. I have even met teams that change the iteration length depending on where they are within the project! (For those interested,[2] they use one-week iterations at the start of the project to avoid the "meander" syndrome described earlier, move to two-week iterations as they hit their stride, and go back to one-week iterations as they near the end, in order to fine-tune the scope-cutting and deal with late-breaking requirements changes and integration errors.)

Too short. Iteration start-up and shut-down is not free, so if the iterations are too short, the team will get frustrated at restarting so often. Even people who like short iterations sometimes comment on the nuisance of having to do planning and estimation every Monday morning. In addition, if you don't have good automated integration and acceptance tests, the testing burden will be too high.

---

[2]   Thanks to Jeff Patton for this note.

Also on an eGroup discussion, Patrick Parato noted about one-week iterations:

The only drawback we have seen is that the development team fizzles out close to the end of the iteration. The tasks will be all complete but people don't want to admit it because the one week iterations make them feel constantly under pressure. The developers don't really like the feeling that they can't vary their effort depending on mood, health, or other external stimuli. Some developers believe that one month long iteration allows them more freedom to vary their pace, and that the one week iteration is too much pressure. Very similar to micromanagement.

Monotony. Patrick's note introduces the topic of monotony. As mentioned earlier, human beings seem built for rhythm, and the need for this shows up in incremental/iterative development. An increasing number of people are reporting that when they do short iterations for a year or two, a feeling of burnout sets in, just from the flatness of their work life. This occurs even when and even though they are delivering good code to their customers regularly.

You can take two steps to prevent this monotony. The first is to attend to your iteration and delivery completion rituals (see Chapter 4). At the end of your iteration, decompress or celebrate, whether that means a walk in the woods or a group trip to the pub. Arrange to do something different after delivering new code. Some teams use the period right after delivering to clean up the mess they created in the code just before delivery (Hohmann 1977), others allocate time for some personal development. People use the reflection workshop and iteration planning to create a change of pace.

The second step applies if you are using shorter iteration lengths, such as one week. Bundle these into some form of supercycle, perhaps every four or six iterations to a supercycle. Arrange a rhythm shift to occur at the boundaries of the supercycle, a team outing, picnic, treat, trip to the movies, half-day off, or some days for development of personal topics.

Some teams like to allocate a quota of time for people to work on miniprojects not directly related to the project. Some put marks in the code or on the whiteboard about ugly places in the code they'd like to have time to clean up. Some allocate time for people to investigate new technologies. Both of these are "investment" activities, which improve the programmers and the system and also provide a change of pace.

A final idea is to allow programmers to spend time with real users of their system in their work environment. This not only breaks the monotony, but, as Tom Poppendieck and others have pointed out to me, developers find it highly motivating.

Chapter 7

Questioned (Frequently Asked)

Readers may be curious about how these ideas arose, how they compare with others in the industry, how far they can be stretched, and what to do when they don't seem to apply. The chapter is presented in question-and-answer form to allow for "talking about" the ideas, everything from philosophical foundations to "How do I get started?"

Crystal Clear works because software development is an economically constrained cooperative game of invention and communication, and the rules of Crystal Clear improve both the invention and cooperation aspects of the team's work.

Paradox though it may seem, it is precisely the lack of requirements and planning documents *together with* having team members in the same room that improve the odds of success. The team members get quick feedback on both the process and the product, and there is only a short distance between them and the people who need to know the information. A person who learns something can pass it along to the others with very little communication cost. A person needing to know something can get an answer with similarly little communications cost. By making it easier to coordinate, with less to coordinate, the team reduces both cost and error.

In this chapter, I start right from the very beginning: the research that gave rise to the recommendations, the underlying idea of software development being an economic-cooperative game, and the philosophical heritage of the embodied worldview. These conversations are fairly heavy and not for every reader. As one person put it, Crystal is "short on practices and long on principles."[1] These questions allow me to

---

[1]   Thanks to Andy Pols of the United Kingdom.

talk about the principles. After the principles, I review the boundary conditions of Crystal Clear, as distinct from Crystal Orange, for example, and the lack of required techniques. I discuss the structure of methodologies in general, and how that influences the structure of this book and Crystal Clear in general. I include a summary chart for Crystal Clear.

After the first four, heavy questions, I discuss the way in which this book is laid out, how Crystal compares with Scrum, XP, and with ISO 9001 and CMM(I) requirements, distributed and larger teams. Finally, the last question, "How do I get started?"

QUESTION 1. WHAT IS THE GROUNDING FOR CRYSTAL?

The first and best grounding is empirical. The empirical evidence started showing up after I was employed in 1991 by the then fledgling IBM Consulting Group to create a methodology for their forthcoming object technology projects. I didn't know anything special about methodology then, so my boss at the time, Kathy Ulisse, suggested that I visit and debrief project teams to find out what they had learned (thank you, Kathy!). From then to now, I visited projects both inside IBM and outside IBM, in all parts of the world. I continue these project debriefings even now, because what people report is both informative and surprising.

What I learned was that most of what had been written in the methodology books was quite irrelevant to life on the project and had very little to do with the project's likelihood of success. In fact, until the arrival of XP, the correlation was inverted; the more occupied the group was with following the strictures of the methodology, the less likely it was that they would deliver the software in a timely fashion.

The projects I interviewed that had succeeded often had a sloppy-looking process. These successful people talked about topics that were not method related, but communication and delivery related: sitting close together, having quick access to expert users, delivering frequently, and getting feedback quickly.

Initially, I took down all these notes, and didn't know what to do with them—after all, I had been charged with writing down a "methodology," which was supposed to consist of roles, work products, milestone standards, and the like. It was only after several years of interviews, three or four attempts to write down a useful methodology, and working directly on projects that the message started to sink in properly: Those really are the core properties of success; the techniques and work-product details of the "methodology" are really a second order success factor. Get the people close together, communicating with goodwill, delivering often and getting quick feedback from the users, and the team will probably sort out the rest on their own, using whatever technology and techniques they know.

Looking back over my notes from ten years of interviewing, these same recommendations surfaced over and over again. I slowly recognized that they form a methodology, one that contains few specific rules, but allows the people to act as educated professionals in their fields and work out the best path to success on their own. The problem that has occupied me for the years since that realization has been just how to write it down in a way that another team could follow, how to identify which pieces are more critical than others, and how to describe the allowable variances. My best current guess is this book.

The second grounding consists of a set of principles distilled from watching software projects in social-anthropologist fashion and from reading literature on human communication and process design. I described these principles at length in *Agile Software Development* (Cockburn 2002), and in my doctoral dissertation, *People and Methodologies in Software Development* (Cockburn 2003a). I list and summarize the principles here:

1. **Different projects need different methodology trade-offs.** This should be completely obvious. Judging from the ongoing initiatives at large companies around the world to create and standardize a single methodology for all their projects, however, it is evidently not obvious. In "Selecting a Project's Methodology" (Cockburn 2000), I proposed two axes for selection: the number of people needing to be coordinated and the degree of damage that could be caused by the system malfunctioning. These two axes explain why Crystal is not a single methodology but a family of methodologies, and serve as a basis for selecting a particular Crystal methodology to start from. Of the two axes, I consider the number of people being coordinated as the most significant to start with; the team can often shape the methodology for the other axis.

2. **Larger teams need more communication elements.** Team size is the critical distinguishing element between members of the Crystal family. Crystal Clear, for example, is only recommended for teams that can achieve osmotic communication. Once the team grows to more than a dozen people, or sits more than thirty seconds' walk from each other, different communication and coordination modes are needed.

3. **Projects dealing with greater potential damage need more validation elements.** A small team of six or fewer people programming the movement of boron rods in a nuclear reaction should, I hope, use more care in their work than the same six people programming a free-time system, perhaps to organize their recipe collection, keep track of the neighborhood's football team scores, or order food for late night work. The difference is in the verification and validation dimension, not in the coordination and communication dimension. For the nuclear reactor, there should be public reviews and walk-throughs of the requirements, the design, the code, and the tests . . . it should be manifestly and publicly clear that the system works. That amount of verification is unlikely to be worth the time, energy, and monetary cost on the free-time projects. Crystal Clear does not natively address the life-critical level of damage. A team working on such a project can only use Crystal Clear as a starting point and must add additional verification elements to fit their situation.

4. **A little methodology does a lot of good; after that, weight is costly.** Not much work has been done on the diminishing returns aspect of methodologies. The surprising

news is that a little goes a long way, and diminishing returns set in very quickly. This is surprising because there seems to be a reflex response that "more methodology is better," meaning that more process, more documents, and more status reporting will improve the likelihood of timely delivery. My interviews indicate the reverse, that less is generally better, as long as one covers the gaps with personal communication. Jim Highsmith gives the advice to start with less than you think you need...that's probably all you need; it is easier to add some as you go along than to remove as you go along. That advice is incorporated into Crystal Clear.

5. **Formality, process, and documentation are not substitutes for discipline, skill, and understanding.** This principle from Jim Highsmith (2003) articulates what is different between agile and traditionally predictive or plan-driven projects. Software is built by people who need to invent and communicate their ideas, based on their skill and understanding. Large corporations often make the mistake of thinking that having people fill out forms, follow particular steps in development, and document the current state of their code will confer upon them skill in inventing solutions. However, the three elements that Jim highlights—discipline, skill and understanding—are all *internal* properties of a person and cannot be substituted for by the external forms.

6. **Interactive, face-to-face communication is the cheapest and fastest channel for exchanging information.** Two or three people standing at a whiteboard, diagramming and talking, are able to take advantage of a wealth of communication channels and get near-instantaneous feedback. They can see each other's expressions and change sentences in mid-utterances. They can move closer and farther, point, gesture, make facial movements, draw, and talk all at the same time, interrupting each other and adding to the drawing as they go. This sort of exchange situation is known as *warm*, meaning that it is rich in information and also in emotion. As the people move to telephone, e-mail, and eventually paper, the richness, speed of interaction, and emotional content diminish, and the communication is known as *cooler*. Although there are certain advantages to using cooler communications channels (asynchrony and isolating social-emotional reactions are two of them), there is a tremendous loss in communication efficiency, which on a software project translates to lost time and increased mistakes. Since most projects are time and cost sensitive, Crystal Clear maximizes rate of progress for time and money expended by keeping the communications close and rich (osmotic communication).

7. **Increasing feedback and communication reduces the need for intermediate deliverables.** Many methodologies are full of what I call "promissory notes." These are documents that promise that the team *will* build such-and-so, which *will* be built at such-and-such a time and *will* look like this or that. These promises are pri-

mary needed because there is such a long time delay between when the promise is made and when the software is delivered. With such a long time delay, it is of course natural that the sponsors, examiners, and users want to know that progress is being made and what the final system will look like. The problem with these promissory notes is that very often the neat plans and designs don't work out as promised. If, in contrast, the team builds something and shows it to the users every month, the time delay is short enough that they don't have to make elaborate promises—they simply show the month's results and learn directly and correctly what is right and what is wrong. Software development is still slow enough and expensive enough that some promissory notes are needed—the delivery plan and use cases being two—but the principle is still that the shorter the time delay, the fewer intermediate "promissory" notes are needed.

8. **Concurrent and serial development exchange development cost for speed and flexibility.** This principle says that properly executed concurrent development can speed development, at a possibly higher salary cost, compared with correctly executed serial development, in which each task is run to completion before the next task is started.[2] The problem with the lower cost serial development is that any mistake in understanding causes a ripple effect of rework, which is expensive. It is predicated upon having very stable requirements and a full understanding of the domain and the implementation technology. It is very rare in software projects that the requirements and the technology are well enough understood to permit these efficiencies to be harvested. The Crystal family is therefore built upon concurrent development, which permits real-time discovery of mistaken assumptions, but at the same time requires better communications between the people (which gets back to close communication and osmotic communication).

9. **Efficiency is expendable in non-bottleneck activities.** The book, *The Goal* (Goldratt 1992), identifies that every process has a "bottleneck" station, one that constrains the speed of the entire enterprise. Software development is no different. What the book does not draw upon, but the Crystal family does, is the corollary, that the non-bottleneck stations can help in certain ways, operating at lower efficiencies. Efficiency becomes an expendable commodity. In software development this manifests itself when people with spare capacity help to write requirements, tests, or documentation; or, when the developers (assuming they

---

[2]   The third chapter of *Simultaneous Management* (Laufer 1998) describes how to mesh concurrent and serial development on the same project to take advantage of each. As interesting as the techniques is the fact that his stories come from civil engineering projects (e.g., building a hospital or an airstrip in the jungle).

have spare capacity) start work before the requirements are finalized, taking upon themselves the likelihood of later rework. Examples of these situations are described in *Agile Software Development.* Identifying the bottleneck station and making use of spare capacity should become a core part of the team's methodology shaping workshops.

10. **"Sweet spots" speed development.** The best of all possible worlds is having (1) dedicated, (2) experienced people who (3) sit within earshot of each other, (4) use automated regression tests, (5) have easy access to the users, and (6) deliver running, tested systems to those users every month or two. Such a project is clearly in a better position to complete successfully than one missing those characteristics. (It is surprising that sponsoring executives do not pay more attention to these important success factors.)

    Crystal Clear is built upon and legislates the last four of those sweet spots. Obviously, it is a rare team that can be staffed with experienced people, and so Crystal Clear works with the assumption that the project is staffed with a mixture of experienced and novice developers (although it does require that the lead designer is experienced). When the team cannot hit one of those sweet spots, then they need to invent a way to get closer to it. The *Focus* property is about allowing the team to get close to the first sweet spot even when they are not fully dedicated to just one project. What to do when some of the other sweet spots are missed is taken up in later questions.

Since it is hard to remember ten principles, I derive them from one idea, that of the economic-cooperative game described at length on my Web site,[3] in *Agile Software Development,* and in "The End of Software Engineering and the Start of Economic-Cooperative Gaming" (Cockburn 2004b).

The cooperative game manifesto says:

Software development is a series of resource-limited, goal-directed cooperative games of invention and communication. The primary goal of each game is the production and deployment of a software system; the residue of the game is a set of markers to assist the players of the next game. People use markers and props to remind, inspire and inform each other in getting to the next move in the game. The next game is an alteration of the system or the creation of a neighboring system. Each game therefore has as a secondary goal to create an advantageous position for the next game. Since each game is resource-limited, the primary and secondary goals compete for resources.

---

[3] http://Alistair.Cockburn.us.

The advantage of this phrasing is that it highlights a couple of critically important aspects of software development:

♦ It is the *people* and their *invention* and *communication* that make software happen. Everything that relates to their speed of invention and communication affects the outcome of the project. This specifically includes proximity, community, amicability, conflict, and trust as have been discussed at length in this book.

♦ There are two goals in motion at every instant: delivering the present system and setting up for the following game. They conflict, requiring some nontrivial combination of short-term "greedy" and long-term "investment" actions.

♦ Every decision, by every person involved, has economic consequences. Since the situation is overconstrained and underresourced, this typically means you will hurt no matter what you do; you only get to choose in which way to get hurt. If you spend too much time in investment actions, you get hurt in the short term (and maybe the long term); if you do too many greedy actions, you get hurt in the long term; and there is probably no middle safe ground. Don't fall asleep.

I generate most of my methodology recommendations and project management strategies from the cooperative game manifesto. Considering the state of the project, the two goals, and the nature of human-to-human communication, I am able to choose where to abbreviate, where to spend extra effort, when to put people closer together, and when to put them further apart. (Yes, there are indeed times to separate them and *reduce* communication! See "The Cone of Silence" (Cockburn 2004b).)

*   *   *

The Swedish researcher Pelle Ehn and Danish developer Peter Naur provide additional grounding to these ideas based on the philosophers Descartes, Marx, Heidegger, Wittgenstein, and Ryle. Ehn examines the first four of these philosophers in his excellent but sadly out of print *Work-Oriented Development of Software Artifacts* (Ehn 1988).[4] I summarize his extensive discussion in a brief and necessarily coarse fashion as follows:

♦ Descartes gives us a worldview that there is an objective reality that can be described. This worldview underlies and informs mainstream traditional software

---

[4]   An extract from Ehn's writing is included in Appendix B of *Agile Software Development*.

development. The assignment of the development team is to capture that reality in their requirements, in their code, and then again in their analysis models, designs, and documentation.

♦ Wittgenstein gives us an opposing worldview, that is, there is no objective reality that we can articulate and agree upon. Rather, we are all engaged in ongoing "language games" that evolve over time and that externalize a meager part of our understanding at any moment in time. The development team never "captures" the requirements, because neither the requirements nor the people's understandings are either expressible or shared. What happens instead is a sort of dance in which the various people perform actions and make utterances, and react to the actions and utterances of everyone else and also themselves. Although this description may seem untidy and vague, it matches my particular understanding of what happens on projects and forms the deepest underlying basis for the Crystal family and Crystal Clear most particularly.

♦ Marx gives us the worldview that every new software system will change the social-power structure. Accordingly, the users, the executive, and the developers should include in their development process an inquiry into how the system will shift power and how to handle that shift. This worldview is taken into account to a small extent by the agile methodologies, who give a larger voice to the users. It was taken deliberately into account by Kristin Nygaard, Pelle Ehn, and the Scandinavian school of development in the 1970s and 1980s, when they were working with the local trade unions on where and how to incorporate computer technology into the unionized workplace.

♦ Heidegger discussed the nature of tools, as being either visible to the wielder as a tool object, or invisible to the wielder, as simply an extension to his body that accomplishes the needed task. While the tool is visible to the wielder ("Gee, this hammer is heavy," or, "Where's that hyphenation key, again?"), the tool interferes with the performance of the task. When the wielder is performing the task at full speed, he does not notice its existence at all. This discussion is important to the designers of the user interface and also of the domain model, both of which can interfere with the system's usability.

♦ Ryle's views are discussed by Peter Naur in "Programming as Theory Building" (Naur 1992). Naur incorporates Ryle's idea of "theory" to describe the way in which a designer-programmer has to understand the domain at hand, the requirements, the technology, and the proposed design solution. For a designer to make sympathetic changes requires him to have an understanding rich enough to be mined for implications and causes. For a group of people to make harmonious design decisions, they have to have in their separate heads theories that are "close" to each other. To me, this explains very neatly the metaphor element of XP: the metaphor is a short phrase which points to the theory of the system's design; the better the team's agreement on the metaphor, the more likely they are to make harmonious design decisions (see *Agile Software Development,* p. 239).

Naur's idea of each person having his own theory of the system and the difficulty of aligning the multiple theories across the development team fit naturally with Ehn and Wittgenstein's notion of language games and the dance of actions and utterances that move people to greater alignment of language and understanding.

Ehn discusses the idea of people laying down markers of their current understandings, so they can refer back to them later. Naur's writing leads one to recognize that the subtlety of people's understandings change over time and that the current design, beautiful or ungainly, really is a mirror of their current understanding.[5] As their theory matures, it becomes more subtle, and they get a more concise and natural design expression.

There is a negative side to having a more subtle theory. The design becomes more subtle over time, which means that the maintainer also needs to develop a similarly subtle theory to take over the code! Really experienced developers find this frustrating, because it means that their best, cleanest, most concise code is virtually unmaintainable! They watch in horror as the people who follow them unpack the design to become bigger, clumsier, and *more evident to the casual observer!*

This observation brings into question the very idea of quality in design. One of the very many dimensions of quality is the ability to maintain and evolve the code. To the more experienced developer, the subtle design is "better." He can, with his subtle understanding, adjust the system to new circumstances with just the smallest of changes. That same code is nearly unmaintainable to the person with a less developed theory. With the less-subtle design, the second person will take longer and have to make more extensive changes, and at the same time find that less subtle design "easier" to maintain and extend. I see no way out of this dilemma; it seems just another of those contradictory situations that infest software development.

Experiential, cognitive, and philosophical groundings suggest that the best way to develop software is to use so few people that everything can be communicated in face-to-face discussions, letting small groups finesse problems by relying on common sense and skill and holding the behaviors and artifacts together by adopting only a few

---

[5]   Ward Cunningham said almost identical words to me back in 1994. I might not have noticed it in Ehn and Naur's writings if Ward had not already mentioned it.

principles of development, such as direct user involvement and tracking by finished products. These are the foundations of Crystal Clear.

Readers who care about such things should examine Ehn and Naur's writings to better understand the philosophical and cognitive underpinnings of the Crystal approach.

*   *   *

There is a mostly unstated bias in Crystal—that of generally trusting people. That bias comes from me. Psychological baggage inevitably seeps from a methodology author into his recommendations, and this one is mine.

It is not a blind trust, though. Although teams perform better and use less energy when they can work in trust, not all people are able to trust others, nor do all people deserve trust. Some people, playing their own game of career survival, are quite willing to take advantage of their teammates or suboptimize the project results if it will enhance their careers. Others are not capable of fulfilling their assignments. Still others simply don't care. In general, every person is watching all the others to see when the trust will fail. This is one reason that the targeted property of Crystal Clear is only "personal safety," and not full trust.

The manager of a "cooperative gaming" team must notice and attend to failures in trust. One dilemma that periodically shows up is this: The executive sponsor asks the programmers how long a set of tasks will take. They answer, the executive sponsor accepts, and the programmers start work. As time passes, the executive sponsor gets this uncomfortable feeling that the programmers are taking advantage of him. Does the assignment really take that long (the programmers are working diligently), or are they taking advantage of the situation and padding their time estimates so they can relax along at an arbitrarily slow pace?

There is no way to resolve the question, either in Crystal or in any other methodology. Either could be true, and I have encountered what I believe are examples of both.

Software development is a game of people working with and against other people. All human motives and emotions apply and must be taken into account, even in Crystal.

QUESTION 2.   WHAT IS THE CRYSTAL FAMILY?

Crystal is a family of methodologies based on a genetic code that allows different family members to be generated for different circumstances. All members will share a family resemblance.

The genetic code consists of:

♦ The economic-cooperative game model just described

♦ A set of *priorities* and *principles* for making choices

♦ Selected *properties* to steer toward

♦ Sample *strategies* and *techniques*

♦ Sample *instances* to copy

The three priorities are project *safety,* development *efficiency,* and *habitability* of the resulting conventions.

The *safety* priority is to get a reasonable business result from the project, given the project's priorities and resource constraints. *Efficiency* in development is a top priority because so many projects are economically overconstrained.

Habitability became a top priority when I started noticing in my project interviews that most programmers have the power to ignore whatever methodology is mandated by their organization. All they have to do is say that it slows them down and they'll miss their deadline if they do all that extra work. That is usually sufficient basis for ignoring it. To be fair, most methodologies are so inefficient that they are correct in their statement, so it is not clear whether they are doing the organization a disservice or a favor by ignoring the methodology (my estimate is that there is an immediate 15 to 30 percent efficiency to be gained in most organizations simply by throwing out most of their process[6]). If the programmers are told they have to do it anyway, they usually find ways to circumvent it. It doesn't matter what the methodology is if it doesn't get used. In other words, *habitability* is a critical success factor of methodology adoption.

Part of habitability is tolerance for human variation. Some like to make lists, others don't; some work best visually, others with text; some like to work alone, others in groups. Some stare at the design for hours, days, or weeks making sure it is right, while others like to "feel" the code taking shape. It is for this reason that Crystal has so much tolerance around techniques—not only do they change all the

---

[6]   As Luke Hohmann points out: "When you want your boat to go fast, it is easier to cut anchors than add horsepower."

time, but different people are drawn to different techniques. The *habitability* priority means that the rules need to be such that the people on the team can live with them.

The priorities interact. *Habitability* means that I accept that a chosen set of rules may not be as *efficient* as possible. The *safety* priority means that the chosen rules should be good enough to get an adequate result (making exception, of course, for poor project managers and greedy sponsors, both of which still exist).

Part of efficiency and habitability is dealing with the fact that every project is slightly different, and so properly needs its own, tailored methodology.

This means that no one methodology will suffice for the range of projects that even a midsized company will encounter.

A company need not define dozens of methodologies though. One company with widely diverse projects was able to get away with just three base methodologies: one for under-four-person projects, another for projects of eight to twenty people, and a third one for systems that have to pass the U.S. Food and Drug Administration process certification. Each team tailors the nearest base methodology to their project's particular requirements, expertise, and technology characteristics.

Of course, they have to do this tuning quickly enough to fit within the business's cost-value horizon. If methodology shaping takes half the project budget, then it would indeed be better to use a suboptimal but standard methodology. The need for efficient methodology shaping is why I describe the methodology shaping and reflection workshop techniques in this book.

Those are the priorities. The properties are just those described in Chapter 2. No strategies or techniques are required for a team, other than incremental development. The set of allowed strategies and techniques is very large, and so I present just a few of the more interesting and less known ones in Chapter 3. Methodology samples are included in *Surviving Object-Oriented Projects* (Cockburn 1998), *Agile Software Development* (Cockburn 2002), and, of course, this book.

To help with choosing a set of rules for to a particular project, I constructed the two-dimensional grid shown in Figure 7-1.

This grid[7] identifies *team size,* the number of people being coordinated, as the primary axis with respect to defining methodologies. A second important dimension is *criticality*, the potential damage caused by an undetected defect: loss of comfort (C), loss of discretionary moneys (D), loss of essential moneys (E), and loss of life (L). We should expect to see the communication and coordination components of

---

[7]   Described in (Cockburn 2000) and in *Agile Software Development*.

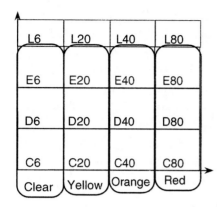

Figure 7-1.   *Crystal's coverage of different project types.*

methodologies change noticeably as the team keeps doubling in size. We should expect to see the validation and verification components change noticeably as the criticality increases up to loss of life (where the FDA process approval can become relevant). In Figure 7-1, the box labeled C6 signifies projects with up to six people working on a loss-of-comfort system.

The name *Crystal* derives from these two dimensions, in an analogy with geological crystals, which also are characterized in two dimensions: color and hardness. I let the team size (more generally, the communication and coordination complexity) correspond to the darkness of the color: clear, yellow, orange, red, maroon, blue, violet, and so on, and the criticality correspond to mineral hardness: soft as quartz for loss-of-comfort systems, hard as diamond for loss-of-life systems.

Figure 7-1 shows sixteen boxes, implying the need for at least 16 methodologies to be defined. My experience is that if a group starts from a previously documented methodology and shapes on the fly with the *Methodology Shaping Workshop* and the *Reflection Workshop*, things can simplified. One suggestion is to put the life-critical projects into their own area, and cluster the rest by team size. This leaves one primary dimension—color—as the distinguishing characteristic for non-life-critical methodologies. I don't have enough experience yet to know how the life-critical methodologies cluster, but the company mentioned above decided that all their FDA-approval projects with less than 20 people could be clustered together. They didn't have any projects at all with more than 20 people, so they simply had three categories, which we might call *clear, yellow,* and *diamond.*

QUESTION 3. WHAT KIND OF METHODOLOGY DESCRIPTION IS THIS?

The predominant way of conveying a methodology is through an element-by-element description of approximately one dozen different types of elements. Figure 7-2 shows a generic and typical set of methodology element types. A little multiplication shows that even a fairly simple methodology requires the description of over a hundred separate elements, plus how each fits with all the others. Most methodologies contain several hundred elements, and Extreme Programming has about four dozen. You can immediately see why methodology descriptions are so long (and boring).

Part of the methodology text describes the "factory" where the software is produced (I don't like the historical connotations of that word but can't find another). The nonfactory part of the methodology describes how the work products are to be described. Figure 7-3 shows the separation of methodology elements into factory and product descriptors (with time flowing downward in the diagram).

On the right, we see the original, fuzzy, and imprecise descriptions of the product (vision and mission statement, conceptual prototypes) at the top, evolving over time into intermediate work products such as requirements and plans, and eventually into source code, tests, packaging, and user manuals. The elements of the methodology covering this evolution live in the realm of notations and techniques. Thus we see

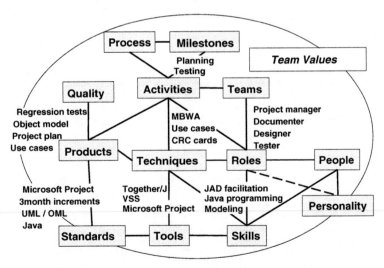

Figure 7-2.   Element types of a methodology with sample elements.

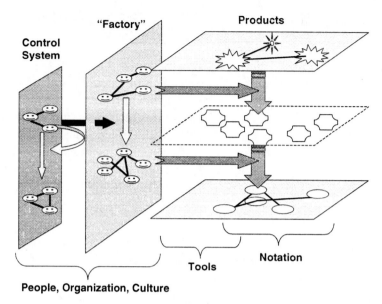

Figure 7-3.   *Division of methodology into "factory" and product descriptors.*

that UML is a product-description notational standard (which explains both why it is useful and still affects the outcome of projects so little).

The two vertical slices on the left are the factory and its control system, both made of people. The people producing the software live in an organizational structure, which changes over time. The people causing those changes live in their own organizational structure, which is also changing over time. The elements of the methodology covering these concern people, organization, and culture. Historically, software development groups have been averse to explicit discussion of their organizational and cultural elements, which has been a continual source of dysfunction in our field.

The horizontal arrows indicate the tools that the people use to create and alter the work products.

I have used these frameworks to describe methodologies for years. Two flaws in them are, however, slowly becoming both apparent and painful.

One flaw is the idealization of people into roles. A methodology description is, by its very nature, a formula intended to cover multiple projects, and the main part that gets abstracted away is *personality*. The problem is that people are simply stuffed full of personality, so that the *people* who show up at work don't have the correct fit with the *roles* that are supposed to be in operation. It is not a "tester" who comes to work in the morning, it is Jim; it is not a "project manager," it is Annika; it is not a "designer," it is Peter. Annika may or may not have the personality needed for a good project manager, Peter may or may not have the skill set needed to be a good designer (see Figure 7-4).

In practice, individual personalities dominate. Peter may get offended by Annika and refuse to turn in reports; Annika may find Jim hard to talk to and ignore him for weeks at a time; or, as often happens, Peter may simply take over the project, ignore Annika, and drive the project in any direction he wants.

The second flaw in the standard presentation of methodology is that there are an arbitrary number of unclassified items that don't fit into the methodology diagram but turn out to be important to the way the project runs. I have encountered as critical "methodological" items the shapes of the desks; the layout of rooms; the presence or absence of ventilation; a cultural tradition of Thursday afternoon volleyball games or Friday night beer busts; the establishment of a cultural signature such as a logo, saying, ritual, or a value such as excellence, working late, or always being laid back; and rules such as "salespeople are not permitted in the programming area after 10:00 A.M." or "no phone calls or conferences between 10:00 and 12:00."

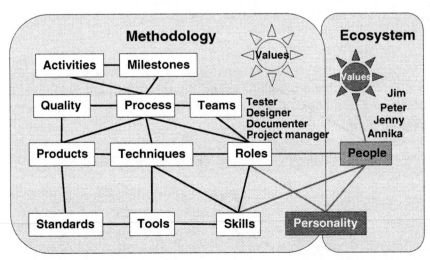

Figure 7-4. *Methodologies idealize personality, but people are stuffed full of it.*

To summarize, I found four knotty issues in methodology descriptions:

+ They are long, intricate, and boring.
+ Factory description gets intertwined with product description.
+ They miss many small rules and issues that have large effect.
+ They miss the effects of individual people with personalities.

I decided to deal with these four issues in the following way:

Different people come to a methodology description from different backgrounds and are able to notice different things (similar to the blind men feeling different parts of an elephant and trying to form their impression of the whole). I therefore have written the chapters in different formats to give different views for different reader backgrounds. I do not legislate techniques, but leave those up to the individuals as professionals in their respective fields. The work products are presented via samples, so that I don't get tied into notational standards that are likely to change every few years. As a result Crystal Clear is primarily a description of the factory: where people sit, how they interact, and so on.

To cover the many small rules that are important to projects, I experimented in describing methodologies using *patterns* instead of the methodology 12-tuple. Much to my delight, I found that I could describe many aspects of a methodology that were important, including the odd little rules, in a way that was easily understood and applied by busy project teams. Those aspects that didn't fit as patterns could simply be expressed as project conventions.

Out of those experiments I learned that *a methodology is nothing more than the conventions the team agrees to adopt!* These conventions drift over time, and so there is nothing more natural than that the team should convene regularly and review their operating conventions. This is, of course, the reflection workshop. Also, conventions are no harder to write down than simple sentences, which means they can be written and posted. This is shown in the example of the *team conventions* work product.

Studying the patterns literature, I discovered that good patterns fall into two sorts: properties and strategies. Some are ambiguously both, but usually one can decide that any one is more one than the other. Patterns fans might like to reconsider Christopher Alexander's patterns in this light. For example, *Light on Two Sides of the Room* is more a property and *Attic Window* more a strategy (Alexander 1977). The book *Design Patterns* (Gamma 1995) contains strategies—it could as well have been called *Design Strategies*. In *Surviving Object-Oriented Projects*, I decided to call the appendix "Risk Reduction *Strategies*" instead of "Risk Reduction Patterns." On the other hand, when we were writing *Patterns for Effective Use Cases*, we deliberately searched for *properties* of effective use cases and use-case-writing processes, rather than strategies.

When it came time to write this book, I tried describing the methodology with patterns. However, they were an unsettling mix of properties and strategies. This is not at all a problem for any one project team—they only care about what they should do themselves. It is problematic when aiming for a wide set of projects, because the strategies should be the discretionary choices of the team. Therefore, I separated the patterns into two chapters: *Osmotic Communication* and *Frequent Delivery* went into Chapter 2, and *Exploratory 360°*, *Walking Skeleton*, and *Incremental Rearchitecture* into Chapter 3. *Reflection Workshop* got split out as a technique, a means to achieve the property *Reflective Improvement*.

The next issue involves the idiosyncrasies of the specific people who show up in the specific buildings to work with specific technologies on the specific problem at hand. This instance of people, project, and environment I refer to as the project "ecosystem" (Cockburn 2002). Dealing with the ecosystem comes in two steps. The first is to recognize that the properties have to be the heart of the matter, and everything else advisory. Thus, Chapter 9 captures the visible properties (six to eight people in one room or adjacent rooms, etc.) plus the properties the group sets into place (*Frequent Delivery,* etc.). It doesn't mention the strategies, techniques, process cycles, or work products. Instead, the group is required to periodically get together and discuss together what its local conventions should be. When someone with a strong personality joins or leaves, the group gets together again to revisit its conventions.

The second part of dealing with the ecosystem is to recognize that a methodology can't solve all of the group's problems. No methodology can correct for the absence of competent and experienced people, or people who dislike each other, or can't make a decision. These are simply exposures, and not just to Crystal Clear, but to every methodology. It is quite possible that a group, otherwise following every recommendation of Crystal Clear, will get together in their reflection workshop, have an argument, and come out not being able to work with each other. That is outside the reach of methodology.

What Crystal Clear can do is to name the rules that give a project team better than even chances of success and room to maneuver.

QUESTION 4. *WHAT IS THE SUMMARY SHEET FOR CRYSTAL CLEAR?*

Project size

Up to 6 or possibly 8 colocated developers. Can be shaped with care to up to 12 people. Not intended for larger teams, as it is missing group coordination.

System's potential for damage

Loss of comfort or loss of discretionary moneys, as in invoicing systems. Can be shaped, with additional testing, verification, and validation rules, up to "essential" moneys. Not intended for life-critical systems as it is missing verification of correctness.

Types of systems

Mainframe, client-server, Web-based, using any type database, central or distributed. Can be shaped for hard real-time systems with additional rules for planning and verification of system timing issues. Not intended for fail-safe systems, as it is missing hard architectural reviews for fault tolerance and fail-over.

The values

Strong on communications, light on deliverables. Short, rich, informal communications paths, including with the sponsoring and user communities. Frequent deliveries with product and process feedback. Reduced overhead and fewer intermediate work products. Tolerance for variations in people's working styles.

Tolerances

The policy standards are mandatory unless an equivalent substitution can be made. For example, use of the Scrum or Extreme Programming techniques for project scheduling and staging is acceptable; use of the TSP project launch and relaunch techniques is acceptable.

Every deliverable has a designated owner or owners. "None" and "Everyone" are acceptable, if explicitly stated. In each of these cases, there must be additional justification as to how the model works (e.g., Extreme Programming declares that everyone owns all code when (and only when) they work in pairs; pair programming creates moment-to-moment dual ownership of code.)

Use of precision

Low precision at first, high precision only in delivered artifacts.
Low precision includes designers talking with users and sponsor, two-paragraph use cases or user stories or feature lists, design drawings on the whiteboard, user screens drawn as pencil sketches, release schedule as short lists and phrases (initially).

High precision includes demo and production screens, final code, test cases, user manuals, or help text.

QUESTION 5. WHY THE DIFFERENT CHAPTER FORMATS?

Methodology books are generally written as a set of rules telling the reader what to do. There are several reasons not to use that format in this book. The first is that Crystal Clear is not so much a set of instructions about how to write software as properties, conditions, conventions, and techniques regularly used to bring a certain class of projects home safely (this is the *safety* priority). The intersection of those successful projects is so small as to not be safe itself, and the union of all of them is too fat. I am trying, in this book, to indicate how to find subsets that are both safe and usable.

Readers come from various backgrounds, which makes a difference in what they look for in the book. Our practice of programming has changed drastically since 1987 and the arrival of objects, and again since 1998, when the object and XP communities brought patterns, refactoring, pair programming, and test-driven development to the fore. Some programmers have kept up with the most recent changes and need to see proper references to those latest practices. Others still operate using the older practices and need to be given detail to catch up with the latest vocabulary. Some readers, already experts at running small-team projects, are looking for new ideas or new words for old ideas. Others, new to leading a small team, want detailed instruction. Here are some of the categories of reader I tried to deal with:

♦ Those arriving cold to the topic of agile development might benefit from the lighter and very contextual e-mail discussion in the first chapter.

♦ Those already very familiar with small-team agile development may want to focus only on the safety properties of the second chapter and use their own ways to get to those properties.

♦ Those getting started with a Crystal Clear way of working will want a starter set of techniques. Some of these techniques will be new, even to experienced people, things they can add to their practice set.

♦ Very few people coming from a traditional software development process history have an operational grasp of the cyclical development processes. Those with a process focus should benefit from seeing the process unrolled in the various ways, and the cycles isolated.

♦ Methodologists, and owners of development processes in general, operate directly from the list of work products, evaluating a methodology based on the list of who produces what and who checks that. The collection of work samples could still give an experienced agile developer some new ideas.

♦ Those coming to the book with a varied set of projects on their active list will want to know how to vary the rules and when to shift to a different methodology entirely.

♦ Those who have read widely will be interested in the economic and philosophical foundations and discussion of how these ideas fit with related and competing ones.

It is not my ambition that every reader should like every chapter and format. Rather, my hope is that through the use of different perspectives, each reader, coming from his particular background, can find some chapter format that conveys what is needed in order to understand Crystal Clear's main ideas.

QUESTION 6. WHERE IS CRYSTAL CLEAR IN THE PANTHEON OF METHODOLOGIES?

There are too many methodologies to compare against, so I'll address this question by showing *how* I answer it and giving just two examples.

Each methodology author selects a couple of priorities to be the methodology's focus or center of attention. That focus could be on *defect reduction*, as in Cleanroom (Mills 1988) and the Dijkstra/Gries's program-derivation method (Gries 1981), *repeatability* as in ISO 9000, *predictability and control* as in the CMM(I), or *productivity* as in XP. I have heard people discuss how to stay "laid back" as they expand, indicating that as a priority. Whatever the author prioritizes becomes a filter for selecting and rejecting possible elements of the methodology. Beware methodology authors who assert that their methodology design satisfies all priorities.

When comparing methodologies, investigators usually list the methodologies' techniques and rules in a table, and let the readers evaluate the list according to their (the readers') personal priorities. This presupposes that the reader already understands the implications of priorities in methodology design. If the reader does understand, then of course he can read the comparison and make a meaningful choice. If not, however (and most readers don't know about methodology priorities), there is an increased chance that the reader will select a methodology not aligned with the team and organization's actual priority set.

Crystal, as a family of methodologies, focuses on *efficiency* and *habitability* as critical elements of *project safety*. All Crystal methodologies try to accomplish as much as possible with as little as possible. However, that drive for efficiency is subject to the habitability imperative. Teams around the world have different backgrounds and values and are faced with projects of differing characteristics and priorities. The *habitability* priority is to give each team and each team member the maximum free choice in working his own way (we want the team not only to succeed, but also be willing to work in a similar way again).

Obviously, the two conflict at some point, and so Crystal allows for teams to choose less-than-optimal ways of working if they so choose. As long as they keep delivering software successfully, I am satisfied.[8]

Crystal Clear is the version of Crystal for small, colocated teams. It has the same priorities and focus of attention, that is, being efficient and tolerant.

As a point of comparison, XP prioritizes for programmer *productivity* and code *evolvability* (*note:* these are my interpretations). XP reduces intermediate work prod-

---

[8]   This is, I believe, a fundamental difference between Crystal and XP.

ucts (increasing productivity) and raises the discipline required of the people (increasing productivity again), but reduces tolerance for individual work styles. The code should be refactored to become easier to evolve, and there is an extensive set of unit tests to help the next person along.

Project sponsors requesting a development team to have ISO-9000 and CMM(I) certification are focusing primarily on *predictability* and *repeatability*. Note that it is not the methodology that gets assessed at the various CMM(I) levels, but the organization itself. To pass certification, the organization needs a documented methodology and that methodology should be designed in a way to facilitate getting certified.

CMM(I), in particular, carries the concept that variation across projects can be reduced through proper attention to statistical control of the process. For CMM(I) Level-4 certification, the organization must show that it measures the process, and for Level-5 certification that it uses the measurements to optimize the process. (Crystal turns the CMM(I) pyramid upside down in a sense, but that discussion belongs in a later question).

I don't know enough to answer what the focus of attention is for the Rational Unified Process (Kruchten 1999), DSDM (Stapleton 2003), or Scrum (Scwaber 2002).

What priorities drive the selection of methodology elements in your organization? When you understand that, you will be in a much better position to decide how to choose or blend other methodologies.

Crystal Clear and XP

XP is similar to Crystal Clear in many ways, particularly with its attention to colocation, short iterations, frequent delivery, and close contact with the sponsors and end users. It is stricter than Crystal Clear in several ways and looser in a few.[9]

♦ XP's iteration cycles are required to be shorter: three weeks in the first-edition XP, one week in the second-edition XP. XP doesn't make any rules about how long the delivery cycle must be (there are some guidelines in second-edition XP).

---

[9]   The first edition of Extreme Programming Explained, says, "XP is a lightweight methodology for small-to-medium-sized teams developing software in the face of vague or rapidly changing requirements." Beck writes in the second edition, "XP is my attempt to reconcile humanity in my own practice of software development and to share that reconciliation." He is describing how he personally prefers to operate. Unlike the first-edition XP, the second-edition XP is not something that one can be held in compliance with. This shift in intention is of more significance than the additions and changes in the practices he describes. My comparison here is based on the first edition of XP. Use the same line of reasoning as show to derive the up-to-date answers as XP evolves.

Crystal Clear on the other hand, requires deliveries to be no longer than three months at worst, but allows the iteration to be as long as the delivery. I have seen otherwise excellent XP projects get into trouble because the delivery cycle was six months to a year. That is clearly a violation of the intent of XP, which is *implicitly* predicated upon frequent deliveries. Crystal Clear is therefore explicit about real deliveries.

♦ XP calls for programming in pairs, which Crystal Clear doesn't. The difference is fundamental: XP aims to be the most effective methodology possible, reducing the team's freedom in making these sorts of choices. Crystal Clear aims to be an *adequately* effective and *tolerant* methodology, giving the team as much freedom as possible in constructing the local set of conventions.

♦ XP calls for automated unit testing with integrations multiple times a day. In Crystal Clear, unit testing is recommended, not mandatory, and the integration period may range from a fraction of a day to several days.

♦ XP calls for a customer on-site, where Crystal Clear only calls for easy access to expert users, with an indicated minimum of an hour a week rather than full time. This is a situation where more is better; for Crystal Clear I am deliberately looking for the minimum that satisfies the *project safety* priority.

♦ XP has the team decide and adhere to common coding conventions, something not required or even mentioned in Crystal Clear. XP's convention becomes understandable when one considers that the programmers change programming partners frequently and have to get to an agreement about coding conventions in order to avoid constant fights and confusion.

♦ XP talks explicitly about simplicity in design and refactoring as part of the development episode and also in the longer term. These are only recommended in Crystal Clear, as discussed in the strategies *Walking Skeleton* and *Incremental Rearchitecture*. While I am clearly in favor of simple designs with ongoing refactoring, the question is, Should it be a required standard in the methodology? My conclusion is that learning to simplify and refactor designs is part of the normal growth path of a professional programmer, and not something for Crystal Clear to attempt to legislate across all project types and programming technologies.

♦ XP does not require documentation and Crystal Clear does. In terms of the two goals of the cooperative game, XP is loud about its focus on the first goal, delivering the software, and silent on the second goal, setting up for the next game.

XP does provide half of the needed investment for the future: through pair-programming rotations, a new person joining a seasoned team can come up to speed on the design and code very quickly. However, as people move on to other projects over time, there is a leakage of team understanding, and it is quite likely that the newcomers will not master and internalize the knowledge as fast as it leaks out. This decay is almost inevitable, which means the team should create other, externalized informing markers, to support the influx of new people. Crystal Clear asks the team to deliberately perform both "greedy" and "investment" actions, balancing the longer term communication paths with the short term.

Looking at these, we see that where XP regulates, it regulates stricter rules, and where it is looser, it is because of absence of a rule. This has two consequences:

◆ You are welcome to adopt any of XP's practices in Crystal Clear. This includes on-site customer, the planning game, programming in pairs, weekly iterations, test-first programming, fully automated unit tests, continuous integration, strict common coding conventions, and simple designs with ongoing refactoring.

◆ If you want to do full-on XP and still meet Crystal Clear, you must do two things: add a commitment to not just iterate, but also *deliver* code regularly; and add reminding and also informing documentation, as part of the investment activities involved in setting up for the next game.

From a techniques point of view, XP provides a rich library of effective techniques for the professional developer to master.

Crystal Clear and Scrum

Scrum focuses on three key practices as well as the properties of close communication and focus:

◆ *Time-boxing*. The subset of the requirements being developed during each one-month iteration is frozen into the "iteration backlog" at the beginning of the iteration. This gives the team the peace of mind (focus) to work on them without fear of them changing. Scrum requires a demo or equivalent after each time-box, not an actual delivery.

◆ *Dynamic backlog*. To compensate for locking the requirements during the iteration, a list ("product backlog") is kept of everything remaining to do. The sponsors are allowed to change the backlog however they wish, whenever they wish. The development team and the sponsors look at the backlog at the start of a new time-box period and select the subset to be frozen for the time-box. That is, they *reprioritize the backlog* before each iteration so each iteration targets the highest priority work each month.[10]

♦ *Daily stand-up.* The team meets briefly (literally standing up) each day to let each person announce what he worked on yesterday, is planning on working on today, and what is holding him back. This binds the team with social and technical interchange and creates an early warning system for when they get off track.

These combine well with the three key practices of Crystal:

♦ *Frequent Deliveries,* not merely demo-ing the system, but actually putting it in the hands of users, a "friendly user" at the minimum.

♦ *Close Communication* for Crystal in general, and *Osmotic Communication* for Crystal Clear, ease of question-and-answer at any time during the day, and over-hearing of information in the small-team setting.

♦ *Reflection Workshop,* tuning of the rules to allow rapid adaptation to local conditions within the project time frame.

Scrum and Crystal fit neatly together, producing what one wit called the *No-Process process.* The No-Process process says, roughly, start anywhere, work in short cycles with high communication and reflective feedback, and eventually you will end up with what you need (a genetic algorithm, if you like).

♦ Time-boxing with real deliveries is the motor to the process.

♦ Periodic reprioritization of the backlog keeps the product on track over the long term.

♦ Postiteration reflection workshops keep the team and process on track over the long term.

♦ Osmotic communication and daily stand-ups keep the team on track over the short term.

You can probably add the No-Process process to your organization's process, no matter what that is. It would be a really wonderful genetic algorithm, except that your

---

[10] Jeff Sutherland is evolving "Continuous Scrum." Using automated planning and tracking tools, the contents of the time-box are allowed to vary daily, not just monthly (see http://wiki.scrums.org/index.cgi?ContinuousScrum). This requires a different approach to managing user relations and sponsor expectations. I look forward to his writings on this.

project probably has a 4-, 6-, or 10-month deadline, and you don't have time to start just *anywhere* and evolve to optimal. You need to start *pretty close*.

Crystal helps you start *pretty close* with its properties, principles, techniques, and examples.

Crystal Clear and RUP

The Rational Unified Process (RUP) is very similar to the Crystal family of methodologies in structure, but in a different way than XP.

Both RUP and Crystal are "methodology generators." Neither is a methodology or process on its own (yes, I know it is called the Rational Unified *Process* but it is not a process, anyway, it is a process generator, or "process framework" in RUP language). Both RUP and Crystal are predicated upon the view that no single process can fit all projects, and, therefore, the project team has to customize the methodology to fit their local situation.

Both RUP and Crystal contain advice about how to custom-tailor the methodology to the organization and project; both describe core techniques and contain work product samples and templates. Both recommend incremental growth of the system using iterative development, good testing practices, close contact to the users, risk management, and feedback from running code.

RUP's *inception* phase is very similar to the *chartering activity* described in this book. RUP's *development cases* for process customizing are just as core to RUP as the methodology shaping workshop is to Crystal (if you aren't tuning RUP to your company with development cases, then you aren't doing RUP just as if you don't do methodology shaping and reflection workshops then you aren't doing Crystal).

At this level of discussion, there is very little to distinguish the RUP process generator from the Crystal methodology generator.

Three core elements differ. RUP sets *architecture, visual modeling*, and *tool usage* as core elements. Crystal considers architecture be a local matter, although I give the same recommendation to build an early, executable architecture. Crystal differs strongly from RUP on the subject of visual modeling, using first the idea that documentation is to be a locally decided matter, and second the idea that documentation should attempt to convey the "theory" of the system (see Question 1), and visual models are only a small part of conveying that theory. Crystal in general is tool-agnostic, and Crystal Clear even somewhat reticent when it comes to modeling tools. The ones that serve Crystal projects best tend to be configuation management, communication, programming, test harness, test code-coverage, and performance profiling tools.

Crystal contains one core practice that easily could be (and should be!) added to RUP: the reflection workshop. There is nothing to stop every team using a RUP instance from simply getting together after each iteration and reflecting on how to do better. The RUP authors can (and should) simply add a technique and work sample showing teams how to do some form of reflective improvement.

There are other differences, some of which are essential and some of which are more mental associations about the methodology's practices and its "feel" in practice. Those mental associations generate their own reality in organizations adopting a methodology and so are not to be ignored.

- *Light and Tolerant.* Each Crystal methodology is intended, in its core values, to be as light, efficient, nonbureaucratic, and tolerant as the project situation will allow. Those are not declared elements of RUP. This gives the result that Andrea Branca described in an email: "It is possible to make any process *look* agile, but hard to make it *feel* agile."

- *Shaping Principles.* Crystal contains a set of principles (described in this chapter) intended to give guidance on how to make shaping choices. Those principles are part of the Crystal "package." RUP recommends tailoring and lists milestones and templates to tailor, but provides no theory about how to make the shaping choices (these can, of course, be added, building on the theory provided in Crystal).

- *Speed of Methodology Shaping.* Crystal calls for the methodology shaping to be done is very short order, usually on the order of days, so that cost of that workshop is repaid by the new efficiencies *within the project time frame*. A Crystal methodology is intended to evolve within the course of the project, which means that methodology shaping has to fast. Shaping RUP need not take months, but often does, which may be why so many companies avoid development cases and adopt the whole package (which is doubly bad, because they get the inefficiency of an untuned methodology with the cost penalty of an overly heavy one).

- *Cut-down versus Buildup.* The approach in Crystal is to start from whatever your team comes up with in the methodology shaping workshop, or whatever you used last time, and build up from there, adding to the methodology only when experience reveals a problem (typically during the reflection workshop). Crystal is deliberately underspecified, committing "errors of omission," if you will. The idea is that it is easier to detect when you are missing something you need than it is to detect that you have something extra you don't need. Crystal is deliberately "stretch to fit."

RUP, in contrast, is "shrink to fit." RUP contains an encyclopedia of work product templates (among other contents). Just as you wouldn't read an encyclopedia from front to back, or prepare all the recipes in *The Joy of Cooking* in sequential order, you shouldn't fill in all the templates in the RUP encyclopedia from front to back. Rather, just as you look into a cookbook or encyclopedia for what you need today, you should look into the RUP encyclopedia and pull out the specific elements you need on this particular project.

The approach in RUP, then, is to start from the full encyclopedia and throw things out during the shaping activity. In this sense, it is overspecified.

The two err in different ways for different organizations. I expect groups to have trouble with Crystal because it is too empty to start with; many have trouble with RUP because it is too full to start with. I see no escape from a dilemma of this sort.

- *Visual Modeling.* As described earlier, visual modeling is a core element of RUP, where it is an elective element in Crystal.

- *Tools.* RUP is designed to be supported by tools, where Crystal is deliberately agnostic on tools, and even slightly against investment in visual modeling tools. My recommendation since 1992 has been to buy whatever tool lets you draw connected shapes the fastest; that includes pencil and paper, whiteboards and cameras, PowerPoint, Visio, and CAD-CAM tools (some of which, I am told, have outstanding usability).

- *Concurrent Development.* Crystal has concurrent development as a core recommendation, with guidance for incorporating just-in-time requirements when it suits your project. RUP contains recommendations for incremental growth of the system, but no guidance on how to incorporate just-in-time requirements and concurrent development.

- *Corporate Support.* There is no escaping the difference that RUP is supported by a dedicated design team, along with marketing, tools development, training, and consulting arms. This is not a difference in methodology definition, but it creates a very great difference in adoption. You can't buy a copy of Crystal; you can only buy a copy of two books (*Agile Software Development* and this one) and raid my Web site (Alistair.Cockburn.us). After that you and your team have to get together and *think, discuss,* and *reflect.* (Okay, for a very limited number of teams, a Crystal methodology expert can be hired to do some coaching.) That is very different from placing an order for books, tools, courses, and consulting to show up at your organization's doorstep.

Can you do Crystal Clear within RUP? Would Crystal Clear be a valid implementation of RUP, assuming of course a colocated team of three to eight people?

Recall that only the first three properties of Crystal Clear are mandatory. Everything else is advisory or at least up for discussion. Those three properties are not conceptually difficult; the question is whether a team doing RUP will actually bring themselves to deliver to a real user every few months, whether the team will move from their private offices to a common area to get osmotic communication, and whether they will sit down, discuss in a reflection workshop and achieve reflective improvement. If they can do these three things, then probably the rest of what they do will fall within Crystal Clear.

It is not obvious to me that Crystal Clear, as written, is a valid implementation of RUP. There may not be enough visual modeling or architecture done or explicit risk management to pass the RUP test. Whether it does or doesn't probably depends on how your development cases come out.

QUESTION 7.   WHAT ABOUT THE CMM(I)?[11]

Crystal Clear was not designed with the intention of meeting requirements of the CMM(I), and it is difficult see how it would move up that ladder. Crystal Clear does address many of the activities called out in the CMM(I), although perhaps not in the way the standard CMM(I) assessor is used to. However, Crystal Clear has a project focus, and the CMM(I) has an organizational focus.

On the other hand, many organizations already certified at CMM(I) level 3 or above should be able to either introduce Crystal Clear or borrow from it to increase efficiency. Let's look at that closer by imagining an organization already doing software development at level 3 of the CMM(I) and wanting to use Crystal Clear.

♦ They have to find a "friendly" user willing to let them deploy the system every few months. This should violate none of their process rules. However, the groups I have encountered that prioritize CMM(I) certification have put their developers so far away from the users and burdened their process so much that it is unlikely that they can deliver running, tested software every quarter.

♦ They have to colocate the team to get osmotic communication. This should break no process rules. However, many CMM(I) organizations are committed to distributed teams.

♦ They have to adopt reflective improvement. It should violate no process rules that people get together and look for ways of working better. The trouble it may cause is that the team is likely to suggest process changes. Many organizations who have gone to the trouble to get CMM(I) certified did not leave room for the process to change. The shift to an evolving process, though difficult, will be a healthy one.

In all three cases, the needed change is not in the process rules, but in mind-set (the harder of the two to change).

Attending to focus, personal safety, and easy access to expert, users should not jeopardize any part of their declared process, but only help the people work better. Similarly, the technical environment with automated testing, configuration management, and frequent integration may take some work, but shouldn't interfere in any way with the certified process.

The work products of Crystal Clear are advisory to start with, and the organization certified at level 3 is likely to have all of the ones I name (and others besides). The

---

[11]   CMMI is broader in scope and more flexible than the "CMM for Software." Indeed, the CMM for Software is no longer officially supported. For the purposes of this discussion, though, there is no significant difference between CMM and CMMI.

organization might adopt some of the ideas shown in the work products section to simplify or improve their work product set (replacing the Gantt schedule charts with earned-value or *burn-up* charts would be a good start).

There are several other differences between Crystal and the CMM(I). The most obvious is that the CMM(I) is hosted and supported by a sizable organization that acts as a resource for training and examination, while Crystal is supported by three books and a handful of expert consultants around the world. Even though with good luck Crystal will get more support, it is unlikely ever to have organizational support at the same level as the Software Engineering Institute (if it did, it would have to be called the Software Gamesmanship Institute!).

The real core of the differences comes from the underlying values and assumptions about software development. The CMM(I) is fundamentally about consistency, predictability, and repeatability. Crystal is fundamentally about efficiency, habitability, and locally optimized rule sets.

Process engineering literature categorizes processes as either *defined/theoretical* (not the CMM(I) meaning of "defined" I hasten to add!) or *empirical*. A *defined/theoretical* process is one that is well enough understand to be automated. An *empirical* one needs human examination and intervention. A textbook in the field has this to say:

> It is typical to adopt the defined (theoretical) modeling approach when the underlying mechanisms by which a process operates are reasonably well understood. When the process is too complicated for the defined approach, the empirical approach is the appropriate choice. (Ogunnaike 1992)

To pull off a *defined/theoretical* process, one must know and be able to adequately measure all the relevant parameters, but more significantly, the system must be non-chaotic. In a chaotic system, even the slightest perturbation in a key parameter sends the system off in a different direction; no amount of measurement and control is enough. The CMM(I) ladder is built on the assumption that these conditions are met.

Personally, I doubt that either the first or the last assumption is met in software development. First, I don't think we know the relevant parameters to measure. Second, I think it quite likely that any team-based creative activity is chaotic, meaning that a tiny perturbation can cause an arbitrarily large effect. Here is a short example from a meeting I attended:

> In a meeting about a new initiative, the people in the room were tense, but seemingly well-behaved. When we took a short break, the woman who was to lead the new initiative turned in her resignation! It seems that one of the (to me) mildly phrased barbs offered by the future CFO was simply "one too much" for her, and she quit on the spot.

Think of the last time that you made what you thought was an innocuous comment and your listener got surprisingly upset. Think of when a key person missed a meeting. Either of those can cascade into an arbitrarily large consequence for the project.

The need to have people detecting things going wrong and intervene in unexpected ways was driven home to me in an e-mail from Glen Alleman, reporting on an organization (CH2M HILL Communication and Information Solutions), which provides nuclear material stewardship applications, ERP, cyber security, and other services to several thousand users under the guidelines of the Defense Nuclear Facilities Safety Board (which controls thousands of buildings contaminated with chemical and radioactive waste). Glen wrote

> We've just come from a "safety stand down," (there's always some safety issue with our business including the IT part). In the lessons learned process one of the questions is, "If you followed the procedure correctly would the problem not have occurred?" The answer from the safety guys is essentially—there are empirical processes that must be present.

This single question allows the organization to detect new, previously unsuspected parameters of importance. At any level of accomplishment, a team should have the humility and healthy skepticism to ask this question and follow where it leads.

For the above reasons, I find it unlikely that the issue will ever seriously arise of a CMM(I) level-3 organization doing Crystal Clear, although a CMM(I)-certified group may borrow ideas from Crystal Clear.

*   *   *

This is the time to explain what I meant in the previous section by Crystal turning the CMM(I) pyramid upside down.

Crystal is built on the concept that *every* methodology and organization needs to be *self-evolving*. What the CMM(I) places at the top level, optimizing, I have as a starting requirement. Every Crystal project uses reflective improvement, guaranteeing that the rules will change over time. If Crystal were to have a certification activity, then even at "Crystal level 2," the team would have to show that they *changed* their process within and across projects!

There is a less distinct inversion of the pyramid, having to do with measurement precision. In order to step into statistical process control, the CMM(I) calls for numerical measurements to take place at level 4. The concept I find missing in this approach to measurement is the idea of *making the measurements more precise at higher levels*, starting off with "fuzzy measures" that are nothing more than adjectives or expressions of feelings.

When a person says in a reflection workshop or status meeting, "that went well," "I'm not comfortable," "I didn't like," "I'm not completely certain," or "there was a wobbliness at the start," he is offering up the integrated response of a professional who has been in many situations in their lives. It is a rolling up of a lot of information gathered from a number of sources, into a single expression. It is a "fuzzy number" in the mathematical sense (McNeill 1994), occupying a range of values with a probability distribution function.

These are great measurement values for many situations, particularly when the important parameters are numerous or unknown, as with a software development project.

The pyramid that would be interesting to me would start with personal, fuzzy measurements of the project at the lower levels. Most projects would benefit greatly from recording and analyzing them. As the organization progresses, they might learn which ones are more significant to track, and find ways to sharpen the measurement value, making it more *precise*, eventually ending up with numbers (which I consider sharp, pointy things when applied to such things as project mood).

QUESTION 8.   WHAT ABOUT UML AND ARCHITECTURE?

The Unified Modeling Language (UML) is a drawing notation standard, not a methodology. In terms of the standard methodology framework (roles, techniques, standards, milestones, etc.), it is one of the standards for one or two of the roles. It is a component of a methodology, but not likely to be a very large factor in the project's outcome.

The UML standard does not make prescriptions or even recommendations about when, where, and how much you draw. With respect to the standard, you can draw out the entire design before starting to program, or you can "think a little, draw a little, code a little," a strategy long recommended by object technology experts and supported by Scott Ambler's (2002) book, *Agile Modeling*.

Discussion of drawing models quickly gets caught up in discussion of architecture and how much design to do when. You will not be surprised to learn that my view is that different people have different preferences and like to think about designs for different amounts of time before starting to program.

Having said that, it is also my view that a design is a "theory," which desperately needs a matching "experiment" to validate it, or, more importantly, reveal its weaknesses. Usually, the design doesn't survive its first encounter with real code. This means that the sooner the design gets tested in implementation, the sooner the designer learns where and how it needs improvement.

Some people have a very short thinking time horizon before they desperately feel the need for an experiment: on the order of five or ten minutes. Others have a medium time horizon, on the order of several hours or a day or two, during which they mentally explore all the pitfalls, weaknesses, and potential change requests they may have to adapt to. Others have quite long thinking time horizons, on the order of a week or two, during which they do the same. My experience is that when designers spend more than a few weeks working out a (software) design, they usually have passed the optimal trade-off point, where it would have been useful to create an experiment with real code to get some real feedback.[12]

Taking all those together, I feel that most architects take too long before they make their first experiment, but it is not necessary to adopt the view that design can be replaced just by refactoring and attention to XP's "once and only once" rule.

---

[12]   I did hear one story of a programmer assigned to program an operating system kernel element, who stared at his design for months, studying its symmetry and aesthetics, until he was totally convinced no symmetry was missing and it couldn't be made simpler, at which point he typed it in (and it worked). Such a situation is extremely rare.

The subjects of UML, drawings, tools, architectural design, and thinking time horizons tend to get confused all together. If you can pull them apart, it frees you up to work in new combinations.

It is, for example, *not* the case that all drawings are UML drawings (see the work products for some examples), nor must architectures be described in UML, or even in drawings, nor must fancy software tools be used to capture either drawings or UML (imagine UML drawn by hand, see the work products for examples), nor does spending time thinking mean sitting at a tool. Finally, and especially, nor is it the case that sitting in front of a UML drawing tool means that any architectural thinking is going on.

The approach typical on a Crystal Clear project is to use the *Walking Skeleton* and *Incremental Rearchitecture* strategies. An early architecture is sketched, programmed and tested in the first iteration, and completed, extended and evolved over subsequent iterations. UML might or might not be used to think through it and document the result.

QUESTION 9.   WHY AIM ONLY FOR THE SAFETY ZONE? CAN'T WE DO BETTER?

Yes, you can do better, and if you're up for it, I encourage you to do so. For example, you can apply all of the XP practices, with test-driven development, full-time pair programming in rotations, automated acceptance tests as well as unit tests, expert users and domain experts on-site full time, continuous and automated builds, shortening the iteration cycle to one or two weeks, and delivering monthly.

You can, and should, if at all possible, institute a weekly one-hour discussion group. People who have done this report back on the increase in trust, capability, and ability of people to discuss their topics with each other. Work your way through several books, including *The Pragmatic Programmer* (Hunt 2001), books on test-driven design (Beck 2003, Astels 2004), refactoring (Fowler 2002) and any number of the design pattern books. In these sessions, show and discuss snippets of code from the project, learning to analyze and compare design-programming techniques. Discuss ways of testing code. Use the sessions to try out new languages and tools.

You can and should pay extra attention to personal safety, and build the basis for trust between people—technical as well as personal trust. You can and should allocate time and money for professional training of the team members, so they stay up to date with our fast moving field. For example, I have totally revised my programming techniques every ten years—I am on my fourth relearning cycle, and that is only for the programming. I haven't even touched usability or user interface design yet, and am woefully out of date on configuration management systems. Where are you? If you haven't significantly changed your habits for design, programming, UI design, and testing in the last five or seven years, you are almost certainly far out of date.

The list of how to do *better* than what I have required in Crystal Clear is long. However, each of those things adds difficulty in adoption, and reduces the number of people who can manage the sum total.

The Crystal family of methodologies is not targeted to be "optimal" for any one dimension of possible project priorities. It does not optimize for productivity, or for traceability, legal liability, freedom from defects, being laid back, distributed teams, maximum use of junior staff, or any of the other priorities you come up with.

Crystal has as priorities: project safety, efficiency, and habitability. The efficiency priority says, play the economic-cooperative game well, allowing good speed of delivery on this game while still paying attention to the next game. The habitability priority says, take into account the natural strengths and weaknesses of humans working together to make the result reasonably pleasant to live in. Project safety means that software comes out the door in a fair time frame, with the project staff intact and willing to go through the same process again.

The efficiency and habitability priorities conflict, as do so many issues that we must attend to in software development. One can be more efficient by being less tolerant. One can be more tolerant by requiring less efficiency.

Hopefully, this book provides enough rigor for your team to get into the project's safety zone, and enough latitude so that you can add whatever next priority you need in your projects.

QUESTION 10. WHAT ABOUT DISTRIBUTED TEAMS?

This is a much more interesting question now than it was when I first formulated Crystal Clear.

Crystal Clear is predicated on having osmotic communication. It takes me about six seconds to push my chair away, walk out of the office to an office down and across the hall, and stick my head in to ask the person a question.

In another six seconds, I can discover the person isn't there and get back to my workstation and keep working without losing my train of thought. Or ask the question, face to face. The point is to limit the amount of time and energy used to get the question placed and have a short, rich conversation about it.

Richard Herring reported on an experiment in which the team, sitting on different floors of the same building, used microphones and Web cameras to simulate "presence and awareness" (Herring 2001). Each person put the web cam photo of each other person as small images on their workstations. With these small images, they could each see whether the other person was busy with heads-down typing, in discussion, or absent. With the microphones and speakers, they could ask and answer questions immediately. Using chat technology, they could ask and answer questions silently and asynchronously (reducing the disturbance factor even more). They even copied code to and from their development environment, so they could exchange real code and not just suggestions about it.

Richard Herring satisfied my concerns about osmotic communication, and it is clear that his group took care of their social personal safety and trust issues as well. This was a very creative manner to deal with one of the "sweet spots" (see the first section in this chapter for a discussion of the sweet spots and simulating them). If you have an only mildly distributed team, try Herring's ideas.

Victoria Einarsson, in Sweden, described using something essentially like Crystal Clear, except that the developers worked out of their homes. Victoria described to me how she spent hours each day on the phone, asking and answering questions and keeping the social connections in place. Several things became clear during our conversation. First, they were indeed effective as a team. Second, they mimicked Crystal Clear in almost every aspect. Third, it wasn't actually Crystal Clear because they didn't have osmotic communication. Fourth, their success was heavily dependent on Victoria's tremendous social-technical skills as the team leader. In other words, if they wanted to set up a second project team, they would have to be very careful in interviewing the new group leader for having outstanding social and technical skills. They were successful, but it is not a project setup I would easily recommend, because it was so dependent on Victoria's skills.

The success of this team raises a relevant point. It is not the case that you have to do everything in Crystal Clear to be successful. A number of teams I visit are successful while dropping elements of Crystal Clear. They operate outside of the general safety zone that Crystal Clear describes, and make up for that by having some outstanding people in key positions on the team. Having such people is also a way to win the game, just not the subject of this particular book.

Teams distributed across more than just one city are more dependent on communication technology and outstanding individuals. There are ways for them to succeed, but those ways aren't Crystal Clear.

QUESTION 11.   WHAT ABOUT LARGER TEAMS?

I had the pleasure of visiting and interviewing Jan Siric, then of Nordea in Denmark, about his sixteen-person project, which matched all the characteristics of Crystal Clear except for team size. Here's what I saw:

> The twelve developers, programming both mainframe and workstation software, sat at three long tables, two per side of each long table. Each table had a workstation at each end. The center section of each table was a whiteboard lying on its side. The monitors were mounted on rails so they could slide into the center section. Jan and three other team leader/manager people sat at tables to the side. A long conference table lay further down the room. The room was airy, spacious, and filled with plants. I immediately noticed the presence of carpeting on the floor and acoustic tile on the ceiling to dampen the noise. As a result, noise was not a problem.

With this arrangement, Jan was able to get the six-second timing even with sixteen people, and people could work alone, in pairs, in clusters or as a group as they needed.

What impressed me the most, however, was Jan's ability to detect cracks in the communication. Hearing an odd comment in the cafeteria one day, he interviewed the programmers and found that a mainframe programmer who had only recently joined their team hadn't fully adjusted to their open conversations with frequent questions and interactions. Jan rearranged the seating, swapped the team managers so that the one with the best social and communications skills was in charge of that particular subteam, and then paid special attention to how the interactions proceeded.

Jan's actions perfectly illustrate Crystal Clear's concept of judging the state of the project in good measure by the quality of the communications.

However, I would not recommend Crystal Clear for teams of sixteen people as a general rule. Jan was able to pull it off because he was outstanding at the social/communication issues involved, and he was able to get both osmotic communication and personal safety in place with that particular team.

Under common circumstances, osmotic communication is very hard to achieve with more than about eight people. XP groups can achieve it with twelve people, using six workstations and two people per workstation. After that, it gets quite difficult.

Crystal Clear is not intended to scale. It is an efficient way to work when you can achieve colocation and osmotic communication. If you can't achieve that sweet spot, then you have to work differently.

QUESTION 12.   WHAT ABOUT FIXED-PRICE AND FIXED-SCOPE PROJECTS?

There is a tendency to think that agile processes only apply to exploratory projects. This is simply not true. All of my early experiences were on fixed-scope projects. I started using these techniques simply because there was no other way to meet the project deadline than to be superefficient as these ideas permit one to be. You should be able to use these, or adaptations of these techniques, on almost any small project (many of the strategies and techniques can be used or adapted for almost any project).

Let's see how blitz planning adjusts for fixed-time and fixed-scope projects.

The fixed-time project. You lay out the cards on the table and walk through the tasks and timing. The answer comes out larger than the time allowed in the fixed-time schedule. One of two things may happen

+ You and your executive sponsor get creative with the cards and find a way to meet the deadline.
+ Despite all your creativity, you can't find a way to meet the timeline.

The first situation shows a good application of the blitz planning technique. It is possible that the technique allowed you to find a strategy that you might otherwise have overlooked.

The second situation does not show a failure in blitz planning, Crystal Clear, or agile techniques. It shows that someone made a wrong bid on the project. Whether you can convince the sponsors to change the bid depends on factors local to your situation. The result may in fact be that you have to live with the given schedule and simply work overtime. The difference is that everyone in the room knows the situation early.

> On one project we went and got the customer-side sponsor and showed him the cards. After working with the cards, he agreed that the project simply couldn't be done in the time given, and changed the terms of the project. I can only hope that you are so fortunate.

The fixed-scope project. You are starting the second, third, or fourth iteration. You lay out the cards on the table, and . . . *you don't change the scope of the project!* There is nothing in agile development that says you *have to* change the requirements in each iteration. Crystal Clear and XP say that *if* you are in a situation where you need to change scope, this is the time and manner in which to do it. For the fixed-scope situation, you simply leave the scope alone.

QUESTION 13.   HOW CAN I RATE HOW "AGILE" OR HOW "CRYSTAL" WE ARE?

Proponents of agile development dread being asked how to evaluate how "agile" a project team is. Nonetheless, the manager of a portfolio of projects will want to track how the teams adopt elements of Crystal Clear. Figure 7-5 shows how I answered the question for a series of projects.

♦ We characterized each project by how many people were being coordinated and the iteration length.

♦ We listed the properties, starting with the seven properties from Chapter 2. We unpacked them to expose their components. Thus, user viewings, automated testing, configuration management, integration frequency, and collaboration across boundaries become separate tracking items.

♦ We identified which strategies and techniques might be interesting to try. In Figure 7-5, I show a dozen worth considering.

We filled out this table, marking *how frequently* the deliveries, the reflection workshops, the viewings, and the integrations had happened. Osmotic communication got a 'Yes' if the people were in the same room, otherwise we wrote down the team's spread. Personal safety got '0,' '1/2,' or 'Yes,' depending on a subjective rating. (If you don't have personal safety on your projects, can you post a '0'?)

For focus, we put down "priorities" if that was achieved, "time" if that was achieved, or 'Yes' if both were achieved. For automated testing, we considered unit and acceptance testing separately (none had automated acceptance testing).

We marked some of the times with '!' if they seemed out of range. Seeing a '!' in one place leads me to look for a compensating mechanism in another part of the chart. For example, both SOL and EVA had only one delivery, after a year. Both received '!' marks by that delivery frequency. However, SOL has a compensating mechanism, a user viewing every week (marked in bold in the table). EVA, the only project in this chart that crashed and burned, has no compensating mechanism (this is a good time to reread the property, "Easy Access to Expert Users.")

The table in Figure 7-5 does not yield a summary score. Instead, it indicates what the team might choose to work on next. I would, of course, post the chart as an information radiator.

Project	SOL	EVA	GS	THT	Ideal
# People	25	16	6	2	<30
Iteration Length	1 month	3 weeks	1 month	1 month	<2 months
Frequent Delivery	1 year!	1 year!	1 month	4 months!	<3 months
User Viewings	**1 week**	1 year!	1 month	1 month	<1 month
Reflection Workshops	1 month	3 weeks	0	1 month	<1 month
Osmotic Communication	1 floor	yes	yes	yes	yes
Personal Safety	yes	1/2	yes	yes	yes
Focus (priorities, time)	yes	yes	priorities	yes	yes
Easy Access to Expert Users	1 day/week	0	0	yes	yes
Configuration Management	yes	yes	yes	yes	yes
Automated Testing	0	unit	0	unit	yes
Frequent Integration	3/week	daily	1/week	1/day	continuous
Collaboration across Boundaries	yes	0	0	1/2	yes
Exploratory 360°	yes	0	0	yes	yes
Early Victory	yes	yes	0	yes	yes
Walking Skeleton	yes	yes	0	yes	yes
Incremental Rearchitecture	yes	yes	0	yes	yes
Information Radiators	yes	yes	yes	yes	yes
Pair Programming	0	yes	0	0	maybe
Side-by-Side Programming	0	0	0	0	maybe
Test-First Development	0	yes	0	0	maybe
Blitz Planning	yes	yes	0	yes	yes
Daily Stand-up Meeting	yes	yes	yes	0	yes
Burn Charts	yes	0	0	yes	yes
Dynamic Priority Lists	0	yes	0	yes	maybe

Figure 7-5.   *A way to track projects' use of the agile ideas.*

QUESTION 14.   HOW DO I GET STARTED?

Do these four things immediately:

1. Review the constraints for Crystal Clear (the June 9 e-mail from Crystal to Alistair). If you can't meet these constraints, go ahead and continue with the next steps, but bear in mind you will need additional rules or practices to compensate for the missing project characteristics.
2. Hold a practice reflection workshop with a few friendly colleagues (this is a process miniature for the reflection workshop).
3. Proceed through the project interviews and proper team reflection workshop as described in the techniques section. In that reflection workshop, walk through this book's description of process cycles, and the work products. Review the team structure and conventions work product, in particular.
4. Identify who will serve as the "friendly user" to your group, to review your system as it grows, before it becomes something you can deploy to all users.

After these steps, you should have discussed what it means to be doing Crystal Clear, where your team's strengths lie, and where the team and project's weak spots lie. You will naturally have discussed automated tests, configuration management, frequent integration, and ways to attain focus. It will take some time for personal safety to be established.

5. Run a short iteration. Make it artificially short, one or two weeks, so that you can hold your first reflection workshop right away and revise your working habits already (this short iteration provides you with a process miniature on Crystal Clear itself). It will also cement the reflection workshop as a group technique, provide an outlet for questions and ideas, and increase personal safety (people will see how their actions are interpreted).

At this point, you are underway. Use this and other books as encyclopedias of ideas to try during successive iterations. Finally,

6. Hold reflection workshops every two weeks for a month or two, and then decide on the interval to use between the next reflection workshops.

There. You are doing Crystal Clear.

Chapter 8

Tested (A Case Study)

Stephen Sykes of Thales Research and Technology in the United Kingdom experimented with an early version of this book and tried it out. Here is his report on the experience, along with the ISO 9001 auditor's recommendations. Many thanks to both Stephen and Thales.

It is a rare treat to be able to include in this book a field report from someone who tried Crystal Clear. It is an even greater treat to read the report of the ISO 9001 auditor who analyzed their project.

Thales Research and Technology UK is an ISO 9001 certified organization. Wanting to know more about Agile development as part of their corporate process improvement activity, they decided to try Crystal Clear on a program for calibrating the camera position for a natural scene recognition system. Stephen Sykes, the initial lead designer for the project, downloaded and worked an early (2002) version of this book for that experiment. The concluding part of the experiment was to have one of their ISO 9001 auditors analyze the project for what should be done differently for when it wouldn't be an experiment.

The top priority for the project team was to complete the prototype by the end of January 2004. The ideal would be to have a deliverable-quality product. In fact, they ended up with a good-quality demonstrator that could be turned into a product at reasonably short notice. The sponsor terminated the project at that point, electing to drop from the project scope the trial of a second calibration algorithm and certain project documentation activities.

The ISO auditor noted the difference between the final project scope and the original with the description: "[T]he project was unfortunately terminated early. However, due to the nature of the CC method, the early termination did not prohibit a useful software product."

In terms of Crystal Clear's attention to the sponsor's priorities, this counts as a satisfactory project outcome ("at the last reflection workshop, the sponsor also said that the advantages greatly outweighed the disadvantages. He's suggested we try it again, on a larger project, provided the fit with our existing procedures can be resolved"). The methodology has become classified as an allowable candidate for projects in the "rapid application development" category, and is slated to be used again in the near future.

Here is the report, trimmed to fit within this chapter.

THE FIELD REPORT

Executive Summary

This report describes a pilot project using the Crystal Clear methodology. The report represents part of a body of knowledge about Agile methodologies built at Thales Research and Technology (TRT UK), as part of its Small Systems Software Engineering activity. Crystal Clear itself was developed by the methodologist Alistair Cockburn.

Crystal Clear is an Agile methodology. "Agile" is an umbrella term for methodologies such as XP, DSDM, and Scrum. In general, Agile methodologies aim to reduce the risk of building the wrong thing, and to deliver value as early as possible. A literature survey of the Agile methodologies was conducted during 2003, and it was decided that Crystal Clear was the one most likely to be useful at Thales.[1] Crystal Clear was selected because it emphasizes

- **Efficiency.** Crystal Clear aims to minimize waste, while focusing the team on the important features.
- **Habitability.** Crystal Clear is designed to be comfortable to use, so that teams do not feel a need to avoid following it.
- **Safety.** The methodology aims to increase the probability of successful delivery.

Crystal Clear is intended for small, low-criticality projects. Compared with XP (which is the most well-known Agile methodology), Crystal Clear is more tolerant of individuals' different ways of working, but includes stronger planning activities.

We ran a pilot project in order to evaluate the methodology. We aimed to test the methodology against the claims made for it, and to determine any issues that might prevent adoption. Project CamCal was chosen as the pilot because it was small and noncritical (which is the kind of project the methodology was designed for), and because its members were willing to be part of the trial. Unfortunately, the project was halted before its planned end date, for reasons outside the scope of the pilot project. The project still succeeded in delivering a product to the satisfaction of its customers.

Our conclusions are summarized as follows. The methodology met its objectives of being efficient, habitable, and safe:

- **Efficiency.** Performance metrics showed high productivity.
- **Habitability.** The team would be happy to use the methodology again.

---

[1]   This was Stephen's view. It is not a corporate Thales position.

◆ **Safety.** The project was converging on its agreed end date until it was curtailed. The project still created a usable product.

The following issues need attention in adopting the methodology:

◆ It may require established roles to change.
◆ It challenges established documentation practices.
◆ It requires a broadly scoped contract.

The TRT UK Quality Assurance team conducted an informal assessment of the project from the perspective of ISO 9001 and TickIT, concluding that the methodology could be made compliant with these standards with the addition of a few extra practices and records. The QA team proposed that Crystal Clear be incorporated into the Quality Management System at TRT UK and proposed further studies using the methodology.

An analysis of the methodology from the CMMI perspective is ongoing at the time of writing. We aim to trial the methodology on a project with more developers.

Introduction

The project developed a program for use in connection with a computer vision system called ZYX. Our pilot project, CamCal, developed a camera calibration tool for ZYX. The purpose of camera calibration is to inform ZYX of where the camera is and where it is pointing. This information is encoded in a calibration matrix that maps 3D world coordinates to 2D image coordinates. The matrix is needed by ZYX in order to understand what it sees.

The starting point was a prototype camera calibration tool that had previously been developed in MATLAB. The purpose of the project was to replace the prototype with something less fragile and more suitable for presenting to customers, and more suitable for use at customer sites. We decided to write our new version in Java, with some of the mathematical components implemented in MATLAB.

CamCal was a small project, with only one and one-half developers and a total cost of just over six man months. The work was funded internally by TRT UK, and there was no immediate external customer.

Project Chronology

The key dates on the project are shown in Figure 8-2. In order to keep this section reasonably short, we present only the most significant events on the project. These include events where there was a change to the requirements or to the schedule.

The project involved the following people. With the exception of Stephen, who is the author of this document, their names have been changed.

- Sam, the project manager in charge of the wider project of which CamCal was a part
- Liam, a computer vision consultant
- Stephen, an engineer with a programming/algorithms background
- Desmond, an engineer with a Java background

Liam's Prototype

Liam conceived the idea of a camera calibration tool. He wrote a prototype, mostly in his own time. The prototype included all the key features required, but it was fragile and not particularly easy to use. What was needed was a tool written to professional standards that we could deliver to customers.

Proposal

Sam and Liam began work on a proposal for a camera calibration project. They would need at least one software engineer. Stephen would be released to work on the camera calibration project on a part-time basis, provided the project used an Agile methodology.

A proposal document was written that laid out the project's initial requirements, the development approach, an initial work breakdown structure, and an estimate for the work. The estimate was for 105 days of effort. The initial allocation of roles was that shown in Figure 8-1.

The proposal document was put to Senior Management and accepted. The project started on August 18, 2003.

The proposal document was based on an early (January 2002) version of Crystal Clear. This did not include project start-up activities. But it was clear that there were issues we needed to resolve before we could begin the iterative development. So, we borrowed the idea of an "Exploration phase" from XP. This was the first phase of the project and is described in Figure 8-2.

Name	Roles
Sam	Sponsor
Stephen	Lead Designer, Coordinator, Writer, Tester
Liam	User, Designer, Business Expert, Writer, Tester

Figure 8-1. *Initial allocation of roles.*

	Event	Effort (days)	Dates
Project Start-up	Liam's prototype		Dec 2002 to Feb 2003
	Proposal		June 2003
	Exploration		Mon 18/8/03 Fri 5/9/03
	Desmond joins project		Tues 9/9/03
	First planning meeting		Wed 10/9/03
Increment 1: Walking skeleton	Development		Thurs 11/9/03 to Fri 17/10/03
	Viewing		Fri 17/10/03
	Reflection Workshop		Mon 20/10/03
Increment 2: CP entry and edit	Planning meeting		Mon 20/10/03
	Development		Mon 20/10/03 to Fri 7/11/03
	Viewing		Fri 7/11/03
	Reflection Workshop		Thurs 13/11/03
Increment 3: Calibration	Planning meeting		Thurs 13/11/03
	Development		Mon 10/11/03 to Fri 5/12/03
	Viewing		Mon 8/12/03
	Reflection workshop		Mon 8/12/03
Increment 4: Consolidate for year end	Planning meeting		Mon 8/12/03
	Development		Tue 9/12/03 to Tue 23/12/03
	Viewing		Tue 23/12/03
	Reflection workshop		Tue 23/12/03
Increment 5: Complete	Planning meeting		Mon 5/1/04
	Development		Mon 5/1/04 to Fri 23/1/04
	Viewing		Mon 26/1/04
	Reflection workshop		Mon 26/1/04

Figure 8-2.   Project chronology. (Note the use of European date format [dd/mm/yy].)

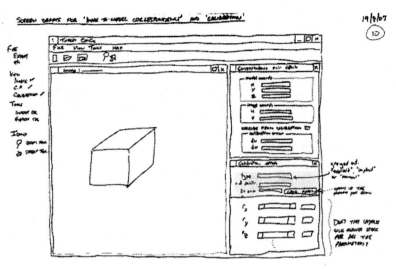

Figure 8-3.   *An example whiteboard printout.*

Exploration

The Exploration phase was a two-week long task in which Stephen and Liam captured more detailed requirements, investigated the key technical issues, and firmed up the estimates.[2]

The proposal document gave a set of high-level requirements, but more detail was needed. Stephen and Liam worked together to flesh out the details, with Liam (as user) being the main source of requirements. They captured the requirements using a printing whiteboard, drawing several draft screen-shots such as the one in Figure 8-3.

The printouts were numbered and kept together in a folder (the printout in Figure 8-3 is number 10). They also started a requirements document.

The proposal document had left open the issue of which language the software was to be written in. This needed to be resolved quickly because it affected the composition of the team. After some investigation it was decided to use Java for the GUI and MATLAB for the underlying mathematics. The MATLAB source-code would be compiled into a DLL compatible with the Java Native Interface.

Crystal Clear expects at least one team member who is thoroughly familiar with the technology, but neither Liam nor Stephen had used Java before. So we asked for

---

2   Readers will recognize this as similar to the *Exploratory 360°* strategy described in Chapter 3.

another team member, and received Desmond, a strong Java developer. Desmond relocated to sit with Liam and Stephen in the same bay.

At the end of the Exploration phase, the project roles were as shown in Figure 8-4. Desmond was allocated to the project 100 percent. Stephen had a commitment to another project so was allocated 50 percent. The other team members were called in when necessary. Stephen is shown as lead designer because that was the original plan. But Desmond had the more relevant skill set, and it was clear that he would lead the development work once he was up to speed with the project.

First Planning Meeting

We conducted a planning meeting using the project planning jam session technique suggested in CC. Sam, Desmond, and Stephen sat round a table and contributed task cards. An example task card is shown in Figure 8-5. Each task card had a title, a brief description, the name of the person, and an estimate in man days. The description did not need to be very long, nor understandable to anybody outside the project. The estimate was in the top right-hand corner in man days. The team adopted the convention that the estimate included any associated unit testing effort.

The key tasks went to Desmond, as the person with the strongest Java experience. We spread the task cards over the table and agreed an ordering that made sense. (A schedule that "makes sense" is one that maximizes the chances of achieving the project objectives, as stated in the mission statement.) We then gave each card a label (at the bottom of the card) so that we could reconstruct the ordering. After the meeting, the tasks were copied into Microsoft Project, which is the standard scheduling tool at TRT UK.

In fact, the majority of the task cards were created before the meeting by Stephen and Liam, who had gone through this process already. Desmond essentially revisited the task descriptions, technology choices, and estimates. Nevertheless, the first plan-

Name	Background (partial)	Role(s)
Sam	Project Manager	Sponsor
Liam	Technical Consultant	User, Business Expert, Writer, Tester
Stephen (50%)	Software engineer, engineering maths	Lead Designer, Coordinator, Writer, Tester
Desmond (100%)	Software engineer (Java expert)	Designer, Tester

Figure 8-4.   *Project roles at end of exploration.*

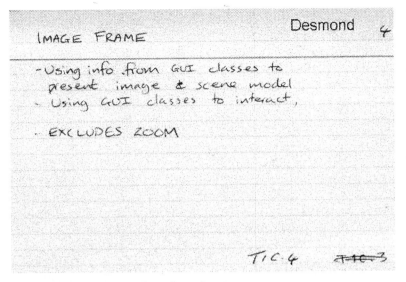

Figure 8-5. *An example task card.*

Figure 8-6. *One end of the table that was covered in task cards.*

ning meeting was a key point in the project. The project had a clear direction, and all had contributed.

By adding up the totals on the task cards, we arrived at an improved estimate for the remainder of the project: 134 man days. Adding the cost of exploration (already spent) gave 154 man days. This was higher than the estimate in the proposal document, but the sponsor was happy for work to continue on the basis of the schedule upon which we had agreed.

Increment 1: Walking Skeleton

The purpose of the first increment was to create a skeletal application incorporating the main architectural features and some core functionality. In Crystal Clear parlance this is called a *Walking Skeleton*. Key tasks would be the creation of the object model and implementation of the software for projecting a scene model onto the screen.

First we had to select and configure our tools. At TRT UK, projects mainly decide for themselves which tools they will use. The tools were chosen by the team members, especially Desmond, on the basis of his experience on other projects. The tools were as follows.

◆ *Design tool.* Together 5.5 was selected. This generates skeletal Java code from UML diagrams. Subsequent changes to the software are automatically reflected in the UML representation.

◆ *Programming tools.* NetBeans 3.5 was chosen as our Java IDE, running on J2SE 1.4.2. MATLAB 6.5 had already been chosen for the calibration software, with Microsoft Visual C++ for the DLL "glue logic" that would connect the compiled MATLAB to Java.

◆ *Unit testing tool.* We selected JUnit.

◆ *Version control tool.* We used Microsoft SourceSafe 6.0, which is standard at TRT UK.

Once the tools were selected and configured, Desmond began creating the architecture for the software, discussing design issues with Stephen using the printing whiteboard. The application was designed using the "Model-View-Controller" paradigm.

At this point we need to say a little more about the application. The application uses a 3D scene model, which describes the objects in the region observed by the camera. The scene model consists of a set of 3D points, which are joined together to form the edges of the objects. The scene model is projected onto the 2D screen according to the location and orientation of a virtual camera. The picture formed by the virtual camera is called the projected scene model.

During increment 1, Stephen wrote the Java code for transforming the 3D scene model into 2D screen coordinates.

Here, there was a change of plan. The original schedule had called for this software to be written in MATLAB, compiled to DLL, and accessed over the JNI. It soon became clear that we were not going to achieve that level of integration in the time available for increment 1. So Stephen wrote the code in Java instead: this way, Desmond would have something to integrate within increment 1. If the software proved to be too slow, it could be rewritten in MATLAB later. (MATLAB is optimized for matrix operations, so we would expect higher performance.) Stephen and Desmond replanned their work by conducting a brief planning meeting.

Simultaneously, the team continued to refine the requirements, with Liam and Stephen working together to produce updated screen drafts. Most of the requirements discussed at this stage concerned usability issues. Liam made one request for completely new functionality (hidden line removal), and this was turned down because it was found to complicate the design too much. We knew that Sam's main concern was to deliver on time, rather than to deliver the most comprehensive product.

By the end of increment 1, the team had succeeded in creating the walking skeleton.

The scene model was only a dummy, consisting of a few geometric shapes (a box, a prism, etc.). The final application would use a scene model that represents the region being viewed, in this case part of a railway station. The user could click and drag the camera icon around the plan view, and the application automatically updated the projected scene model.

It was only a start, but enough to demonstrate some core functionality.

Toward the end of the increment, Sam gave the team its mission statement. This is one of the work products required by Crystal Clear. It is the only work product asked of the sponsor.

At the end of increment 1, we held a viewing and a reflection workshop.

Viewing 1

The viewing meeting was held on Friday, October 17, 2003, at the end of increment 1.

Desmond demonstrated the application to Liam and Sam. The meeting was cordial, with Liam and Sam taking a keen interest in the details of the product. Several

Camera Calibration Mission Statement

The mission of the camera calibration project is to:

◆ Develop a maintainable, simple to use, portable, and extendable software tool that will enable intelligent video surveillance system installers and repairers to rapidly, accurately, and efficiently calibrate their system cameras with respect to a predefined three-dimensional scene model.

◆ Establish a basis for developing a future tool set that can manage all aspects of intelligent video surveillance system installation and repairers' activities. Such a tool set will include the camera calibration tool, and will add scene model creation capabilities. It will be able to grow with the technology growth of the video surveillance market.

◆ Develop and trial the use of new software development methodologies and processes, with a view to improving the software development process used within Thales, for small- to medium-sized software projects.

The development priorities are

Sacrifice others for this:	Complete by end of January 2004. Ensure accuracy and quality
Retain if possible:	Usability, potential to grow into a more extensive tool
Sacrifice these first:	Execution speed, portability, additional interfaces, internal format storage.

Figure 8-7.   *CamCal Calibration mission statement.*

issues were raised in connection with the software and these were recorded on the printing whiteboard. The whiteboard printout is shown below in Figure 8-8. At the end of the viewing the team had a view of the product status that was shared, complete, and reasonably positive.

On CamCal, we chose to have a viewing at the end of every increment. This is more than Crystal Clear demands as the methodology only calls for a minimum of two per release.

Reflection Workshop 1

At the end of increment 1, the team held a reflection workshop. Its purpose was to identify which aspects of the process were working and which needed to be changed. The notes from the reflection workshop are shown on the whiteboard printout in Figure 8-8.

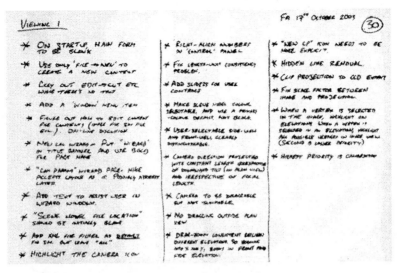

Figure 8-8. *Whiteboard printout from Viewing 1.*

The main points were

- **All to spend a day reading CC.** The team had not been trained in using the methodology. The only training material that was available was the manual on CC, so it was suggested and agreed that each team member should spend a day reading it.

- **Desmond as lead designer.** Desmond had been making the key technical decisions, because of his experience with Java. Stephen had just been acting as "process champion." It was proposed to acknowledge this situation by nominating Desmond the lead designer. Desmond was unsure, but agreed to think about it.

- **"Keep this" statements.** The team found much about the methodology that they wanted to keep. In particular, the team members were working well together. Several of the team members had worked together before on projects that had been run differently: they were finding it easier to work together on this project.

- **Absence of team members.** Apart from Desmond, all of the team members had significant commitments to other projects. The team recognized this as a problem. Agile methods rely on tacit knowledge, so are vulnerable if the people are not present.

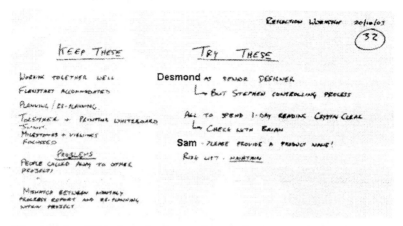

Figure 8-9.   *Whiteboard printout from reflection workshop 1.*

◆ **Mismatch with TRT UK procedures.** Sam was uncomfortable with the fact that he was formally responsible for the project, but not in control of its schedule.[3]

Increment 2: CP Entry and Edit

The objective for increment 2 was to enable the user to enter and edit "Correspondence Pairs" (CPs). A correspondence pair specifies an association between a vertex in the scene model, which is three dimensional, and a point in the image, which is two dimensional. CPs are entered into CamCal by mouse operations. The user clicks on a point in the image, and drags to the intended vertex in the projected scene model. The CPs are ultimately used as the input to the calibration algorithm, which computes the calibration matrix required by ZYX.

Increment 2 began with a planning meeting (Monday, October 20, 2003) in which the project schedule was rebuilt based on the current situation. The main change from the original plan was that Stephen would not be available for increment 2. He had a commitment to another project and would not have time. After discussing the options, the decision was made to delay his contribution until increment 3.

In the new schedule, some time was allocated to address the issues captured at Viewing 1, but the priority was to press ahead with the high-risk aspects of the project, such as calibration and the integration with ZYX.

By the end of the increment, the facility to add and edit correspondence pairs was ready for demonstration. It used a real scene model instead of just geometric shapes.

---

[3]   We'll see discussion of this point at the end of the field report.

We held another viewing session, and another reflection workshop. The viewing generated more issues, which were recorded on a whiteboard printout. Again, the team had achieved a shared view of the status of the product.

This reflection workshop generated fewer points than the first one had. The main outputs from the reflection workshop were

- At the previous reflection workshop, the team members had agreed to read up on the methodology, but they had not found the time. Desmond agreed to do this in increment 3.
- The project was not meeting certain parts of the methodology. The peer reviews had not happened. The risk list had not been maintained. The requirements document had not been firmed up. We agreed to address these in increment 3.

Increment 3: Calibration

The increment began with a planning meeting. The tasks for this increment are summarized below. They were all completed by the end of the increment.

- Peer code review.
- Implement the calibration algorithm in MATLAB, and integrate this with Java.
- Implement GUI facilities supporting calibration.
- Initial system test.
- Desmond to read CC.

The integration between MATLAB and Java had been considered a risk area, so it was a relief to achieve it.

We tried posting the task cards for the increment on a whiteboard in the team's working area. This proved to be very effective at communicating the schedule, and we retained the practice for the remainder of the project.

In addition to these scheduled tasks, the requirements continued to be refined on an ongoing basis. Liam's original requirement had been that CamCal support two particular calibration algorithms. But when integration was discussed, we learned that only one algorithm was compatible with our target system. Since the purpose of the project was to develop a calibration tool for that system and the team had a tight schedule, the decision was made to omit the second algorithm.

Stephen firmed up the requirements document, and had it reviewed by Liam and Desmond. There was also more discussion about detailed GUI behavior. We will relate some details of the discussion to give a feel for the kind of decisions that were taking place.

During increment 1, Stephen and Liam had sketched out a user interface that was wizardlike, so that the user would be guided through the activities that calibration involves. Each page of the wizard would have panels of fixed size and position. Desmond, who was more experienced at GUI design, felt that this would be too restrictive and favored a more flexible design, giving the user the ability to move, resize, and show/hide the windows. He had implemented the software so that this aspect of its appearance could readily be changed. The difficulty was that by giving the user this level of control, the wizardlike nature of the application was lost, and it might not be obvious to the user what he needed to do.

What was needed was a resolution to the question of how the GUI should behave. At the planning meeting, Desmond had taken a task to sort the issue out. Desmond created a design in which the user could select between views using radio buttons. The views were

◆ **Manual alignment.** Here, the projected scene model reflected the position and orientation of a virtual camera that the user could control.

◆ **Algorithmic calibration.** Here, the projected scene model was formed using the calibration algorithm.

◆ **Xxxxx calibration.** This was a dummy option. Desmond left it in place to show that the user interface could be extended to contain more than one calibration algorithm.

Liam felt this arrangement was still not ideal, because the controls for the "manual alignment" view were visible when the first calibration was selected.

We presented the system at a viewing on Monday, December 8, 2003. At this stage, most of the core functionality of the application was present. One could load an image and a scene model, add correspondence pairs, and run the calibration algorithm. The calibration algorithm finds a transformation that fits the scene model over the 2D image, so that the wire-frame projection of the scene model is aligned to objects in the image.

For this viewing, a QA representative had been invited. This was the first QA involvement with the process. Subsequently, a QA representative was invited to every meeting on the project. (The QA perspective is presented separately, following this field report.)

Increment 4: Consolidate for Year End

The main objective for this increment was to bring the project to a state where it could be closed relatively painlessly. There was a possibility that issues outside the scope of the project might lead to it being closed at the end of the increment (which coincided with the end of the year). In fact, this requirement did not affect the planning too much. The key tasks that needed to be done for our target date of end of January 2004 needed to be done anyway. The tasks for this increment are summarized below. All were complete by the end of the increment.

◆ Create a CD of the application, including an installation tool.
◆ Integrate with ZYX. This involved having CamCal create a calibration file and testing that ZYX could make use of it.
◆ Start a User Manual. (It could not be finished until the user interface was complete.)
◆ Code reviews and associated actions.

At this point, the project had a page of issues from each viewing. Liam prioritized them, and they were copied into an issues list that Desmond had created in Microsoft Outlook. Using Outlook meant that we would all have instant access to the most recent list.

The increment terminated with a viewing and a reflection workshop. For this viewing, we ran the software directly from the installation CD to demonstrate that this worked. Only a few points were raised in the viewing, everybody knew that there wasn't time for big changes. The reflection workshop was quiet as well with nobody suggesting any changes to the process.

Increment 5: Complete

The Christmas holiday period provided a natural break between increments, and the fifth increment began on Monday, January 5, 2004.

At the end of 2003, there was a decision, made outside of the scope of the project, that CamCal should be completed cheaply at the start of 2004. To achieve this, the decision was made to omit the acceptance tests and code reviews that had previously been scheduled. The justification was that the software had already passed various test and review activities, and this had created a degree of confidence in the code. The main tasks for the increment were

◆ The prioritized issues list. After some negotiation, it was agreed that Desmond would work down the issues list, addressing all the issues until either he ran out of time, or until a certain point in the prioritized list was reached, whichever came first.

◆ Liam to finish the user manual.

◆ Desmond and Stephen to write a maintenance handbook.

At the end of the increment, we held a final viewing. Compared with the previous increment, it was generally a bit tidier and more polished. This was the result of Desmond's work addressing the items in the prioritized issues list. Sam accepted the application as ready to demonstrate to customers, and asked that it be installed on the ZYX presentation system.

We held a final reflection workshop. This turned into a general discussion about how the methodology went overall. The team members' views were generally very positive. The only substantial issue raised was the fit with TRT UK procedures. If this could be satisfactorily resolved, then all the participants would be happy to work this way again.

(In fact, there is a procedure at TRT UK for addressing QMS issues of this sort: any employee may raise suggestions for process improvement.)

Compliance with Crystal Clear

In this section we summarize the extent to which our pilot project was consistent with Crystal Clear. We evaluate compliance against the following aspects of Crystal Clear: the properties, the roles, the life cycle, and the work products.

◆ Properties
The CC properties were achieved.

◆ Roles
The pilot project allocated roles to the people as Crystal Clear asks. There were some deviations from the ideal:

The lead designer role had to be shared between Stephen and Desmond. Stephen took the methodology aspect of the role, and Desmond took the technical leadership. This division was necessary because the lead designer role requires knowledge both of the technical issues and the methodology. While Desmond was the lead designer in the literal sense, he had not been trained in the methodology and so Stephen had to take that part of the role. This division of responsibility caused some confusion in places, and the project would have worked better had the role been taken by a single person.

There was a deviation in the role of user. The product had two intended uses: (1) as a demonstration tool to be used by senior figures at TRT UK, and (2) as an installation tool to be used by installation engineers. Liam is a real user of the former category. We did not have a user in the latter category.

◆ Life cycle
The pilot project initially used an early draft of the methodology that did not include the Crystal Clear project start-up activities. These were therefore omitted. In other respects the project followed the Crystal Clear life cycle. We note the following:

a) The methodology calls for frequent release of software to users, so as to obtain feedback. Our pilot project achieved that by having a user on the team. The user was given an updated copy of the program every so often.

b) Crystal Clear calls for a minimum of two viewings per release. We had more viewings than this, having made the decision to have a viewing at the end of each increment. All of the viewings were useful, but the later viewings were less useful because the product had changed relatively little between increments.

◆ Work products
The pilot project created most of the work products required, apart from the following:

1. Since there was only one release, the release sequence and release schedule reduced to a single end date.

2. The migration code work product is for database applications and was not applicable for our pilot project.

3. The acceptance tests were removed from the schedule when the project was curtailed, so there were no acceptance test results.

Analysis

Performance against Estimates

The priorities for the pilot project, as stated in the mission statement were

Sacrifice others for this:	Complete by end of January 2004
	Ensure accuracy and quality
Retain if possible:	Usability, potential to grow into a more extensive tool

The project was steered so as to meet these priorities. Note that the primary objective was the end date, not the final cost. So whenever the end date or usability

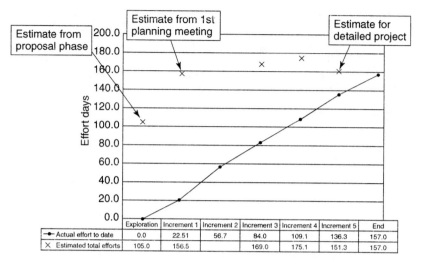

Figure 8-10. *Estimation accuracy (actuals and estimates at the start of each increment).*

	Exploration	Increment 1	Increment 2	Increment 3	Increment 4	Increment 5	End
Actual effort to date	0.0	22.51	56.7	84.0	109.1	136.3	157.0
X Estimated total efforts	105.0	156.5		169.0	175.1	151.3	157.0

appeared threatened, the team reacted by spending effort to solve the problem. The team was able to do this because only one of its members was working on the project full time. The others had some flexibility in how much time they committed to the project.

This is reflected in the graph of estimated versus actual effort shown in Figure 8-10. The estimates increase gradually from the first planning meeting to the fourth. The fifth planning meeting shows a reduced estimate that reflects the decision to curtail the project. (The curtailed project met the underlying business need, which was for a demonstrable product, not a deliverable one.)

The proposal phase was not conducted according to the Crystal Clear process, so does not form part of our experiment. It created an estimate that was found, within a few weeks of starting the project, to be a considerable underestimate. The main reason for the problem was that the proposal phase did not include sufficient time to determine the technology that would be used or the staff who would do the project.

In fact, the figures were not computed until after the project. In hindsight we feel it would have been advantageous to have computed the figures on the fly.

Analysis from the ISO 9001 Viewpoint

(The field report contained an excerpt from the auditor's analysis. A longer excerpt from his report is presented separately, following this field report.)

Conclusions

This section presents our evaluation of Crystal Clear. We evaluate the methodology against the claims that are made for it. We also present a number of issues where care is needed in using the methodology.

Evaluation of Crystal Clear against its Claims

The claims made for Crystal Clear are that it is efficient, habitable, and safe. On the basis of our pilot project, we support these claims.

◆ Efficiency

The final productivity metric for the project was 81.7 lines of noncomment code (system code plus unit test code) per day. This metric was computed by dividing the total number of lines of code generated, by the total effort expended, including all the noncoding effort. (*Note:* Unit test code was 26.4 percent of the Java code.)

The project did not include acceptance tests, but this would not have changed the overall figures very much. Acceptance tests would probably have found some small errors that we would then have corrected, but overall, we knew that the user and sponsor were already content with the product and it had already been subject to various tests.

This high level of productivity arose, first, from the skills of the designer (Desmond). The methodology helped by keeping the development focused, and by reducing waste. Waste, in this context, means anything that does not contribute to the final product.

◆ Habitability

All of the team members would be happy to use this methodology again. Several positive comments were received from the team, including:

Liam (User). "Overall, taking part was an enjoyable experience, and one which I would be happy to repeat."

Desmond (Designer). "I usually felt very focused and energized. . . . I felt generally in control."

Sam (Sponsor). "Communications were excellent . . . the team worked together well . . . the software was delivered in a satisfactory working condition."

Further comments from the team are presented further on. Sam had some concerns about the fit between the role definitions in Crystal Clear and those expected at TRT UK. Sam's approval of the methodology was contingent on this issue being satisfactorily resolved.

- Safety

  A safe methodology is one that increases the likelihood of the project succeeding. The pilot project succeeded in that it created a product that satisfied the sponsor. Beyond that, several aspects of the project were demonstrably safe: the plans were always meaningful, hard issues were resolved in a timely manner, and the team was always focused on the most important features.

The initial estimate for the project was incorrect, but this was conducted outside of the Crystal Clear experiment.

Crystal Clear does require an experienced and competent lead designer in order to be safe. Crystal Clear does not define "techniques" (for configuration management, testing, etc.), and the intention is that the lead designer fills this gap.

Issues Requiring Attention During Adoption

The following aspects of the methodology need attention during adoption:

- It may require established roles to change.

  Crystal Clear gives people roles that may not match the established organizational roles.

  At TRT UK, each project has a project manager who is held responsible for delivering the project on time and within budget. On our pilot project, this was Sam's role. A TRT UK project manager would expect to own the project schedule. But under Crystal Clear, scheduling was a communal activity led by the lead designer. This was a safer arrangement since it brought the skills of all the team members to bear on the scheduling problem. But it created a situation where Sam had the same responsibility that he would normally have, but with reduced power to influence events.[4]

- It challenges established documentation practices.

  Crystal Clear expects initial requirements in the form of a mission statement, an actor-goal list, and some use cases. These are not expected to be sufficiently precise to define every aspect of the product. The details are intended to emerge through interaction between representatives of the developer and customer organizations.

  Crystal Clear also places great reliance on tacit knowledge over written documents. But tacit knowledge is only available to other team members, when the

---

[4]   I discuss options that Sam might have in the Commentary afterward.

people are simultaneously present. It follows that in order to achieve the greatest efficiency, the team members should work together continuously on the same project.

◆ It requires a broadly scoped contract.

Crystal Clear expects the detailed requirements to emerge as the project proceeds, but is silent on the question of how this could fit into a contractual framework.[5] One approach would be to adopt the DSDM practice of base lining the requirements at a high level. DSDM has been used successfully in conjunction with the CMMI, so it is unlikely that this approach would create a CMMI or ISO compliance problem.

Recommendations for Future Work

This pilot project exercised many aspects of the methodology, but was limited by its small size. We recommend a trial on a larger project, having more than one and one-half developers and more than a single release. A larger trial would still need to be within the Crystal Clear scope, having no more than eight team members.

Crystal Clear is designed to accommodate practices drawn from XP, such as test-first design and pair programming. We would recommend that these practices be incorporated into a future trial.

A study on the fit between Crystal Clear and our standard internal methodology is planned for later in 2004. If possible we would also like to conclude the work on the fit between Crystal Clear and the CMMI.

Comments from the Team

The following comments are unedited except where indicated.

Liam's Comments (User)

December 11, 2003:
I have never worked on a project in which team members have such a clear picture of the state of the project's progress. The regular viewing sessions and generated to-do/bug lists being posted on a whiteboard, creates a single point of access which all team members can share. The Project Plan, and associated task lists being posted-up also helps.

---

[5]   This is discussed in Chapter 7.

The only down-side I have experienced is the high-level of conversation/discussion that takes place around the main board, disturbing thought when one is not involved in a team discussion. An ideal solution would be having the space to move board and discussion away from non-involved team members, during such meetings.

February 3, 2004:

The manner in which the Agile/Crystal Clear methodology roles had to be modified to fit with existing company procedures, led to a degree of reactivity in the evaluation process. For example, the senior-designer/coordinator (Stephen) appeared to be questioned over the management of project costs by the sponsor, when in fact only the sponsor (Sam) had full access to the cost information. If the approach evaluated had been fully integrated with company procedures these issues would not have arisen. Overall, taking part was an enjoyable experience, and one which I would be happy to repeat.

Desmond's Comments (Designer)

Focus and Efficiency

As a designer/developer, I usually felt very "focused" and "energized." During each increment I felt I had a clear idea of which features we would be adding, roughly how they should work, how long they should take, and which were the most important. I felt generally "in control."

The short length of the increments and the clear idea of a goal at the end also helped maintain focus on essentials. Each short increment had a clear goal: a set of functionality to be implemented and a demonstration of it to the users. The overall feeling was that we were being fast and efficient. That we were focused clearly on valuable features, and that we made efficient progress.

On other developments one might get a chance to "disappear" for a few months, working towards one big goal. Having contrasted this with Crystal Clear, it now seems to me that Crystal Clear is much more efficient: there is always a slight pressure to deliver, to concentrate on the essentials, that feels like it delivers real value. Or rather, that it avoids some of the inefficiencies in the old approach.

This energized, focused feeling is produced by various factors:

- Involvement in the planning of each increment.
- Familiarity with the set of requirements and the users' priorities (in value terms) for them.
- Sense of achievement as each increment is completed, and within increments, as each feature was added.

◆ To a lesser extent, being freed from the perceived "drudgery" of heavier processes. In fact, it didn't feel like much was actually being dropped. But the knock-on effects of using the lighter process definitely contributed to the good feeling.

"Deliverability" and Control

At nearly all times on the project it felt like we had a working product, with clear ideas of how to proceed, and confidence that something useful would be delivered. So we did not feel out of control, or worried about whether we would actually produce something at the end.

Differences with "Traditional" Methods

From my point of view—from the point of view of someone moving from "traditional" development procedures to Crystal—there are two principles that seem to differentiate Crystal Clear from the old way of working:

1) Minimum necessary overhead: do everything in the "lightest" way possible, consistent with achieving the results. It took a while to become comfortable with the lighter weight processes and documentation. But after a while it became quite easy to stick to, and quite liberating.

2) View feedback from users in a positive way. Don't view oversights or changes as problems, but as discoveries. I had to keep re-emphasizing this to myself.

Sam's Comments (Sponsor)

Communications

Communications were excellent: the core team was co-located in a single area. A printing whiteboard was used to record information, which was then held in a file: this proved to be a time saver. However, it would have been good to have more space to post the information for the team to view.

Viewings and reflection workshops were held each month and certainly kept the whole team up to date with the demonstrable progress of the project. However, the number of iterations and viewings increased from 3 to 5, and this was excessive.

Planning/Project Management

From a project manager's viewpoint, I felt a little out of control for two reasons:

◆ The day-to-day management was delegated to the lead designer.
◆ I was not familiar with the Crystal Clear methodology.

Although not part of Crystal Clear, the project proposal promised that the scope of work could be varied to keep within the original budget. This was not achieved in practice and the project had to be curtailed at a point prior to full completion.

For future projects, the role of project manager needs to be very carefully thought out. Crystal Clear does not fit in well with existing TRT UK procedures and so some changes will be required.

People

The team worked together well, although this project was not typical, in that most of the development was performed by one person. The concept of having little documentation did not work well in the early stages because team members were on holiday or committed to other work. It is a credit to the team that the project was so successful in spite of this.

Deliverables

The software was delivered in a satisfactory working condition. The requirements' document, user manual, and maintenance handbook are all in draft form, because they were produced late in the project and the project curtailment prevented them from being reviewed and issued. Had the documents been produced earlier, there would have been time to review and approve them. They would also have been of use to guide the development work. In practice, an ISO 9001 audit would have caused some problems for the project.

Because the project was curtailed, the software is not yet ready for release to customers, although it can be used for demonstrations.

Summary

For projects that can be clearly specified at the beginning, Crystal Clear does not appear to offer significant advantages over a *well-run* lightweight project that follows standard TRT UK processes. However, it is accepted that for projects such as this, with a large human–computer interface component, where the requirements are difficult to express clearly, Crystal Clear offers some advantages.

The use of paper documents, printing whiteboards, and co-located working may not be practicable for widespread use, and a better approach would be to use electronic documents as is current practice in TRT UK. The problems with team members being on leave at critical times would have been reduced by drafting earlier, more detailed documentation. However the viewings and reflection workshops were very important and should be retained as face-to-face meetings.

(End of report.)

THE AUDITOR'S REPORT

(CamCal was a process experiment. The auditor analyzed what *would* need to be done in order for a Crystal Clear project to pass an ISO 9001 audit. The auditor's text follows.)

Scope

This audit is supplementary to the Management System Audit Plan and was performed at the request of the lead designer on the CamCal elements of the ZYX project.

Crystal Clear (CC) is a software development methodology that is currently being established to enable close, collaborative working of a small software team. The method is considered "lightweight" when compared with a full mission-critical or safety-critical development (e.g., Mil Std 498, ESA PSS-05-0, etc.) and follows a hybrid incremental/evolutionary life cycle. This type of approach is described as Rapid Application Development (RAD) within the TickIT Guide.

CC calls for close interaction between the customer and developers and defines a number of distinct roles.

CamCal had adopted a modified version of the CC method as a conscious experiment in lightweight software development.

The objective of this audit was to assess the CC design methodology as applied to CamCal against the requirements of ISO 9001:2000 and the associated TickIT Guide. Inevitably, the specific implementation as applied to CamCal influenced the approach and findings of the audit.

Two checklists were prepared from the TickIT Guide. The first was against Part D, "Guidance for Auditors" and the second was against Part E, "Software Quality Management System Requirements—Standards Perspective."

Findings

Both ISO 9001:2000 and TickIT are defined within the framework of a full QMS. Consequently, as CamCal (or any other internal project that follows the CC methodology) will operate within the TRT-UK QMS, only the following project-specific elements of ISO 9001:2000 were examined.

Planning of Product Realization

ISO/TickIT require planning of processes for product realization. While CamCal has an overall project plan[6] (which includes the quality requirements) and schedule,

---

[6]   "Project plan" refers not to the project schedule, but to a plan for the *processes* used.

there is no detailed project plan for the CamCal development, but proposal document CamCal-01-003 was referenced from the project plan.

Proposal document CamCal-01-003 had been issued and covered initial planning of CamCal. This gives brief descriptions of the method and a proposed three-iteration life cycle. One of the key features of CC is that each planned iteration (there were five planned later) includes a planning meeting that allows the project to be dynamically replanned. An iteration consists of three mandatory stages: planning; design, code, integrate; and reflection workshop. In addition, an iteration may be followed by a viewing attended by the user and possibly by the sponsor.

In order to be fully compliant with this clause of ISO 9001, the QMS would need modification to provide detail of the working practices associated with CC to avoid the need to reproduce this detail in the PP for every RAD project. A dedicated project plan would then need to reference the QMS or modify the practices as necessary. The project plan would also need to include or reference the following (as appropriate): customer quality requirements; risks or risk management process; methods, tools, standards, etc.; statutory and regulatory requirements; deliverables, including documents; other documents; verification and validation approach; approvals, authorizations, acceptance; roll-out; prototyping; and release.

CC specifies a risk list that needs to be maintained. It is recommended that the normal TRT-UK risk management process is followed.

Determination of Requirements Related to the Product

ISO/TickIT require determination of requirements related to the product. CamCal has a sponsor mission statement and an evolving requirement document (RD) CamCal-02-003 as required by CC, which contained an actor-goal list and a number of use cases. The mission statement has numbered and prioritized objectives, the RD has been evolving throughout development.

These documents are capable of satisfying the ISO/TickIT requirements.

It was suggested that in future it would be useful to have two separate documents to distinguish between contractual requirements (mission statement plus actor-goal list) and the evolving CC requirements document which would contain use cases and lower-level details and could be treated as design detail rather than formal requirements under ISO 9001.

Review of Requirements Related to the Product

ISO/TickIT require review of requirements related to the product. CamCal involved review and approval of the mission statement and ongoing review of the RD. The review of the RD was carried out with the user rather than sponsor, and there had been no formal issues (document remained at Issue 1 Draft C at end, although the project had been prematurely terminated).

In order to be fully compliant with this clause of ISO 9001, the RD should undergo a draft revision (with comments maintained in Visual SourceSafe) for each project iteration or preferably undergo an approved up-issue for each iteration. This would provide visibility of latest stable requirements for each iteration and the mandatory records of review required by ISO 9001.

If Contractual Requirements were treated separately from design detail, as suggested earlier, contractual requirements only should be subject to review at the proposal stage as required by ISO 9001.

Customer Communication

ISO/TickIT require customer communication to take place. The involvement of the customer (normally sponsor and user) is central to CC through viewings and reflection workshops during each iteration.

Consequently this aspect is well covered. CamCal held these meetings and maintained whiteboard records.

CC requires close cooperation with customer representatives over a long period. Careful choice of team members can reduce the risk of poor cooperation.

Design and Development Planning

ISO/TickIT require planning of the design and development activities. In TRT-UK this detail would normally be contained in (or referenced from) the project plan and schedule. For CC, most of the practices and proposed iterations could be in these same documents. CamCal did not have a detailed project plan for CamCal but did have a proposal document and did maintain the schedule.

In order to be fully compliant with this clause of ISO 9001, the requirements defined in 7.1 would need to be followed. The schedule would need to reflect the latest planning meeting (as it does on CamCal).

In CC plans may be changed at the planning meeting associated with each iteration. This should be recognized in the project plan, and the scope of changes that may be made without revision of the project plan should be defined.

Design and Development Inputs

ISO/TickIT require definition of the design and development inputs. CamCal placed this information into a requirement document (RD) CamCal-02-003 as required by

CC. The RD included most of the topics required by TickIT. Unfortunately, the RD was never formally issued.

If contractual requirements were treated separately from design detail, as suggested earlier, this requirement would be met.

In common with clause 7.2.2, *to be fully compliant with this clause of ISO 9001*, the RD should undergo a draft revision (with comments maintained in VSS) for each project iteration or preferably undergo an approved up-issue for each iteration. This would provide visibility of latest stable requirements for each iteration and the mandatory records of review required by ISO 9001.

Design and Development Outputs

ISO/TickIT require attributes relating to the design and development outputs. CamCal did not issue all the defined outputs following early termination of the project. Unit code underwent peer review and checking through the Together suite. Acceptance testing was not carried out because project was curtailed.

In order to be fully compliant with this clause of ISO 9001, each project would need to ensure all software tools and embedded COTS had been, or were to be, evaluated. Executable code would need to be verified during development, and each release would need to be adequately defined and validated.

Design and Development Review

ISO/TickIT require review of the design and development. CC specifies "viewings and reflection workshops." CamCal carried these out and kept whiteboard records.

In order to be fully compliant with this clause of ISO 9001, whiteboard records would need to indicate who was involved with the viewings and workshops. In addition, the sponsor and/or user should be present at some or all in order to ensure reviewer independence. Actions should be clearly identified to enable tracking at the next workshop. The whiteboard records would need to be kept for the mandatory records of review required by ISO 9001.

Design and Development Verification

ISO/TickIT require verification of the design and development. CC specifies verification of work products, and CamCal did carry out unit test (although no records were kept) and demonstration/review by the user during viewings. Failures were also not formally recorded during test.

In order to be fully compliant with this clause of ISO 9001, records of tests performed (including test cases/stimuli) and results obtained would need to be taken for the mandatory records required.[7] Review of performance against current requirements should be carried out at planned stages.

Design and Development Validation

ISO/TickIT require end-to-end verification of the design and development. CC specifies test cases, test records, and defect reports, CamCal did not produce these due to early termination.

In order to be fully compliant with this clause of ISO 9001, records of tests performed (including test cases/stimuli) and results obtained would need to be taken for the mandatory records required. Some form of tracing would be necessary for those requirements not tested or demonstrated.[8]

Control of Design and Development Changes

ISO/TickIT requires control of changes during design and development. Dynamic change is central to CC, which controls changes on two levels; changes to the mission or requirements would be made in the deliverable documents; changes in the design are less formally controlled through workshops and planning meetings. CamCal kept actions lists and recorded completion at viewings. Regression testing was used to verify the effects of changes, but formal records were not kept.

In order to be fully complaint with this clause of ISO 9001, whiteboard records would need to indicate who was involved with the viewings and workshops in order to provide the mandatory records required for review of changes. As discussed earlier, records of regression tests performed (including test cases/stimuli) and results obtained would also need to be taken.

Conclusions and Recommendations

Project CamCal adopted the Crystal Clear rapid development method as a trial and demonstration within TRT-UK of how the process could be used. The customer for the project was internal (hence protecting any external "real" customers from the experiment), but the project was unfortunately terminated early. However, due to the nature of the CC method, the early termination did not prohibit a useful software product.

---

[7]   Here is where automated unit and acceptance regression tests come in handy—Alistair.

[8]   This refers to usability and other requirements that don't have a function test.

This audit assesses the CC methodology against ISO 9001:2000 and the associated TickIT Guide, using CamCal as a case study. Inevitably, the detailed processes followed by the project had some bearing on the observations and findings.

CC is generally compliant with ISO 9001, particularly considering that the TickIT Guide acknowledges and accommodates Rapid Application Development (RAD). Full compliance would require a few extra disciplines/records as described under findings.

It is recommended that:

◆ The TRT-UK QMS is enhanced to provide a generic framework for the CC methodology (preferably named something like "Rapid Development Method" as CC is something of a trademark). The enhancements should include the ISO mandatory requirements.

◆ Each CC project should still create a project plan to adopt or modify the generic approach.

◆ Further in-house developments are carried out to CC, in order to fully understand the implementation and develop the new procedures.

Once established, external customers are given the choice of development methodology, including information on the processes, potential benefits, and their obligations.

REFLECTION ON THE FIELD AND AUDIT REPORTS

First of all, I wish to thank both Stephen and Thales Research and Technology for the excellent field report, complete as it is with photos and interviews, and for permission to publish it, even in excerpted form. Speaking as someone who has read a lot of experience reports, I find it unusually clear and informative, with useful detail and candor.

I left all of the participants' questioning and worrying about Crystal Clear in place because I suspect these will be common reactions in many organizations, and it is useful for you to see them laid out in front of you.

In this section, I consider two of their worries and discuss how to deal with them in different contexts. With luck, this will help Thales in the future, and also you.

Reallocation of Power

The project manager and sponsor, Sam, mentioned several times that he felt somewhat disempowered, not having control over the task time estimates and day-to-day management. Responsibility without authority is a worrisome thing. Sam quite reasonably requests a review of the project manager's role in Crystal Clear.

In discussing this with Stephen, we discovered a number of issues and strategies surrounding this issue.

First, power really does get reallocated, in one of two directions.

The sponsor has the responsibility to provide clear priorities and preferred outcomes when direction trade-offs need to be made. The developers have the responsibility of estimating how long the tasks will take. Together, they have joint responsibility to name all the tasks, and to generate the optimal strategy that will produce the best outcome for the project given the task list, task estimates, and project priorities.

In some companies, the project manager runs the show, naming the tasks, the estimates, and the strategies. Having been in this position for years, I can say that this is a losing proposition. It is almost impossible for the project manager to correctly guess all the tasks that need to be done and their estimates. Starting from the day I first saw Jens Coldewey run a joint planning session, I realized just how impossible.

In other companies, the programmers run the show, telling the sponsor what they will do and when they might be done, never minding what the business's priorities happen to be. This is also incorrect.

In each case, someone is likely to feel displaced by the reallocation of power in Crystal Clear (and other agile methods). The key to success is the recognition that everyone is in this together, the project is a joint activity, and both groups need to provide the information they possess in order to get the best outcome.

Second, the sponsor is still not without power.

Suppose that the planning session produces a timeline that the sponsor considers unacceptable. She has three recourses:

◆ Remove some of the items to be delivered or extend the time allowed.

◆ Get more creative about the plan: offload the team members, do more in parallel, or buy packages that accomplish part of the work. Much can be done with some creative brainstorming.

◆ Reduce all the time estimates by a percentage. Yes, this is a drastic measure, but it is still an alternative. Imagine that the sponsor says, "All very well, but we can't live with that schedule and we can't cut any more scope. I'll give you 80 percent of the time listed on each card, so that we can make the final date." At this point, everyone has seen the cards, so they know the original estimates. The team can track to both the original and reduced estimates and report against both in their status charts. Visibility will be kept high. I suspect that if the sponsor feels she must resort to this alternative, then there isn't a different development methodology that will produce a better result anyway. I also suggest that the team keep brainstorming for a better strategy.

"It requires a broadly scoped contract"

The field report concludes, "Crystal Clear expects the detailed requirements to emerge as the project proceeds, but is silent on the question of how this could fit into a contractual framework. One approach would be to adopt the DSDM practice of baselining the requirements at a high level."

CamCal was based on an early draft of Crystal Clear. I hope that I have managed in this final version to show how it can work in a contractual framework.

Crystal Clear does not *require* the detailed requirements to emerge as the project proceeds, although it *permits* them to. You are not at all obliged to change the requirements at the start of an iteration. If you have detailed requirements at the start that are not permitted to shift, then simply don't shift them!

It may be that you have committed to a scope, price, and time without having had time to properly investigate the requirements and plausible architectures (this is distressingly normal in our industry). You discover part of the way through the project that the original bid was simply wrong. You have several options, none of them pretty:

◆ Go back to the sponsors/buyers and renegotiate. This is not a matter for Crystal Clear or any other methodology to deal with. This has everything to do with how good your executive's relations are with the buyers and what they can change. They may be able to rebid the project, or they may not.

◆ Carefully prioritize your work to deliver the maximum business value in the time available, so that the features left out at the deadline are obvious to everyone as being the least important ones. Having delivered what is clearly the most valuable business functionality is the best bargaining chip you can give your executives to work with.[9]

◆ Be very creative in your strategy generation and find a way to deliver the bid.

◆ Get ready either to work overtime or change jobs. Even the best agile methodology can't change your social rules (but it may make you a more attractive hire).

*   *   *

I should round out this reflection with a final note about "Sam," the sponsor. Stephen writes, "[A]t the last reflection workshop, the sponsor also said that the advantages greatly outweighed the disadvantages. He's suggested we try it again, on a larger project, provided the fit with our existing procedures can be resolved."

Relevant to the tests for methodology design, the project delivered an adequate result for the sponsor, and the people (including the sponsor) are willing to use it again.

---

[9]   See the discussions in *Early Victory* (p. 48), *Burn Charts* (p. 94), and *Essential Interaction Design* (p. 80).

Chapter 9

Distilled (The Short Version)

At the end, it is time to roll it all back up again: What is the core of Crystal Clear, and what puts the team farther into the safety zone? This chapter is very short.

Crystal Clear is a highly optimized way to use a small, co-located team, prioritizing for *efficiency, habitability,* and *safety* in delivering a satisfactory outcome. The brief description of Crystal Clear for level-3 practitioners is just this:

> The lead designer and two to seven other developers
>> in a large room or adjacent rooms,
>> using information radiators such as whiteboards and flip charts,
>> having easy access to expert users,
>> distractions kept away,
>>> deliver running, tested, usable code to the users
>> every month or two (quarterly at worst),
>>> reflecting and adjusting their working conventions periodically.

The team members establish the safety properties below using the techniques they consider appropriate. The first three properties are required in Crystal Clear; the next four get the team further into the safety zone.

1. *Frequent Delivery*
2. *Reflective Improvement*
3. *Osmotic Communication*
4. Personal Safety
5. Focus
6. Easy Access to Expert Users
7. A Technical Environment with Automated Tests, Configuration Management, and Frequent Integration

All the other pages in this book only expand on this page.

References

(Adams 2002) Adams, B., Webb, R., "Trust in Small Military Teams," from the 7th International Command and Control Research and Technology Symposium, available online at http://www.dodccrp .org/Activities/Symposia/7thICCRTS/Tracks/pdf/006.PDF.

(Adolph 2002) Adolph, S., Bramble, P., *Patterns for Effective Use Cases,* Addison-Wesley, Boston, MA, 2003.

(Alexander 1977) Alexander, C., Ishikawa, S., Silverstein, M., *A Pattern Language: Towns, Buildings, Construction*, Oxford University Press, Oxford, England, 1977.

(Ambler 2002) Ambler, S., *Agile Modeling: Effective Practices for Extreme Programming and the Unified Process,* John Wiley & Sons, New York, NY, 2002.

(Andrews url) Andrews, M., "Seating Layout for 20 Please," http://www.wrytradesman.com/blog/ archives/000006.html

(Astels 2003) Astels, D., *Test Driven Development: A Practical Guide*, Pearson Education, Upper Saddle River, NJ, 2003.

(Beck 1999) Beck, K., *Extreme Programming Explained: Embrace Change*, Addison-Wesley, Boston, MA, 1999.

(Beck 2000) Beck, K., Fowler, M., *Planning Extreme Programming*, Addison-Wesley, Boston, MA, 2000.

(Beck 2003) Beck, K., *Test Driven Development: By Example*, Addison-Wesley, Boston, MA, 2003.

(Berczuk 2003) Berczuk, S., Appleton, B., *Software Configuration Management Patterns: Effective Teamwork, Practical Integration*, Addison-Wesley, Boston, MA, 2003.

(Boehm 2003) Boehm, B., Turner, R., *Balancing Agility and Discipline: A Guide for the Perplexed*, Addison-Wesley, Boston, MA, 2003.

(Borning 2003) Borning, A., Freeman-Benson, B., "YP and Urban Simulation: Applying an Agile Programming Methodology in a Politically Tempestuous Domain," http://agiledevelopmentconfer- ence.com/2003/schedule/researchpapers.html#P1

(Cockburn 1998) Cockburn, A., *Surviving Object-Oriented Projects*, Addison-Wesley, Boston, MA, 1998.

(Cockburn 2000) Cockburn, A., "Selecting a Project's Methodology," *IEEE Software, 17*(4), July/Aug 2000, pp. 64–71.

(Cockburn 2001a) Cockburn, A., "Using CRC Cards," http://alistair.cockburn.us/crystal/articles/ucrcc/ usingcrccards.html

(Cockburn 2001b) Cockburn, A., *Writing Effective Use Cases*, Addison-Wesley, Boston, MA, 2001.

(Cockburn 2002) Cockburn, A., *Agile Software Development*, Addison-Wesley, Boston, MA, 2002.

(Cockburn 2003a) Cockburn, A., *People and Methodologies in Software Development,* Ph.D. dissertation, Institute for Informatik, University of Oslo, Oslo, Norway, 2003.

(Cockburn 2003b) Cockburn, A., "The Cone of Silence (and other Project Management Strategies)," http://alistair.cockburn.us/crystal/articles/cos/coneofsilence.htm

(Cockburn 2004a) Cockburn, A., "Extending An Architecture As It Earns Business Value," http://alistair.cockburn.us/crystal/articles/eaaaiebv/extendinganarchitecture.htm

(Cockburn 2004b) Cockburn, A., "The End of Software Engineering and the Start of Economic-Cooperative Gaming," *ComSIS Journal, 1*(1), 2004, pp. 1-32, available online at http://www.comsis.fon.bg.ac.yu/ComSISpdf/Volume01/InvitedPapers/AlistairCockburn.htm

(Cockburn 2004c) Cockburn, A., "What the Agile Toolkit Contains," http://alistair.cockburn.us/crystal/articles/wtatc/whattheagiletoolboxcontains.htm

(Cockburn 2004d) Cockburn, A., "Earned-Value and Burn Charts," http://alistair.cockburn.us/crystal/articles/evabc/earnedvalueandburncharts.htm

(Cockburn 2004e) Cockburn, A., "What the Agile Toolbox Contains," CrossTalk magazine, available online at http://alistair.cockburn.us/crystal/articles/wtatc/whattheagiletoolboxcontains.htm

(Cockburn url eie) Cockburn, A., " Expert in Earshot," http://c2.com/cgi/wiki?ExpertInEarshot

(Cohn 2004) Cohn, M., *User Stories Applied: For Agile Software Development,* Addison-Wesley, Boston, MA, 2004.

(Constantine 1999) Constantine, L., Lockwood, L., *Software for Use*, Addison-Wesley, Boston, MA, 1999.

(Costa 2002) Costa, A., "The Role of Trust for the Functioning of Teams in Organisations," http://www.sses.com/public/events/euram/complete_tracks/trust_within_organizations/costa.pdf

(Cunningham url crc) Cunningham, W., "Crc Card," http://c2.com/cgi/wiki?CrcCard

(DeMarco 1999) DeMarco, T., Lister, T., *Peopleware: Productive Projects and Teams, 2nd Ed.*, Dorset House, New York, NY, 1999.

(Denne 2003) Denne, M., Cleland-Huang, J., *Software by Numbers: Low-Risk, High-Return Development,* Pearson Education, Upper Saddle River, NJ, 2004.

(Ehn 1988) Ehn, P., *Work-Oriented Development of Software Artifacts*, Arbetslivscentrum, Stockholm, 1988.

(Evans 2003) Evans, E., *Domain-Driven Design: Tackling Complexity in the Heart of Software*, Addison-Wesley, Boston, MA, 2003.

(Fleming 1988) Fleming, Quentin W., *Cost/Schedule Control Systems Criteria, The Management Guide to C/SCSC*, Probus, Chicago, 1988.

(Fowler 1999) Fowler, M., *Refactoring: Improving the Design of Existing Code,* Addison-Wesley, Boston, MA, 1999.

(Fowler 2003) Fowler, M., *UML Distilled: A Brief Guide to the Standard Object Modeling Language, Third Edition*, Addison-Wesley, Boston, MA, 2003.

(Gamma 1995) Gamma, E., Helm, R., Johnson, R., Vlissides, J., *Design Patterns*, Addison-Wesley, Boston, MA, 1995.

(Goldratt 1992) Goldratt, E., *The Goal*, North River Press, Great Barrington, MA, 1992.

(Gries 1981) Gries, D., *The Science of Programming*, Springer-Verlag, New York, NY, 1981.

(Hass 2003) Hass, A.M., *Configuration Management Principles and Practice*, Addison-Wesley, Boston, MA, 2003.

(Herring 2001) Herring, R., Rees, M., "Internet-Based Collaborative Software Development Using Microsoft Tools," in *Proceedings of the 5th World Multiconference on Systemics, Cybernetics and Informatics* (SCI'2001). July 22-25, 2001, Orlando, Florida., available online at http://erwin.dstc.edu.au/Herring/SoftwareEngineeringOverInternet-SCI2001.pdf

(Highsmith 2000) Highsmith, J., *Adaptive Software Development*, Dorset House, New York, NY, 2000.

(Highsmith 2003) Highsmith, J., *Agile Software Development Ecosystems*, Addison-Wesley, Boston, MA, 2003.

(Highsmith 2004) Highsmith, J., *Agile Project Management: Creating Innovative Products*, Addison-Wesley, Boston, MA, 2004.

(Hohmann 1997) Hohmann, L. *Journey of the Software Professional*, Prentice-Hall, Upper Saddle River, NJ, 1997.

(Hunt 1999) Hunt, A., Thomas, D., *The Pragmatic Programmer: From Journeyman to Master,* Addison-Wesley, Boston, MA, 1999.

(Hunt 2004) Hunt, A., Thomas, D., *Pragmatic Unit Testing in C# with NUnit,* The Pragmatic Bookshelf, Dallas, TX, 2003.

(Keil 1995) Keil, M., Carmel, E., "Customer-Developer Links," in *Communications of the ACM,* May, 1995, pp. 33-44.

(Kerth 2001) Kerth, N., *Project Retrospectives: A Handbook for Team Reviews,* Dorset House, New York, NY, 2001.

(Kramer 1996), Kramer, R., Tyler, T., *Trust in Organizations,* Sage Publications, Thousand Oaks, CA, 1996.

(Krutchen 1999) Krutchen, P., *The Rational Unified Process*, Addison-Wesley, Boston, MA, 1999.

(Larman 2003) Larman, C., *Agile and Iterative Development: A Manager's Guide*, Addison-Wesley, Boston, MA, 2003.

(Laufer 1996) Laufer, A., *Simultaneous Management: Managing Projects in a Dynamic Environment,* American Management Association, New York, NY 1996.

(Lett 1998) Lett, Steven, "An Earned-Value Tracking System for Self-Directed Software Teams," European Software Engineering Process Group, 1998, available online at http:www.benchmarkqa.com/PDFs/software_teams.pdf

(Low 2004) Low, L., "First Things First," *CIO Magazine,* March 15, 2004, available online at http://www.cio.com/archive/031504/case.html

(Mathiassen 2001) Mathiassen, L., Pries-Heje, J., Ngwenyama, O., *Improving Software Organizations*, Addison-Wesley, Boston, MA, 2001.

(McCarthy 2002) McCarthy, J., McCarthy, M., *Software for Your Head: Core Protocols for Creating and Maintaining Shared Vision,* Addison-Wesley, Boston, MA, 2002.

(McConnell 1998) McConnell, S., *Software Project Survival Guide*, Microsoft Press, Redmond, WA, 1998.

(McNeill 1994) McNeill, D., *Fuzzy Logic: The Revolutionary Computer Technology That is Changing Our World,* Simon and Schuster, New York, NY 1994.

(Mills 1988) Mills, H., Poore, J., "Bringing Software Under Statistical Quality Control," *Quality Progress*, Nov. 1988, pp. 52-55.

(Mishra 1996), Mishra, A., "Organizational Response to Crisis: The Centrality of Trust," in Kramer, R., Tyler, T., *Trust in Organizations,* Sage Publications, Thousand Oaks, CA, 1996, pp. 261–287.

(Naur 1992) Naur, P., "Programming as Theory Building," in *Computing: A Human Activity*, ACM Press, New York, NY, 1992, pp. 37-48.

(Ogunnaike 1992) Ogunnaike, B., Ray, W., *Process Dynamics, Modeling, and Control,* Oxford University Press, Oxford, England, 1992.

(Olson 2000) Olson, G., Olson, J. "Distance Matters," *Human-Computer Interaction,* Vol. 15, 2001, pp. 139-179.

(Patton 2002) Patton, J., "Hitting the Target: Adding Interaction Design to Agile Software Development," in *SIGPLAN Notices,* 2002(3), available online at http://oopsla.acm.org/extra/pracreports/HittingTheTargeReport.pdf

(Patton 2003) Patton, J., "Unfixing the Fixed Scope Project," Agile Development Conference 2003, available online at http://agiledevelopmentconference.com/2003/schedule/experiencereports.html#R13

(Poppendieck 2003) Poppendieck, M., Poppendieck, T., *Lean Software Development: An Agile Toolkit for Software Development Managers*, Addison-Wesley, Boston, MA, 2003.

(Schwaber, 2002) Schwaber, K., Beedle, M., *Scrum: Agile Software Development*, Prentice-Hall, Upper Saddle River, NJ, 2002.

(Simone url) Simone, C., "According To Script: Steps to Scriptability," http://www.mactech.com/articles/develop/issue_24/according.html

(Snyder 2003) Snyder, C., *Paper Prototyping: The Fast and Easy Way to Design and Refine User Interfaces,* Morgan Kaufmann, San Francisco, CA, 2003.

(Stapleton 2003) Stapleton, J., DSDM Consortium, *DSDM: Business Focused Development, Second Edition,* Addison-Wesley, Boston, MA, 2003.

(Thomas 2003) Thomas, D., Hunt, A., *Pragmatic Version Control using CVS*, The Pragmatic Bookshelf, Dallas, TX, 2003.

(Weick 1979) Weick, K., *The Social Psychology of Organizing,* McGraw-Hill, New York, NY, 1979.

(Williams 2002) Williams, L., Kessler, R., *Pair Programming Illuminated,* Addison-Wesley, Boston, MA, 2002.

Index

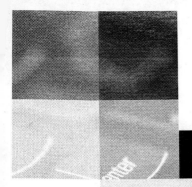

informIT

YOUR GUIDE TO IT REFERENCE

Articles

Keep your edge with thousands of free articles, in-depth features, interviews, and IT reference recommendations – all written by experts you know and trust.

Online Books

Answers in an instant from **InformIT Online Book's** 600+ fully searchable on line books. For a limited time, you can get your first 14 days **free**.

Catalog

Review online sample chapters, author biographies and customer rankings and choose exactly the right book from a selection of over 5,000 titles.